THE
NEUROPHYSIOLOGICAL
BASIS OF MIND

THE PRINCIPLES OF
NEUROPHYSIOLOGY

BY

JOHN CAREW ECCLES

PROFESSOR OF PHYSIOLOGY, THE AUSTRALIAN
NATIONAL UNIVERSITY, CANBERRA

BEING

THE WAYNFLETE LECTURES

DELIVERED IN THE COLLEGE OF

ST. MARY MAGDALEN, OXFORD

IN HILARY TERM

1952

OXFORD

AT THE CLARENDON PRESS

1953

Oxford University Press, Amen House, London E.C.4

GLASGOW NEW YORK TORONTO MELBOURNE WELLINGTON
BOMBAY CALCUTTA MADRAS KARACHI CAPE TOWN IBADAN

Geoffrey Cumberlege, Publisher to the University

PRINTED IN GREAT BRITAIN

£1.50 10

Rosemary Lacey.

THE
NEUROPHYSIOLOGICAL
BASIS OF MIND

THE PRINCIPLES OF
NEUROPHYSIOLOGY

PREFACE

THIS book is built upon a series of eight lectures that were delivered at Oxford in Hilary Term 1952. The occasion was provided by the President and Fellows of Magdalen College who kindly invited me to give the Waynflete Lectures on the subject of the research work that had been done in the Dunedin laboratory on synaptic transmission. Eventually this rather restricted subject was broadened to the scope covered by this book, but to a considerable extent the subject of synaptic transmission has remained dominant, and the contributions of the Dunedin laboratory have been given disproportionate emphasis.

Though the lectures have been considerably modified and amplified, as far as possible their original form has been preserved. In particular this book gives an account which links together the hierarchy of functions in the nervous system from the simplest to the most complex. To give such an account has entailed the selection of certain investigations as providing the theme at each stage of the hierarchy. Much important work, for example the whole of the investigations on metabolism, has necessarily been neglected or merely mentioned in passing because it could not be profitably assimilated at this stage. Evidently there is room at present for several parallel accounts, whose synthesis must await a more profound understanding. This book, then, must be regarded not as a monograph, but merely as the report of a series of lectures, written as they were given, one each week.

As indicated by the sub-title *The Principles of Neurophysiology*, the scope may be described as covering the whole field of neurophysiology—the reactions of the single nerve or muscle fibre, the reactions of the single neurone, the

reactions of the simpler synaptic levels of the nervous
system, the plastic reactions of the nervous system and the
phenomena of learning, the reactions of the cerebral cortex,
and finally the relationship of the brain to the mind.
Broadly speaking, it is an attempt to see how far scientific
investigation of the nervous system has helped us to under-
stand not only the working of our brains, but also how
liaison between mind and brain could occur. As such it
tries to answer, so far as is at present possible, some of the
most fundamental questions that man can ask: What manner of being are we? Are we really compounded of two
'substances' spirit and matter? What processes are concerned in perception and in voluntary action? How are
conscious states related to events in the brain? How can
we account for memory and the continuity of mental experience that gives the 'self'? How is that entity called
'self' interrelated to that thing called a body? Descartes
failed to answer these questions because his science was
too primitive, and his dualist-interactionist explanation
has consequently been discredited. The remarkable advances that have been made possible largely by electronic
techniques now make it worth while to try to answer these
questions in at least some of their aspects. Cartesian
dualism and interactionism thus become valid working
hypotheses in the attempt to obtain a further scientific
insight into the nature of man. This was essentially the
theme of Sherrington in his remarkable book *Man on his
Nature* (1951). I am attempting to follow the lead that he
gave. To use a popular phraseology (Ryle, 1949), I am
arguing that, before we exorcize the 'ghost' from the
'machine', we should at least carefully scrutinize the machine. We may then find where the 'ghost' comes in, or at
least how the 'ghost' could come in. But that will come in
the last chapter. For it, in a sense, the other seven chapters

are a preparation. But they are essentially concerned in the Neurophysiological Basis of Mind.

Very recent advances in technique have made it possible to offer satisfactory explanations of many of the basic reactions of the nervous system. Inevitably, much of the first seven chapters will be concerned with new methods of investigation and the hypotheses developed as a consequence. One such method is the recording of electrical potentials from the interiors of single nerve fibres and nerve cells; another is the use of radio-tracers in measuring the fluxes of ions across surface membranes. It will emerge that the work on the single fibres provides the basis for an explanation of reactions of the more complex synaptic structures and hence of the central nervous system even in its highest level, the cerebral cortex.

Unfortunately many sections of these earlier chapters will prove to be the most difficult in the book. It is suggested that, if they are proving too difficult, much of the sections giving the experimental testing of hypotheses (pp. 7–52, 69–95, 114–49) could be omitted at the first reading. However, these sections describe most of the recent fundamental advances and are of the greatest importance not only for their own sake, but also in giving a sound scientific basis for the more speculative sections of the book.

Where practicable, brief statements of hypotheses have preceded the accounts of experimental investigations and the developments of the hypotheses arising therefrom. It is hoped that this sequence will make it easier for the reader, and it also conforms with the usual pattern of a scientific inquiry: some hypothesis is tested experimentally and consequently modified. Even in the more speculative last chapter the method is essentially scientific, since attempts are there made to formulate hypotheses which lead to predictions that in part at least are testable.

My thanks are due to my numerous friends and col-
leagues who contributed so much to this book not only by
their researches and publications, but also by their discussion of many of the problems and in many cases by reading
and criticizing parts of the manuscript. I would like also to
thank the audience who provided me with so much stimulus and encouragement during the lectures themselves.

J. C. E.

AUSTRALIAN NATIONAL UNIVERSITY
CANBERRA
August 1952

ACKNOWLEDGEMENTS

GRATEFUL thanks are due to the following publishers and editors for their generosity in giving permission for the reproduction of figures: *Journal of Physiology*; *Journal of Neurophysiology*; *Journal of General Physiology*; *Biological Reviews*; The Royal Society; *Compt. Rend. Soc. Biol.*; *Journal of Comparative Neurology*; Ciba Foundation; Oxford University Press; *Nature*; E.E.G. Society; Society for Research in Nervous and Mental Diseases, and Charles C. Thomas.

CONTENTS

I

THE IONIC HYPOTHESIS AND THE RESTING MEMBRANE

A. INTRODUCTION

IT is now over a century since the discovery of the action current of the nerve impulse. The immense volume of work since that time has established the prime importance of the nerve impulse in the working of the nervous system. It can be regarded as the universal currency of the nervous system, for all actions in the nervous system at greater than microscopic distances are mediated by the brief propagated electrical events that are called nerve impulses. Provisionally a nerve impulse may be defined as a wave of electrical negativity that travels without decrement along nerve-fibres. We may say that all 'information' is conveyed in the nervous system in the form of coded arrangements of nerve impulses. The principal tasks confronting me in my attempt to give an account of the working of the nervous system are therefore to give adequate descriptions firstly of the nerve impulse, and secondly of the ways in which it is generated and the manner in which it exerts its effects. In order to simplify this task I will concentrate on those nerve-fibres that are most suitable for rigorous investigation—the invertebrate giant nerve-fibres. In this context it may be noted that for our purposes vertebrate muscle-fibres closely resemble the nerve-fibres of both vertebrates and invertebrates, and have also been subjected to rigorous investigation.

Both nerve and muscle-fibres may be regarded as indefinitely extended cylinders of uniform diameter which are filled by a watery medium of special composition, axoplasm or myoplasm respectively (Fig. 1). They are bathed in a watery medium of very different composition, which is an ultra-filtrate of blood. The external medium is separated from the internal by an exceedingly thin membrane. This plasma membrane of lipoid-protein structure is so thin (values of 50 to 100 A are commonly assumed) that it has not been directly observed by ordinary microscopic technique. However, it is now being successfully studied

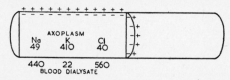

FIG. 1. Diagram of giant axon of squid, partly cut away in order to show the electric charge across the surface membrane. The approximate internal composition of a fresh fibre is shown for sodium, potassium, and chloride in mM, i.e. millimol. per Kg. of water. The composition of the external fluid is also shown in mM.

by electron-microscopy and its existence has been of course established by more indirect evidence. For example, the boundary between the nerve- or muscle-fibre and the external medium has special electrical properties and offers very high resistance to the diffusion of substances, especially ions.

In the first instance we can build up hypotheses which explain the behaviour of nerve- or muscle-cells at rest and during activity in terms of the properties of the plasma membrane, and the compositions of the media on either side of it, but ultimately the properties of the membrane and the behaviour of nerve- and muscle-fibres are dependent on metabolism of the axoplasm or myoplasm, and are, for example, changed when this metabolism is depressed or modified by anoxia or by enzyme poisons (cf. Arvanitaki and Chalazonitis, 1949; Ling and Gerard, 1949b).

B. THE IONIC HYPOTHESIS OF THE IMPULSE

1. *Historical development*

In 1902 Overton published a remarkable series of investigations on the effects of ions on muscle and nerve,

which gave him an amazing insight into the ionic processes that occur during the propagation of the impulse
(cf. Katz, 1952). A clear formulation of an ionic hypothesis of the nerve impulse was first proposed by Bernstein
(1902), who postulated that the resting plasma membrane
was selectively permeable to potassium, and that it broke
down to give a temporary phase of non-selective membrane permeability during the impulse. However, this
hypothesis failed to explain the important new observation of reversed membrane potential during the action
potential of the impulse, that was made as soon as intracellular electrodes were employed on giant nerve-fibres
(Hodgkin and Huxley, 1939, 1945; Curtis and Cole, 1940,
1942). At about the same time Conway (Boyle and Conway, 1941; Conway, 1946, 1947) showed that the resting
plasma membrane of muscle-fibres was freely permeable
to the chloride ion as well as to potassium, and that both
the distribution of these ions and the resting membrane
potential were attributable to a Donnan equilibrium across
the plasma membrane.

The confused position that prevailed subsequently (cf.
Eccles, 1948) was terminated by a brilliant contribution
by Hodgkin and Katz (1949), who not only formulated a
new ionic hypothesis to replace the Bernstein hypothesis,
but also subjected this hypothesis to precise quantitative
tests. Since that time this new hypothesis has survived
such a rigorous series of experimental investigations that
it can now be regarded as providing, at the first stage of
analysis, a substantially correct explanation of the properties of the surface membranes during rest and activity
of nerve- and muscle-fibres; and, specifically, it gives a
precise explanation of the nerve impulse. A simple statement of the hypothesis will precede a brief description of
the principal experimental tests which in this chapter will
be restricted to the resting membrane. Three reviews
(Hodgkin, 1950, 1951; Keynes, 1951c) have been of the
greatest value in this task.

2. *Statement of the ionic hypothesis*

The resting membrane is readily permeable to potassium and chloride ions, which exchange across it solely by diffusion and hence are distributed according to a Donnan equilibrium between the inside and the outside of the fibre (cf. Fig. 1). On the other hand the resting membrane is sparingly permeable to sodium ions, and an active sodium-pump mechanism removes them from the interior as fast as they diffuse in. The sodium-pump is located in the membrane, but it derives energy in some way from metabolic reactions within the fibre, and it operates to keep the sodium concentration within the fibre normally at about 10 per cent. of the external concentration. As a consequence of this sodium distribution and of a high internal concentration of impermeable anions, such as are provided by glutamic and aspartic acids, the potassium and chloride ions are distributed very unequally under the condition of Donnan equilibrium, the internal potassium being twenty to fifty times more concentrated than the external, while a reciprocal relationship obtains for chloride, i.e.

$$\frac{(K)_i}{(K)_0} = \frac{(Cl)_0}{(Cl)_i} = 20 \text{ to } 50$$

where $(K)_i$ and $(K)_0$ are the concentrations of potassium ions respectively inside and outside and similarly for chloride ions.

The resting membrane potential, E_r, being the potential obtaining in a Donnan equilibrium, is related to the relative concentration of potassium or chloride ions by the equations:

$$E_r = \frac{RT}{F} \log_e \frac{(K)_i}{(K)_0} = \frac{RT}{F} \log_e \frac{(Cl)_0}{(Cl)_i}. \qquad (1)$$

It is assumed that the activity coefficients of these ions are the same inside and outside which seems not unreasonable in view of the observations by Hodgkin and Keynes (1950) on ionic mobility in axoplasm.

At room temperature Eq. 1 may be written:

$$E_r \text{ (in mV)} = 58 \log_{10} \frac{(K)_i}{(K)_0}. \tag{2}$$

Thus for a Donnan ratio of 20 to 50 it would be predicted that the outside would be 75 to 100 mV positive to the inside (cf. Fig. 1). Such a potential compensates for the concentration gradient so that the electro-chemical gradient for potassium or chloride ions is virtually zero, i.e. no work is done if a small quantity of potassium or chloride ions is transferred in either direction across the membrane. Or, alternatively, if the concentration (or more strictly the activity) of potassium is say fifty times greater inside than outside, potassium ions will bombard the membrane fifty times more intensely on the inside; hence a potential difference (about 100 mV, cf. Eq. 1 and 2) across the membrane is necessary in order to equalize the inward and outward potassium fluxes. If the potential is less than this value, there will be an excess outward flux of potassium ions each carrying a charge, until the equilibrium potential is attained, and vice versa if the potential is greater than the equilibrium value.

However, when this resting potential is slightly diminished (depolarization) by an applied electric current (at the cathode) or by the flow of electric currents in local circuits due to a change in membrane potential in some adjacent part of the fibre, the surface membrane immediately develops a high specific permeability to sodium ions, due, it is assumed, to the operation of a 'sodium-carrier' mechanism (Hodgkin, 1951). As a consequence sodium ions are carried inwards along their steep electro-chemical gradient (Fig. 2 A), their positive charges rapidly discharging the resting potential, and hence progressively adding to the activity of the sodium-carrier mechanism. Thus eventually the potential approaches that of a sodium electrode, and so will be a reversed potential (Figs. 2 A and B), the inside being positive to the outside (cf. Eq. 8, where $(Na)_i/(Na)_0$ equals about $1/10$. As this peak of the action potential is reached, the sodium-carrier is already failing, and soon completely fails, while potassium permeability is increased far above the resting level. There is

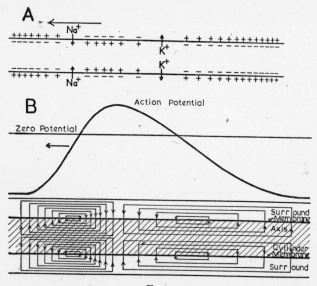

FIG. 2.

FIG. 2 A. Diagram showing postulated movement of sodium and potassium ions across the membrane during an impulse advancing in the direction of arrow, and the resulting alteration of charge on the membrane and its recovery.

FIG. 2 B. Upper part shows potential distribution of impulse along nerve- or muscle-fibre, while lower part shows the resulting flow of electric current both in the external medium and within the fibre, while lower part shows the resulting flow of electric current both in the external medium and within the fibre. Note the reversal of membrane potential during the spike. Fig. 2 B is drawn so that the impulse is at approximately the same position as in Fig. 2 A.

thus a rapid net outward flux of potassium ions (Fig. 2 A), for, during the falling phase of the action potential, the 'potassium-carrier' operates effectively in this direction along an electro-chemical gradient, each potassium ion carrying a positive charge outwards. In this way the original resting potential is rapidly restored (often within a millisecond), at which level there is according to the hypothesis zero electro-chemical gradient for potassium.

The propagation of an impulse receives an immediate explanation by this hypothesis, for the change in potential at the activated area will cause currents to flow (Fig. 2 B) which depolarize an adjacent region of the nerve or muscle fibre to the critical level so that the sodium-carrier mechanism is activated there also, and so on indefinitely.

The action potential is thus explained by a cycle of permeability changes at any region of membrane. The immediate source of energy for propagation of the impulse is the uptake of a small quantity of sodium ions and the loss of a small quantity of potassium ions. Ultimately an equivalent amount of sodium ions must be extruded by the sodium-pump, the potassium ions being probably passively absorbed. Metabolic energy is thus eventually required for a complete restoration of the *status quo*, but the fibre contains a large reserve of energy on account of its high potassium and low sodium content, hence the activity of the sodium-pump does not need to be geared accurately to the level of activity of the fibre, the sodium ions gained in bursts of activity being slowly pumped out later during periods of rest.

C. EXPERIMENTAL TESTING OF THE IONIC HYPOTHESIS

1. *Distribution of electrolytes on either side of the membrane*

On account of their large size, about 0·5 mm. in diameter (Young, 1939), it is possible to extrude the axoplasm of the giant squid axons and directly analyse it, but for other tissues more indirect procedures are necessary. Activation analysis by neutron bombardment (cf. Keynes and Lewis, 1951*b*; Lewis, 1952) has been used for single giant axons of sepia, and the figures for frog muscle in Table 1 are derived by chemical analysis with due allowance for extracellular space. After excision squid and sepia giant fibres rapidly lose potassium and gain sodium and chloride, but as far as possible the figures of Table 1 are corrected to give the original *in vivo* composition.

TABLE I

Distribution of electrolytes on either side of the membrane

(Cf. Hodgkin, 1951; Keynes, 1951)

Tissue	Concentrations inside in mM			Concentrations outside in mM			Approximate ratios inside/outside		
	Na	K	Cl	Na	K	Cl	Na	K	Cl
1	2	3	4	5	6	7	8	9	10
Squid: 500 μ axon .	49	410	40	440	22	560	1:9	19:1	1:14
Sepia: 200 μ axon .	43	360	..	450	17	540	1:10	21:1	..
Carcinus: leg nerve .	52	410	26	510	12	540	1:10	34:1	1:21
Frog: sartorius muscle	15	125	1·2	110	2·6	77	1:7	48:1	1:64

In the last two columns it will be seen that there is approximately the predicted reciprocal relationship between the relative potassium and chloride concentrations. The deviations from prediction (cf. p. 4) are possibly attributable to the failure to allow adequately for the changes that occur during dissection of the giant axons, and for the amount of extracellular space in muscle (cf. Hodgkin, 1951). Other possibilities would be either that some of the internal potassium is bound in chemical combination with proteins or other large molecules, or that the activity of the internal potassium ions is lower than that outside. However, it has been shown that in the giant axons neither of these latter factors is of significance (Keynes, 1951*b*; Keynes and Lewis, 1951*a*; Hodgkin and Keynes, 1950; Hodgkin, 1951). Thus it appears that the observed distribution of potassium and chloride ions accords at least approximately with the postulates of the ionic hypothesis: that the membrane is relatively freely permeable to both potassium and chloride; and that a Donnan equilibrium obtains *in vivo*.

The relative permeability of the surface membrane to potassium and chloride is also shown by experiments in which the external concentrations of the various ions were altered. For example, if solid potassium chloride was added to the Ringer's solution, muscle-fibres showed merely a transient shrinkage, and there was a permanent net entry of potassium chloride in direct proportion to the amount added to the external fluid (Boyle and Conway, 1941; Conway, 1947). If the added potassium chloride was compensated by abstraction of an iso-molar concentration of sodium chloride from the Ringer's solution, potassium chloride also entered the muscle-fibres, but was accompanied by water so that the internal potassium concentration remained approximately constant (Boyle and Conway, 1941). Similarly the membrane of crustacean nerve-fibres has been shown to be permeable to potassium and chloride (Shanes, 1946).

2. *The resting membrane potential*

Direct methods have now been employed in measuring the membrane potential of a wide variety of cells. Originally a fine capillary tube was inserted along a giant axon (Fig. 3 A) so that the potential could be measured at least 10 mm. from the area damaged by the insertion (Hodgkin and Huxley, 1939, 1945; Curtis and Cole, 1940, 1942; Hodgkin and Katz, 1949). But a more generally applicable method was introduced by Gerard and co-workers (Graham and Gerard, 1946; Ling and Gerard, 1949a) who found that a glass tube of less than 1 μ diameter (the micro-electrode) could be introduced through the membrane of a cell without causing appreciable damage (Fig. 3 B). The membrane appears to self-seal around the electrode, which, being filled with salt solution, provides an insulated lead from the interior of the cell. When this micro-electrode is filled with 3M-KCl, it is probable that there would be a relatively small liquid junction potential with the cytoplasm of nerve or muscle (Nastuk and Hodgkin, 1950),

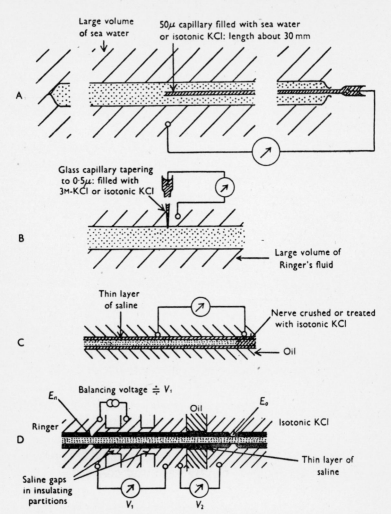

FIG. 3. Diagrams showing methods of recording the potential across the surface membrane of nerve- or muscle-fibres (Hodgkin, 1951). A. Longitudinal insertion of internal electrode in giant axon of squid. B. Insertion of fine glass micro-electrode across membrane of cell. C. External electrode method used for single fibre. Membrane potential can be calculated from ratio of resistance of unit length of axis cylinder to that of external fluid. D. Special system of Huxley and Stampfli (1951a) for medullated nerve. When balancing voltage is adjusted so that V_2 registers zero potential, then V_1 registers the difference between membrane potentials at E_n and E_o, i.e. the potential across E_n minus the liquid-junction potential at E_o, which is immersed in isotonic KCl.

and the membrane potential will be accurately given by the measured potential difference between the internal micro-electrode and the external electrode.

Table 2 reveals that, as determined in this way, the resting membrane potential has a small range of variation with a wide variety of excitable membranes. It is further

TABLE 2

Sizes of Resting and Action Potentials (largely from Hodgkin, 1951)

Potentials are expressed as outside minus inside potential and the resting potentials have been corrected for liquid-junction potentials

Tissue	Fibre diameter (μ)	Resting potential in mV		Action potential of spike in mV	
		Ob-served	Calcu-lated on K_i^+/K_0^+ ratios of Table 1	Ob-served	Calculated as potential of column 4 minus potential calcu-lated on Na_i^+/Na_0^+ ratios of Table 1
1	2	3	4	5	6
Squid: non-myelinated axon . . .	500	61*	74	89	129
Sepia: non-myelinated axon . . .	200	62*	77	120	136
Carcinus: non-myeli-nated axon . .	30	82*	89	134	147
Frog: isolated medul-lated axon . .	15	71	..	116	..
Frog: striated muscle-fibre . . .	80	88	98	119	148
Frog: striated muscle-fibre *in vivo* . .	..	95	98	..	..
Dog: cardiac muscle-fibre . . .	30	90	..	121	..
Kid: cardiac muscle-fibre . . .	65	94	..	135	..
Cat: motoneurone .	70	75	..	110	..

* These values were recorded for an external potassium concentration of 10 mM and would be lowered by several millivolts at the external potassium concentration used in the calculation of column 4.

of importance that, as the micro-electrode is being in-serted, it suddenly leads off the full size of the resting potential, an observation which indicates the very tenuous character of the membrane that supports the whole resting potential (Nastuk and Hodgkin, 1950).

According to the ionic hypothesis the resting membrane potential, E_r, is related to the relative external and internal potassium or chloride concentrations in accordance with Eq. 1 or 2 (pp. 4, 5). It was argued above that *in vivo* there is approximately a reciprocal relationship between the ratios of potassium and chloride concentrations on either side of the membrane (cf. Table 1), and, since the potassium ratio is more accurately measurable than the chloride ratio, only the resting potentials calculated from the potassium ratios by Eq. 2 are shown in Table 2, column 4. The agreement is satisfactory, particularly for carcinus nerve and frog muscle, but in every case the observed potential is lower than the calculated value.

Though some uncertainty is introduced into the observed and the calculated values by the allowance for the liquid junction potential and by the assumption of equal activity coefficients, respectively, there is no doubt that the principal cause of the discrepancy is that the potential measurements are made on excised tissues not in the steady state which the ionic hypothesis assumes to exist under resting conditions. Direct determinations show that there is a net uptake of sodium and chloride and a net loss of potassium (cf. p. 17). The significance of this effect is revealed by the observed value of 85 mV for the resting potential of frog muscle *in vivo*, a value which is in close agreement with the calculated value of 98 mV, when allowance is made for the liquid junction potential by adding on 10 mV. Hence much of the discrepancy between the observed and calculated values in columns 3 and 4 of Table 2 may plausibly be attributed to the non-steady state that supervenes immediately the tissue is excised. Further reference to this problem will be made when discussing the observed ionic fluxes across the resting membrane (p. 21).

An important inference from the ionic hypothesis is

that alteration of the external potassium concentration should produce an immediate change in the resting potential, the potential being proportional to the logarithm of

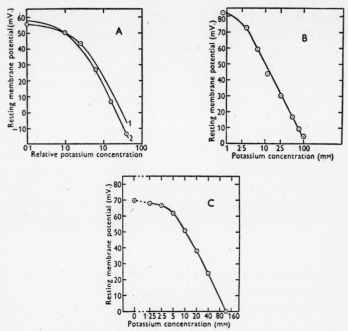

FIG. 4. Relation between potassium concentration in external solution plotted on logarithmic scale and potential difference across the resting membrane (Hodgkin, 1951). External positivity of membrane is plotted upwards. No corrections applied for liquid junction potentials. A. Squid giant axon: plotted points give data of Curtis and Cole (1942), as determined by method of Fig. 3 A; lines give curves drawn according to Eq. 3 for two different assumed values for $P_K:P_{Na}:P_{Cl}$ (cf. Hodgkin and Katz, 1949). Potassium concentrations as multiples of a standard solution of 13 mM. B. Frog sartorius muscle from data of Ling and Gerard (1950) as determined by the method of Fig. 3 B. C. Frog medullated nerve from data of Huxley and Stampfli, 1951b, as determined by the method of Fig. 3 D.

the ratio of the potassium ions on the two sides of the membrane (Eqs. 1 and 2). Strictly, time should be allowed for the ionic fluxes across the membrane to restore equilibrium, but Boyle and Conway (1941) showed that there was no appreciable change in $(K)_i$ of muscle if the increase of $(K)_0$ was accompanied by an iso-molar decrease in $(Na)_0$, which has been the usual procedure in this type of experiment (cf. p. 9). Actually with single myelinated nerve-fibres (cf. Fig. 4 c) the potential change followed the change of the solutions to within one second (Huxley and Stampfli 1951b), while with the squid giant axon (cf. Fig. 4 A) the membrane potential became stabilized at the new value within 2 to 3 minutes (Curtis and Cole, 1942), periods which are satisfactorily accounted for by diffusion time. Eq. 2 would predict a slope of 58 mV per ten-fold alteration of $(K)_0$. As shown in Fig. 4, the observed slopes approach this value for high values of $(K)_0$, being 50, 45, and 50 mV for squid axon, frog muscle, and frog nerve respectively. However, at low potassium concentrations all three curves deviate widely from the predicted linear relationship. Hodgkin and Katz (1949) have shown that this deviation is to be expected because the excised tissues are no longer in a steady state, but are gaining sodium and losing potassium. Further they show that in such a non-steady state the resting membrane potential would be given approximately by an equation derived from the constant-field theory of Goldman (1943):

$$E_r = \frac{RT}{F} \log_e \frac{P_{\mathrm{K}}(\mathrm{K})_i + P_{\mathrm{Na}}(\mathrm{Na})_i + P_{\mathrm{Cl}}(\mathrm{Cl})_0}{P_{\mathrm{K}}(\mathrm{K})_0 + P_{\mathrm{Na}}(\mathrm{Na})_0 + P_{\mathrm{Cl}}(\mathrm{Cl})_i} \qquad (3)$$

where P_{K}, P_{Na}, and P_{Cl} are the permeability constants for the respective ions. Assumed relative values for P_{K}, P_{Na}, and P_{Cl} are used in plotting the curves in Fig. 4 A, which are seen to be in good agreement with the observed potentials.

Thus the alterations in membrane potential produced by varying the external potassium concentration would appear to deviate from the predicted effects largely because the excised tissues are not in the steady state that would prevail *in vivo*. With high external potassium concentration the relationship approximates to the predictions from Eq. 2, but with low potassium concentrations the fraction of the potential attributable to the sodium and chloride ions dominates the contribution by the potassium ions, and, with potassium concentrations lower than that normally obtaining *in vivo*, the observations deviate widely from prediction (Figs. 4 A, B, C). The same explanation, therefore, is offered for the deviations from the predicted linear relationship in Fig. 4, and for the discrepancy between observed and calculated values in columns 3 and 4 of Table 2. Further consideration of the steady state condition is deferred until the ionic fluxes have been discussed.

3. *The ionic fluxes across the membrane*

(a) *Measurements of fluxes*

The fluxes of sodium and potassium ions across the surface membrane of the giant axons of sepia have been directly measured by means of the radioactive isotopes, ^{24}Na and ^{42}K (Keynes, 1951*b*; Keynes and Lewis, 1951*b*). It is shown that the levels of radioactivity do not have a deleterious effect on the tissues.

Essentially, the experiment is carried out for potassium by soaking the axon for a measured brief interval in an artificial sea-water in which a known proportion of the potassium ions is ^{42}K. The axon is then mounted over a Geiger counter in a thin-bottomed chamber through which an inactive solution, i.e. normal artificial sea-water, rapidly circulates. Extracellular ^{42}K ions are thus rapidly washed away and an exponentially decreasing radioactivity remains (cf. Fig. 5 A), which is attributable to intracellular ^{42}K. The time-constant of the isotope decay was allowed for. From the time-constant of this decrease, the outward flux, m_o, of potassium ions may be calculated provided that the total internal concentration of potassium, C_i, and the axon diameter, d, are known, for

$$m_0 = \frac{kdC_i}{4} \qquad (4)$$

where k is the exchange constant (the reciprocal of the time constant of the decrease) and d is the diameter of the axon (the surface/volume ratio being thus $4/d$).

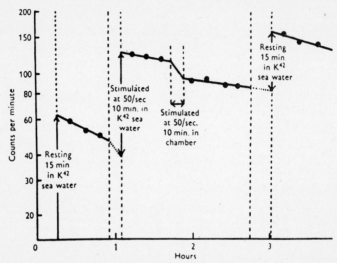

FIG. 5 A. Movements of ^{42}K in a sepia axon 168 μ in diameter. Counts per minute are plotted logarithmically as ordinates. For entry of ^{42}K, 1 count a minute was equivalent to $1\cdot17 \times 10^{-11}$ mol. K per cm. axon (Keynes, 1951b).

The inward flux, m_i, is simply calculated, for, by testing between a series of brief immersions in sea-water containing ^{42}K, it is shown that the rate of uptake of ^{42}K, dY/dt, is constant for some hours (Keynes, 1951b). Thus

$$m_i = \frac{dY/dt}{S_0 A},\qquad (5)$$

where S_0 is the proportion of potassium ions that is radioactive, and A is the surface area of the axon whose radioactivity is being measured (Keynes, 1951c).

Similarly the inward and outward fluxes of sodium ions may be calculated by using ^{24}Na, but a complication is introduced by the much higher concentration of sodium ions in the soaking fluid; hence, as shown in Fig. 5 B, up to 8 minutes have to be allowed for the extracellular ^{24}Na to be washed out by the normal artificial sea-water.

The ionic fluxes for sepia axons as determined in this way are shown in Table 3, together with the potassium fluxes of carcinus axons, and the most complete set of

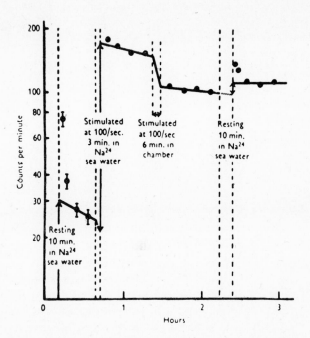

FIG. 5 B. Movements of ^{24}Na in a sepia axon 170 μ in diameter plotted as in Fig. 5 A. For entry of ^{24}Na, 1 count a minute was equivalent to $4\cdot25 \times 10^{-11}$ mol. Na per cm. axon. The vertical bars drawn through the first four counts indicate $\pm$ the S.E.; for the remainder of the counts the S.E.'s were not large enough to be shown in this way (Keynes, 1951*b*).

values for frog muscle (cf. Keynes and Lewis, 1951*a*; Keynes, 1951*b*; 1951*c*; Hodgkin, 1951).

Clearly the sepia axons in Table 3 were not in a steady state, since they were rapidly losing potassium and gaining sodium. A less rapid rate of change is shown by two axons that were specially gently treated (figures in brackets). On the other hand the carcinus axons and the frog muscle were much closer to a steady state for potassium.

TABLE 3

Ionic fluxes across resting membranes (Hodgkin, 1951)

Tissue	Ion	Concentration in mM, i.e. m.mol./ kg. water		Flux in $\mu\mu$mol. cm.$^{-2}$ sec.$^{-1}$		$\dfrac{Inward\ flux}{Outward\ flux}$	
		Outside	Inside	In- wards	Out- wards	Ob- served	Predicted (see text)
1	2	3	4	5	6	7	8
Sepia axon	K$^+$	9·7 (9·7)	272 (330)	17 (11·1)	58 (33)	0·3 (0·33)	(0·35)
	Na$^+$	458	110	61	31	2·0	..
Carcinus axon	K$^+$	11·3	255	19	22	0·86	0·89
M. adductor longus dig. IV (frog)	K$^+$	2·5	110	5	6	0·83	..
	Na$^+$	120	..	12	..	..	..

(b) *Ionic flux and membrane potential*

The ionic hypothesis postulates that, for any given permeability of the membrane, the flux of potassium ions is determined solely by the concentration and potential gradients across the membrane. Ussing (1949*b*) and Teorell (1949) have pointed out that under such conditions the ratio of the fluxes in the two directions depends only on the electro-chemical activities of the ions on either side of the membrane. Assuming equality of activity coefficients (cf. p. 8),

$$\frac{m_i}{m_0} = \frac{C_0}{C_i} e^{EF/RT} \tag{6}$$

where m_i and m_0 are the respective fluxes in and out, C_0 and C_i are the respective concentrations outside and inside, and E is the electrical potential across the membrane, which may be assumed to be 62 mV (Table 2). Thus for the values in brackets in Table 3 the predicted flux ratio would be 0·35, which is in close agreement with the observed ratio of 0·33. For equality of potassium flux the resting membrane potential E_r would be (cf. Eq. 2)

$$58 \log_{10} \frac{330}{9·7} \text{mV} = 89 \text{mV}.$$

The actual potential is lower than this value, and the fluxes of potassium correspondingly modified, on account of the contribution made by the fluxes of sodium and chloride (cf. Eq. 3). Similarly the predicted flux ratio for carcinus axon was 0·89, which is in good agreement with the observed value of 0·86. Thus good experimental support is provided for the postulate of the ionic hypothesis that the potassium flux across the resting membrane is determined entirely by diffusion along electro-chemical gradients. There is no evidence for a special secretory mechanism for potassium at a significant level.

Similar calculation for the sodium flux of the sepia axon gives a very different result, for the calculated flux ratio is 50 as against the observed ratio of 2. If the whole of the inward sodium flux (61 $\mu\mu$mol. cm.$^{-2}$ sec.$^{-1}$) is diffusional, the diffusional outward flux would be only 1·2 $\mu\mu$mol. cm.$^{-2}$ sec.$^{-1}$, leaving almost 30 $\mu\mu$mol. cm.$^{-2}$ sec. $^{-1}$ to be otherwise accounted for. In part this may be attributable to the exchange diffusion of Ussing (1949a), but the outward sodium flux showed no immediate decline when the axons were transferred from sea-water to a solution in which NaCl was replaced by iso-osmolar choline chloride or dextrose (Keynes, 1951b), which should eliminate exchange diffusion. Thus sodium must be actually pumped out against a steep electro-chemical gradient. The resting metabolism of sepia axons is adequate to operate a sodium-pump extruding the 30 $\mu\mu$mol. of sodium per sq. cm. per sec. if the pump efficiency is as low as 6 per cent. However, a much higher value (10 to 40 per cent.) would have to be assumed for the efficiency of the sodium-pump in frog muscle (Hodgkin, 1951). In this respect, at least, the functioning of the membrane is intimately dependent on the metabolism of the underlying cytoplasm. The effect of anoxia and metabolic poisons on the sodium-pump and on the resting membrane potential should be further investigated (cf. Arvanitaki and Chalazonitis, 1949; Lorente de Nó, 1947a; Ling and Gerard, 1949b).

Relative permeabilities to sodium and potassium ions may be calculated from Table 3, on the assumption that the inward fluxes of both are entirely due to diffusion. For the sepia axon sodium is forty-seven times more concentrated than potassium outside, yet its inward flux along the same potential gradient is only 3·6 times the potassium flux. Thus the permeability to potassium is thirteen times greater, which is to be compared with the value of twenty-five times assumed for squid axons by Hodgkin and Katz (1949). Similarly for frog muscle in Table 3 the potassium permeability is calculated to be twenty times greater.

(c) *Ionic flux and membrane conductance.*

The electrical conductance of the membrane is determined by the ease with which ions traverse it. Hodgkin and Huxley (cf. Hodgkin, 1951) have shown that, for a system in a steady state, if the contribution of a univalent ion to membrane conductance is G_n and the flux of that ion is m_n, then

$$G_n = \frac{F^2}{RT} m_n. \tag{7}$$

In Table 3 carcinus axons are sufficiently near to a steady state for a calculation of membrane conductance attributable to potassium ions. The calculated value of 8×10^{-5} mho cm.$^{-5}$ is about half the observed total conductance (15×10^{-5} mho cm.$^{-2}$, the reciprocal of value in Table 4, column 5). Presumably flux of chloride ions accounts for much of the remaining conductance. But more accurate investigations are needed on tissues close to the steady state, for example on frog muscle. Only very approximate calculations are possible for the sepia axons of Table 3 because they are so far removed from the steady state. However, it is of importance in the meantime to find that there is at least agreement in orders of magnitude between the results of tracer measurements of ionic flux and electrical measurements of membrane conductivity.

(d) *Comparison of isolated and* in vivo *conditions.*

The isolated giant axons must be regarded as being in a state of progressive deterioration, far removed from the *in vivo* steady state in which the net sodium, potassium, and chloride fluxes must be zero (cf. Table 3). The simplest initial explanations would be either that the sodium-pump was working inadequately or that the membrane was abnormally leaky to all ions. It is of importance to note that these measurements of ionic fluxes and of membrane potential have been made on giant axons immersed in artificial sea-water which has a potassium ion content (9·7 to 10 mM) far below the values for blood, which are respectively 22 and 17 mM for squid and sepia (cf. Hodgkin, 1951, Table 2). However, increase in the external potassium to such levels and various other procedures (Weidmann, 1951*a*) have not been effective in maintaining the axons in a steady state. Further work is therefore needed before an explanation is available for the steadily deteriorating condition of the isolated giant axons. If substitution can be made for the missing factor or factors, the isolated giant axon will become even more useful in the investigation of the plasma membrane of excitable cells.

If the sodium-pump extrudes sufficient sodium to equalize the inward and outward sodium fluxes, which presumably is the normal condition for the resting membrane *in vivo*, the fluxes of sodium ions would make no *direct* contribution to the membrane potential, which would then be determined almost exclusively by the diffusion of potassium and chloride ions, and hence by their relative inside and outside concentrations (or more strictly activities) as shown in Eq. 1 (cf. Table 2 for frog striated muscle *in vivo*). Under such conditions there would be zero electro-chemical gradient across the resting membrane for both potassium and chloride ions, and alterations of the membrane permeability to either or both would produce merely the same proportional increase in both the inward and outward fluxes, so that there would still be no net flux of either potassium or chloride. Thus the membrane potential would be unchanged, which is in contrast to the situation in the isolated giant axon where an increased membrane potential is produced by a selective increase in permeability to potassium (Hodgkin and Katz, 1949; Hodgkin and Huxley, 1952 a, d, e). These considerations are of great importance when the mechanism of the inhibitory hyperpolarization is being discussed (cf. p. 163).

(e) The sodium-pump

According to the ionic hypothesis a large part of the resting metabolism is utilized in driving the sodium-pump and so maintaining constant the ionic composition of the nerve- or muscle-fibre (cf. p. 7). The sodium-pump could operate in two ways. (i) It could extrude sodium ions as such, and so cause an outward sodium current, which in the steady state would exactly balance the leak of sodium ions into the cell. In this case switching off the sodium-pump, e.g. by some metabolic inhibitor, should cause a rapid fall of membrane potential because of the now unbalanced inward leak of sodium ions. Secondarily this potential change would cause a net loss of potassium ions and a net gain of chloride ions, effects which would slowly lower the Donnan ratio across the membrane, and hence the potential determined thereby (Eq. 1). Sudden restoration of the sodium-pump would cause a rapid rise in the resting potential, perhaps even above its normal value (cf. Hodgkin, 1951, p. 368). (ii) On the other hand the sodium-pump might have no immediate effect on the membrane potential, as for example, if sodium ions were extruded in exchange for other cations such as potassium, or in combination with internal anions. Switching off the sodium-pump would then result merely in a slow fall in membrane potential as the potassium ions leaked out and altered the Donnan ratio (Hodgkin, 1951; Keynes, 1951c). At present the experimental evidence is indecisive because it has not been possible to secure an adequate control of the sodium-pump. For example, anoxia causes a lowering of resting potential of nerve- and muscle-fibres (Lorente de Nó, 1947a; Shanes and Hopkins, 1948; Ling and Gerard, 1949b) and anoxia plus iodo-acetate is still more effective. In part the lowering of the potential could be explained by the increase in external potassium, i.e. to explanation (ii) (Shanes and Hopkins, 1948; Fenn and Gerschman, 1950). But explanation (i) also seems to obtain, for the lost potassium is reabsorbed on cessation of the anoxia (Shanes and Hopkins, 1948; Shanes, 1950). Measurements of the outward sodium flux would give more direct evidence, but so far the only report is the finding that blockage of the oxidative metabolism of sepia axons and frog muscle by cyanide has no effect on the activity of the sodium-pump (Keynes, 1951c). Keynes therefore suggests that the energy-rich phosphate bonds might provide the immediate source of energy for the sodium-pump.

Further investigation of sodium extrusion is of the greatest significance for understanding the *in vivo* steady state. In particular a systematic study of enzyme inhibitors is indicated. Somehow the sodium-pump must be geared to the metabolism of the cell so that the excess sodium influx during activity is subsequently extruded and the initial resting condition restored. The ionic hypothesis in its present form postulates that the sodium-pump in some way determines the level at which the internal sodium concentration is set, and hence the Donnan ratios for potassium and chloride ions and the membrane potential relatable thereto. The simplest hypothesis would be that the internal concentration of sodium is the factor determining the activity of the sodium-pump.

The inadequacy of our knowledge regarding the sodium-pump must be regarded as the most serious deficiency of the present ionic hypothesis. Possibly valuable clues in this perplexing field may be derived from the study of ionic fluxes in such different tissues as frog skin and mammalian erythrocytes (cf. Hodgkin, 1951, p. 369).

4. *Electrical properties of the membrane*

The ionic hypothesis postulates that the various electrical properties of the membrane arise, as it were, secondarily to the relationship of the membrane to the ionic media that lie on either side of it and to the ionic exchanges between these media. Since this has already been implicit in much of the preceding treatment, the electrical properties need only be presented in summary form.

(a) *The resting membrane potential* (E_r)

The exterior is positive to the interior by 61 to 95 mV as shown in Table 2. In the steady state its magnitude is determined in accordance with Eq. 1, while in excised tissue it is in accordance with Eq. 3. The internal and external potassium and chloride ions may be regarded as functioning as the battery for this potential, capable of giving very large ionic currents during electrical activity (Hodgkin, 1951).

(b) *Electrical conductivity of the membrane* ($G_m = 1/R_m$, *cf. column* 5, *Table* 4)

The measurement of electrical conductivity of the plasma membrane has been fully described (cf. Cole and Curtis, 1939; Hodgkin and Rushton, 1946; Hodgkin, 1947; Katz, 1948). The conductivity (which is the reciprocal of membrane resistance, i.e. $1/R_m$, cf. column 5, Table 4) is extremely low when the thinness of the membrane is taken into account. For example, conductivities range from 140×10^{-5} mho cm.$^{-2}$ for the giant nerve-fibres of the squid, 25×10^{-5} mho cm.$^{-2}$ for muscle-fibres of the frog, 15×10^{-5} mho cm.$^{-2}$ for giant nerve-fibres of the crab, to the very low value of 8×10^{-5} mho cm.$^{-2}$ for the sepia giant fibres (Weidmann, 1951*a*). Some idea of the minuteness of the value 8×10^{-5} mho cm.$^{-2}$ can be given by com-

TABLE 4

Electrical constants of muscle and non-medullated nerve-fibres at rest

Tissue	Fibre diameter	Membrane potential	Length constant	Membrane resistance	Membrane capacity	Time-constant	Specific internal resistance	Specific external resistance
1	2	3	4	5	6	7	8	9
	D	E_r	λ	R_m	C_m	τ_m	R_i	R_0
	μ	mV	cm.	Ω cm.^{2}	μF cm.$^{-2}$	msec.	Ω cm.	Ω cm.
Squid axon	500	61	0·25	700	1·5	1·0	30	22
Sepia axon*	200	62	0·6	12,000	1·1	13	40	22
Carcinus axon	30	82	0·2	6,700	1·35	9	60	22
Frog muscle (a) Large fibre sartorius	135	86	0·24	4,100	8	34	250	87
(b) Small toe muscle ext. dig. IV	45	..	0·11	4,000	4·5	18	260	87

* Selection of more reliable values from Weidmann's table (1951a).
Table largely composed from Cole and Curtis (1939); Hodgkin (1947, 1951); Katz (1948); Fatt and Katz (1951); Weidmann (1951a).

paring it with the sea-water in which the sepia axons were bathed. A layer of sea-water 100 A thick (the assumed thickness of the membrane) has a conductivity of $4\cdot5 \times 10^4$ mho cm.$^{-2}$, i.e. a value of $5\cdot5 \times 10^8$ times greater than for the membrane of the sepia axon, that is the flux of ions through the membrane is hundreds of million times slower than in sea-water. One must assume that both the velocity and density of ions are much lower in the membrane than in the bathing fluids. The relationship of ionic flux to membrane conductivity has already been discussed (cf. p. 20).

(c) *Capacity of the plasma membrane* (C_m) (*column 6, Table* 4)

The membrane also has the properties of a condenser, and one can assume that the space charges of the two layers of ions which give it the resting potential are equivalent to the two plates of a condenser that are separated by the lipoid material of the membrane. The capacities of the membranes of giant nerve-fibres of squid, sepia, and crab range from 1·0 to 1·5 μF cm.$^{-2}$ (cf. Cole and Curtis, 1939; Hodgkin and Rushton, 1946; Katz, 1948; Weidmann, 1951a), while a much larger value 4·5 to 8 μF cm.$^{-2}$ is observed for frog muscle-fibres (Katz, 1948; Fatt and Katz, 1951). If a dielectric constant of 3 be assumed for the membrane, it could only be 27 A thick in order to give a capacity of 1 μF cm.$^{-2}$. It is commonly assumed that the membrane capacity behaves as a perfect condenser, and no significant errors appear to arise in making this assumption. However, Cole (1949) points out that the capacity does vary with the duration and frequency of the applied potential in much the same way as with many solid dielectrics, and this behaviour may well give a dielectric constant of 10 or more. Hence an explanation is available for a capacity of 1 μF cm.$^{-2}$ for a lipoid membrane 100 A thick. However, the very high membrane capacitance of frog muscle-fibres and the still higher capacitance of crab muscle-fibres (Fatt and Katz, 1952c) would seem to require the postulate either of a much thinner membrane or of an ultra-microscopically folded membrane.

(d) *Electric time constant of the membrane* (τ_m)

Since the membrane has a capacity, C_m, and resistance, R_m, any small potential change (hyperpolarization or depolarization) produced across the membrane will tend to decay exponentially to the normal resting potential, the time-constant of decay, τ_m, equalling $R_m . C_m$. τ_m is the time to decay to $1/e$ of the initial value. Such a simple situation will arise only when the whole surface is uniformly polarized, so that the charge on any particular part of the membrane is not affected by current flow from other parts.

According to the ionic hypothesis, if the potential gradient across the membrane has been changed so that it no longer balances the concentration gradients for potassium and chloride ions (cf. Eq. 1), there will be a net flux of both ion species until the potential has been restored to the initial level. For example, if the membrane is hyperpolarized there will be a net inward flux of potassium ions and a net outward flux of chloride ions.

Values of τ_m vary considerably for different tissues. Thus relatively direct determinations give values of 1·0 msec., 9 msec., and 13 msec., for squid, crab, and sepia axons respectively and 18 to 34 msec. for frog muscle-fibres, while more indirect measurements (from the decay of junctional potentials) give approximately 2 msec. for muscle-fibres of the rat diaphragm and 4 msec. for cat motoneurones (cf. pp. 138–42).

(e) *Length constant of the fibre* (λ)

Since the conducting core of a nerve- or muscle-fibre is separated from the external conducting medium by the resistance of its surface membrane, it will have the properties of a cable. If a steady potential change is produced at some transverse zone of a fibre, as by the application of a current, there will be a distribution of current along the length of the fibre, just as with a cable. In a few milliseconds the membrane capacity will cease to pass current, and thereafter, if no active response of the membrane supervenes (cf. Chap. II), at any point the change produced in the membrane potential will be proportional to the intensity of the current across the membrane (Fig. 6 A). The intensity of the membrane current, and hence the potential change (Fig. 6 B), will decay exponentially from the focus in accordance with the cable equation

$$P_x = P_0 e^{-x/\lambda} \tag{8}$$

where P_0 and P_x are the potential changes occurring at the focus and x cm. therefrom respectively, and λ is the length constant of the fibre (cf. Katz, 1939, p. 67).

$$\lambda = \left(\frac{r_m}{r_i + r_0}\right)^{\frac{1}{2}} \tag{9}$$

where r_m, r_i, and r_0 are respectively the resistances of unit length of fibre for the surface membrane, the core and the external medium. When the fibre is immersed in a large volume of external conducting medium, r_0 is so small relatively to r_i that it can be neglected (cf. Katz, 1947b) and $\lambda = (r_m/r_i)^{\frac{1}{2}}$.

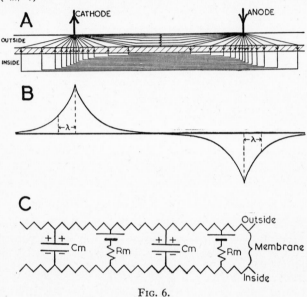

FIG. 6.

FIG. 6 A. Diagram showing flow of electrical current between an anode and a cathode that are applied to the thin film of conducting medium that surrounds a non-medullated nerve- or muscle-fibre, whose membrane is shown in section as the hatched strip. It is assumed that a steady current has been passed for several milliseconds so that at all points the membrane capacity has reached a steady potential, and also that the current is so weak that activation of the sodium and potassium carriers is negligible.

FIG. 6 B. Distribution of membrane potential for condition shown in Fig. 6 A, depolarization being plotted upwards and hyperpolarization downwards. The space constant, λ, is shown as the distance over which the membrane potential decays to $1/e$.

FIG. 6 C. Diagram showing electrical properties of a small segment of the surface membrane, the capacity element, C_m, being shown in parallel with the resistance-voltage element, and the longitudinal resistances of core and of external medium also being shown.

As a cable conductor a nerve- or muscle-fibre is extremely inefficient. Thus both in its insulation, r_m, and its core conductance, $1/r_i$, the fibre is millions of times inferior to a submarine cable, hence its length constant is millions of times shorter. However it will be seen that, for the purpose of propagating impulses, the nerve- or muscle-fibre is a sufficiently good cable (cf. p. 63).

(f) *Summary of the electrical properties of the membrane*

The electrical properties of the membrane can be represented in the conventional diagram of Fig. 6 c, the capacity elements being shown in parallel with the resistance-voltage elements, and the conductivity of the internal and external media being also conventionally represented. The specific resistance of the cell interior has been indirectly evaluated at 30 to 60 Ω cm. for giant axons of marine invertebrates, about 250 Ω cm. for frog muscle, and about 110 Ω cm. for frog medullated nerve-fibres (Huxley and Stampfli, 1951a). This latter value is only about 20 per cent. greater than iso-osmotic Ringer solution, which indicates that the internal potassium ions as well as the anions are almost as freely mobile as in the external Ringer's solution.

II

THE IONIC HYPOTHESIS AND THE ACTIVE MEMBRANE

A. PROPERTIES OF THE ACTIVE MEMBRANE

1. *The action potential of the spike*

ACCORDING to the ionic hypothesis the action potential of the nerve impulse (the spike) is generated by the influx of sodium ions that occurs when the membrane suddenly becomes highly and selectively permeable to them. If it were infinitely permeable to sodium ions, so that the flux of other ions made a negligible contribution, the equilibrium potential would be that of a sodium electrode, E_{Na}, where

$$E_{Na} = \frac{RT}{F} \log_e \frac{(Na)_i}{(Na)_0}. \tag{10}$$

Since $(Na)_i$ is only about 10 per cent. of $(Na)_0$ (Table 1, col. 8), this potential would be about 50 mV in the reverse direction from the resting potential. Thus, under such conditions, the height of the action potential for a fibre in the steady state would be the difference between the potentials given by the potassium and sodium ratios according to Eqs. 1 and 8 respectively. Such calculated potentials in column 6 of Table 2 are seen to be considerably higher than the observed action potentials (column 5). Thus the ionic hypothesis adequately accounts for the action potential, for several factors would make the observed potential lower than the theoretical maximum. For example, the resting potential was lower than the potassium potential, and the summit of the action potential would be expected to occur before equilibrium was established and so to fall short of the *equilibrium potential* for sodium.

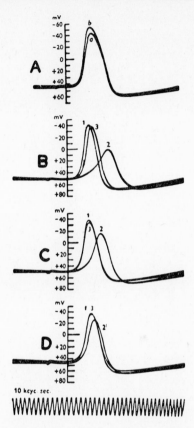

FIG. 7. Action potentials set up by single propagated impulse and recorded as in Fig. 3 A from a squid giant axon when concentration of external sodium was varied, being 1·56, 0·33, 0·5, and 0·71 times normal in *A*, *B*, *C*, and *D* respectively. *B*, *C*, and *D* each show normal action potential (1), action potential after equilibration in the medium with altered sodium (2), and finally action potential after return of axon to normal sodium solution (3). In *A*, *a* is normal and *b* response in 1·56 times normal sodium (Hodgkin and Katz, 1949).

2. *Effect of external sodium concentration on the action potential*

This investigation provides one of the severest tests of the hypothesis that the action potential is caused by the influx of sodium ions. According to Eq. 8 the voltage of the action potential is determined by the logarithm of the ratio of sodium concentrations on the two sides of the membrane. The results of a series of investigations (Hodgkin and Katz, 1949; Nastuk and Hodgkin, 1950; Huxley

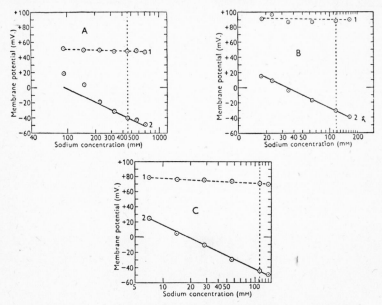

FIG. 8. Relation between sodium concentration in external solution and potential differences across resting and active membrane. Plotted as in Fig. 4 so that resting potentials are positive on ordinate scale and spike potential is plotted downwards from the resting level. External sodium concentration is plotted on logarithmic scale, the perpendicular broken lines giving the normal concentration in Ringer's fluid or sea-water. The continuous lines are drawn with a slope of 58 mV. for a ten-fold change in sodium concentration (Hodgkin, 1951). A. Squid giant axon (Hodgkin and Katz, 1949). B. Frog sartorius muscle (Nastuk and Hodgkin, 1950). C. Frog medullated nerve (Huxley and Stampfli, 1951*b*).

and Stampfli, 1951*b*) are shown for squid giant axons (Figs. 7, 8 A), frog sartorius muscle (Fig. 8 B), and frog myelinated nerve (Fig. 8 c) respectively, the sodium concentrations being plotted on a logarithmic scale. It will be seen that a reduction in sodium concentration causes a small increase in resting potential, but a large decrease in the reversed potential difference across the active membrane. The plotted points of Fig. 8 lie very close to the predicted diminution of action potential of 58 mV for a tenfold diminution of the external sodium (cf. the lines drawn at the predicted slopes in Fig. 8). Within limits set by the damaging effects of high osmotic pressure this relationship also holds for an increase in external sodium concentration to 1·5 times normal (cf. Fig. 7 A). Thus, with the exception of the values of Fig. 8 A obtained with very low sodium concentration on the squid axon (cf. Hodgkin and Katz, 1949; Hodgkin, 1951), the effect of changes in external sodium is in precise accord with prediction from the ionic hypothesis. Furthermore, the rate of rise of the spike, i.e. the rate of entrance of sodium ions, is found, as predicted, to be directly proportional to the external sodium concentration (Hodgkin and Katz, 1949). A more crude test shows that removal of sodium from the external medium reversibly abolishes the ability of nerves to conduct impulses, and that lithium is the only cation that is generally effective as a substitute for sodium (Hodgkin, 1951). This test was first applied by Overton (1902) and has since been carried out on a wide variety of excitable tissues. However, with the smaller medullated fibres of the frog a wide variety of quaternary ammonium ions can substitute for sodium (Lorente de Nó, 1949).

3. *Ionic fluxes across the active membrane*

As predicted by the ionic hypothesis, radio-tracer investigations have shown that there is a large increase in inward sodium flux during activity of a sepia giant axon (Keynes, 1951*b*). Fig. 5 B shows the great increase in uptake of ^{24}Na during stimulation of a sepia axon for 3 minutes at 100 a second, and it also shows that there is a large increase in outward sodium flux. Values determined in this way are respectively 10·3 and 6·6 $\mu\mu$mol. cm.$^{-2}$ per impulse, giving a net uptake of 3·7 (Table 5). Similarly (Fig. 5 A) the potassium fluxes are 0·4 and 4·7 $\mu\mu$mol. cm.$^{-2}$ per impulse, there being a net loss of 4·3 (cf. Table 5). Thus the net gain in sodium per impulse is approximately balanced by the net loss of potassium. A similar result is observed for the net changes as determined by neutron activation analysis (last column of Table 5) both for sepia and squid axons (Keynes and Lewis,

TABLE 5

Ionic fluxes across active membranes

(Keynes, 1951a, b; Keynes and Lewis, 1951a, b)

Tissue	Ion	Concentration in mM, i.e. m. mol./ kg. water		Flux in $\mu\mu mol.\ cm.^{-2}$ per impulse		Net flux in $\mu\mu mol.\ cm.^{-2}$ per impulse	
		Out-side	In-side	In-wards	Out-wards	Difference of columns 5 and 6	Activation analysis
1	2	3	4	5	6	7	8
Sepia axon	K⁺	9·7	272	0·4	4·7	4·3 loss	3·6 loss
	Na⁺	458	110	10·3	6·6	3·7 gain	3·8 gain
Squid axon	K⁺	9·7	255	..	..	..	3·0 loss
	Na⁺	458	149	..	..	..	3·5 gain
Carcinus axon	K⁺	9·7	260	0·5	3·0	2·5 loss	..

1951b). With crab axons the potassium outward flux shows the same relative preponderance (Keynes, 1951a), but there are no determinations of sodium flux. A more indirect method (Hodgkin and Huxley, 1947) had earlier given comparable results for the net potassium flux across Carcinus axon.

The most important conclusion from these measurements of ionic fluxes during activity is that the magnitudes of the net ionic fluxes are more than sufficient to account for the observed potential changes during an impulse, i.e. the ionic hypothesis is supported by direct measurements in this important respect. For example, for sepia axons the action potential is 120 mV and the capacity 1·1 μF cm.$^{-2}$ (Table 4), hence $120 \times 10^{-3} \times 1\cdot1 \times 10^{-6}$ coulombs must flow in through the membrane during the rising phase of the action potential. This quantity of charge would be carried by $(120 \times 10^{-3} \times 1\cdot1 \times 10^{-6}/96,500)$ mol. of sodium ion = 1·4 $\mu\mu$mol. of sodium. Thus the observed net influx of sodium (3·7) is more than twice the amount required to give the action potential in the way postulated by the ionic hypothesis.

Similar calculations also show in squid axons an inflow of sodium in excess of that required for the action potential. Hodgkin (1951) has further pointed out that the large outflow of sodium during activity (6·6 $\mu\mu$mol. cm.$^{-2}$ in Table 5) indicates that the action potential is due to the postulated large increase in sodium permeability, and hence sodium flux in both directions, and not to an inhibition of the sodium-pump.

The net potassium fluxes outwards are likewise more than adequate to restore the membrane from the summit of the action potential to the resting potential. The magnitude of this flux for the sepia axon is also given by the above calculation, i.e. 1·4 $\mu\mu$mol. cm.$^{-2}$ of potassium per impulse; hence the observed net flux outwards (about 4 $\mu\mu$mol. cm.$^{-2}$) is more than double this minimum requirement. With carcinus axon there is also an excess outward flux of potassium, but it is only about 50 per cent.

Thus the accurate evaluation of sodium and potassium fluxes during the impulse has shown that in every respect the ion fluxes are more than adequate to account for the action potential on the basis of the ionic hypothesis. Several problems, however, have arisen.

Firstly, an explanation is required for the measured fluxes being much larger than needed to bring about the electrical changes. Overlapping exchange provides a plausible answer (cf. p. 52).

Secondly, the problems of replacement of the lost potassium and extrusion of the excess sodium arise as soon as long-continued activity is considered. However, a squid axon loses only about one-millionth of its potassium per impulse. Presumably increased activity of the sodium-pump could eliminate the excess sodium (cf. p. 23), and paralleling this postulated activity there is the well-known prolonged increase in nerve metabolism following activity. The positive after-potential may be, in part at least, caused by this increase in activity of the sodium-pump (Hodgkin and Huxley, 1947). Furthermore an increased rate of potassium uptake has been observed after activity (Hodgkin and Huxley, 1947; Shanes, 1950). However, the excised axons are dying tissues often far removed from the *in vivo* steady state, so no complete restitution of ion composition would be expected after activity.

Thirdly, it might be argued that the ion fluxes observed during activity were merely secondary to membrane potential changes that were produced by quite another mechanism. However, this explanation has been refuted by showing that the actual membrane potential changes during an impulse would lead to net ion fluxes of a much smaller order than those observed and even in the opposite direction (Keynes, 1951*b*).

Fourthly, the time-courses of the ion fluxes are not measurable by the radio-tracer technique, which merely gives their cumulative magnitude over minutes. Hence another technique, as described in the next section, is required to give information on the precise time-courses of the ion fluxes. In the first instance this method merely gives the net current conveyed by the ion fluxes across the membrane, and it has to be specially developed in order to identify the ion species.

4. *Effect of membrane voltage on membrane current*

In order to secure the simplest conditions, Hodgkin, Huxley, and Katz (1949, 1952) and Hodgkin and Huxley (1952 *a*, *b*, *c*, and *d*) developed the technique devised by Cole (1949) and Marmont (1949) for subjecting a considerable length of giant axon (about 7 mm.) to uniform electrical conditions. These electrical conditions were applied between a central core electrode and an external electrode, and special precautions were taken to restrict the conditions to the length of axon under investigation. By means of an electronic feed-back device it was possible suddenly to change the potential across the membrane to a pre-determined value and hold it there regardless of any electrical activity of the membrane. The intensity-time course of the current applied by this device, or 'voltage-clamp', is accurately recorded. Initially an extremely brief (total duration only 0·05 msec. with a rapidly reacting 'voltage-clamp') and intense current has to be delivered by the voltage-clamp in order to change the potential of the capacitative element of the membrane to the pre-determined value (Hodgkin *et al.*, 1952). As would be expected, this capacitative current is precisely reversed with reversal of the direction of the change in the membrane potential. This capacitative current is too brief to be seen in Figs. 9 and 10 and will not be further considered.

Subsequent to the capacitative current the membrane potential is maintained constant by delivering with the voltage-clamp a current which would exactly equal the flow of ions across the membrane; for under such conditions the charge on the membrane capacity would remain constant, the capacity itself (and hence the membrane potential for a given membrane charge) being not significantly affected by activity of the membrane (Cole and Curtis, 1939). Thus, because the voltage-clamp maintains the membrane potential at a constant level, the intensity-time course of current delivered by it gives a precise measure of the net ionic current across the membrane. Since the area of the membrane can be directly determined (it was usually about 10 sq. mm.) the density of the net ionic current may be calculated.

In Fig. 9 A there is a remarkable difference between the currents delivered by the voltage-clamp according to the direction of the change that it produces in the membrane potential. When this potential is increased (hyperpolarization) even by as much as 42 mV, a barely detectable steady current has to be applied, i.e. with such potential changes there is only a very small steady ionic current inwards.

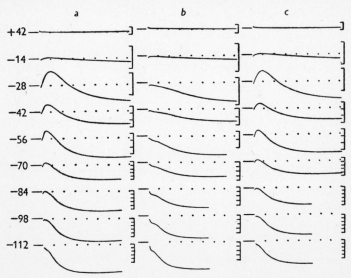

FIG. 9. Records of membrane current of squid giant axon during 'voltage-clamps' in which the membrane potential was suddenly altered and then maintained constant. The alteration of potential is indicated in millivolts by the figures to the left of the curves a, axon in sea-water; b, axon in choline sea-water; c, after returning axon to sea-water. Inward current is shown upwards, one division on the vertical scales always equalling 0·5 mA per cm.² Dots indicate milliseconds on time-scale. Temp. 8·5° C. (Hodgkin and Huxley, 1952a).

For inward current the membrane behaves virtually as an ohmic resistor having a value of over $2,000\,\Omega$ cm.² (cf. Table 4, column 5). In contrast in order to maintain a depolarization of 42 mV, firstly a brief phase of inward current has to be applied, but after less than 2 msec. there is reversal to an outward current which gradually builds up to a steady value, i.e. there is a brief inward ionic current across the membrane which soon reverses to a large maintained outward ionic current. The brief inward current is interesting because it is in the opposite direction to the current flow that would be expected in a simple electrical system. But for the stabilizing influence of the voltage-clamp, this inward current would rapidly cause a further depolarization of the membrane. In fact calculation shows that it would produce a rate of depolarization of the same order as occurs in the rising phase of the spike (Hodgkin et al., 1952). Hence, according to the ionic hypothesis, this inward ionic current should be due to the net inward flux of sodium ions. The inward current with the voltage clamped at various degrees of depolarization is shown in Fig. 9 A, and will be discussed later (p. 40).

The suggestion that the inward current is due to sodium has been rigorously tested (Hodgkin and Huxley, 1952 a and e). In the first place, as shown by Figs. 9 B and C, replacement of the external sodium by choline completely but reversibly removes the transient inward ionic current, which is replaced by a small brief outward current that can be seen preceding the growth of the large outward current (see particularly depolarizations of 56 mV or more in Fig. 9 B). This latter current is but little changed. A simple explanation of the initial hump of outward current is that the membrane depolarization is associated with a large increase in permeability of the membrane to sodium ions which consequently move much more freely along their electro-chemical gradient. When there is a moderate depolarization (for example −28 to −70 mV in Fig. 9 A) and a normal external sodium concentration, the electro-chemical gradient for sodium would be inward, hence the brief inward current. But with zero external sodium the electro-chemical gradient would be outward at all membrane potentials, hence the initial brief hump of outward current would be caused by the internal sodium freely moving outwards across the permeable membrane.

This explanation in turn can be tested by observing the effect of varying both the level of depolarization and the external sodium. With increase of the depolarization be-

yond a critical value there is diminution of the initial inward current and eventually reversal to an initial outward
current. In Figs. 9 A and 10 A the critical reversal points
are about −98 mV and −105 mV respectively, i.e. with
clamping of the membrane potential at such depolarizations the total membrane current is small for about 0·5

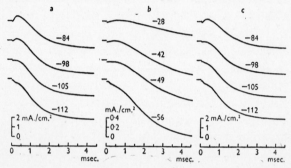

FIG. 10. Records of membrane current of squid giant axon during
'voltage-clamps' as in Fig. 9, but close to equilibrium potential for
sodium. *a*, axon in sea-water; *b*, axon in 10 per cent. sodium sea-water,
i.e. only 10 per cent. of the sodium of sea-water, the remainder being replaced by choline; *c*, axon returned to sea-water. Note ordinate scale
is larger in *b* than in *a* and *c*. Temp. 8·5° C. (Hodgkin and Huxley, 1952*a*).

msec. For the axon of Fig. 10 A we may therefore take a
potential of −105 mV as the equilibrium potential for
sodium ions. This value is in good agreement with the
value calculated by substituting in Eq. 8 the measured
internal and external sodium concentrations.

The 'sodium' explanation may be further tested by varying the external sodium. When it is reduced to 10 per cent.,
Fig. 10 B shows that the equilibrium potential is about
−49 mV, i.e. the value is 55 mV more positive for a ten-
fold change in external sodium, which is very close to the
value of 55·6 mV as determined from Eq. 8 at 8·5° C.
Similar good agreement has been obtained in several such
experiments with diminution of the external sodium
(Hodgkin and Huxley, 1952*a*).

It may be concluded that the experimental tests illustrated by Figs. 9 and 10 have established that, on clamping

the membrane potential at a considerable level of depolarization, there is an initial current attributable to the flux of sodium ions along their electro-chemical gradient. With lower depolarization, e.g. 14 mV in Fig. 9 A, the inward sodium current may be barely detectable (cf. p. 53).

With a maintained depolarization the initial inward current always reverses to a prolonged outward current (Figs. 9 A, 10 A). This current of course is in the same direction as would be expected for such a maintained potential in an ohmic resistor, but differs in its delayed onset and slow rise to a maximum as well as in its enormously greater size (fifty to one hundred times) when compared with the current that flows in the reverse direction during hyperpolarization. For example compare the records at $+42$ and -42 mV in Fig. 9 A. Since this delayed outward current in Figs. 9 A and 10 A is but little affected by changing the external sodium concentration (Figs. 9 B, 10 B), it is highly improbable that it is a sodium current. On the other hand it has the direction and magnitude that are required to explain the repolarization of the membrane during the falling phase of the spike, and which has been postulated as due to the outward potassium current (p. 6).

The identification of the delayed outward current as a potassium current has been tested by measuring the outward flux of potassium ions by radio-tracer technique using ^{42}K (Hodgkin and Huxley, 1952e). As expected, the outward flux of potassium ions is diminished during hyperpolarization and greatly increased during depolarization. In a maintained depolarization there is good agreement between the total electrical charge transported outwards across the membrane, as measured electrically, and the charge that would be carried by the observed outward flux of potassium ions, i.e. approximately 96,500 coulombs per mol. of potassium. Hence it can be concluded that the delayed outward current is attributable to the outward flux of potassium ions. The membrane is so permeable to potassium that its resistance falls to the very low value of about 30 Ω cm.[2] (Hodgkin *et al.*, 1952), i.e. to about 1·5 per cent. of its value for current in the hyperpolarizing direction. This phenomenon of 'delayed rectification' was first accurately investigated by Cole and Curtis (1941).

5. *Sodium and potassium conductances with depolarization and repolarization of the membrane*

There is now good evidence that for about the first 0·5 msec. of depolarization the potassium current is negligible (cf. Fig. 10 A at −105 mV), and also that after several milliseconds the sodium current falls to a negligible level, as is shown by testing with zero external concentration of sodium (Fig. 9 B). In the intermediate zone the two currents overlap, but may be separated by employing the data given in Fig. 9 and making the simple assumptions that variation of the external sodium merely alters the size of the inward sodium current, but not the time-courses of the sodium and potassium currents, and that for a brief initial period the potassium current is negligible. From the time-courses of the sodium and potassium currents so obtained, the respective conductances of the membrane can be directly calculated, since the voltages driving the currents are the differences between the actual potential and the respective equilibrium potentials of the membrane for sodium and potassium, all of which are known (Hodgkin and Huxley, 1952a, 1952e). Values so determined are plotted in Fig. 11 for various levels of depolarization.

These curves represent the time-courses of the sodium- and potassium-carriers that are activated by depolarization. The sodium-carrier rises along a steep inflected curve to an early maximum, and then declines with an approximately exponential decay. On the other hand, after a delayed onset the activation of the potassium-carrier rises relatively slowly to a maintained maximum. Fig. 11 further

shows that, with increasing voltages of the depolarization, there is an approximately proportional increase in
the rates of activation of both carriers, and with a depolarization of about 100 mV maximum levels of activation are attained, both conductances then being about 30

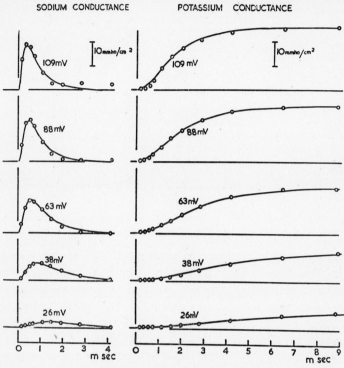

FIG. 11. Changes in sodium and potassium conductances of the membrane of the squid giant axon when it is clamped at the indicated potentials of depolarization. The circles are experimental estimates and the
smooth curves are solutions of equations used to describe these changes
(Hodgkin and Huxley, 1952a, 1952e).

m. mho/cm.^{2} It is of interest also that the rising phases
of both conductances have a high temperature coefficient,
the T_{10} value being about 3.

In order to utilize these measurements of sodium and
potassium conductances in developing a quantitative interpretation of the respective conductance changes during

the nerve impulse, it is necessary also to know the time-courses of the conductances during repolarization of the nerve membrane; for during the nerve impulse repolarization follows rapidly on depolarization (cf. Figs. 7, 14 A). Hodgkin and Huxley (1952*b*) analysed this effect for many levels of repolarization applied at a wide range of intervals after the onset of the depolarization.

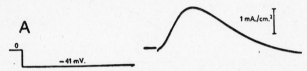

A

0

−41 mV.

1 mA./cm.²

FIG. 12 A. Membrane current produced by 'voltage-clamp' as in Fig. 9 A, the voltage change being shown to left.

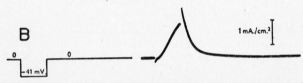

B

0   0

−41 mV.

1 mA./cm.²

FIG. 12 B. Membrane current during brief (0·84 msec.) application of same 'voltage-clamp' as shown in curve to the left. Temp. 6° C.

The simplest situation is illustrated in Fig. 12 B when a repolarization back to the resting level occurs at the height of the inward sodium current (Fig. 12 A). It causes a sudden large increment in this inward current, and then an approximately exponential decay to zero membrane current. Only a small brief fraction of the sudden increment is attributable to current surge into the membrane capacity, and all except this brief capacitative fraction disappears when the external sodium is replaced by choline. Thus on repolarization there is a sudden increment in sodium current, which is precisely the effect that would be expected from the increase so produced in the electrochemical gradient for sodium, provided that the sodium conductance does not instantaneously revert to the resting level. As shown in Fig. 12 c, the sodium conductance calculated as for Fig. 11 falls along an exponential curve to the resting level, there being no appreciable discontinuity at the moment of repolarization (Hodgkin and Huxley, 1952*b*).

Similarly there is a sharp discontinuity in the outward potassium current at the moment of repolarization (Fig. 12 D), but the potassium conductance calculated there-

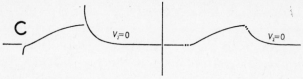

FIG. 12 C. On left is plot of membrane current for brief (1·5 msec.) application of 'voltage-clamp' as in Fig. 12 B, but 29 mV depolarization, and to right is calculated curve of sodium conductance (cf. Fig. 11). Temp. 4° C.

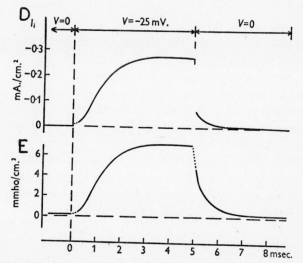

FIG. 12 D. Plot of current during a prolonged (4·9 msec.) application of a 'voltage-clamp' of 25 mV depolarization, the axon being in choline sea-water (cf. Fig. 9*b*) in order to eliminate inward sodium current.

FIG. 12 E. Potassium conductance for Fig. 12 D calculated as for Fig. 11 (Hodgkin and Huxley, 1952*b*).

from (Fig. 12 E) is seen to decay exponentially from the moment of repolarization (Hodgkin and Huxley, 1952*b*).

Thus repolarization affects both sodium and potassium conductances similarly in that both decay exponentially from the moment of repolarization. However, the time-constant of decay is much briefer for sodium than for potassium, the respective values being 0·1 and 6 msec. at 6° C. (Hodgkin and Huxley, 1952e). In comparing the decays in Figs. 12 C and E allowance should be made for the high temperature coefficient, the T_{10} value being about 3 for both. When, for any given depolarization, the amount of repolarization is varied (and not just equal to the depolarization as in Fig. 12), the rate of fall of the conductance increases continuously as the repolarizing potential is raised. This effect recalls the approximate direct proportionality shown in Fig. 11 between the rate of rise of the conductances and the levels of the respective depolarizations.

In conclusion we may tabulate the important findings on sodium and potassium conductances during depolarization and repolarization.

(i) Both conductances rise along an inflected curve when the membrane is depolarized and decline exponentially without appreciable inflexion with repolarization, the rates of rise and fall being approximately proportional to the induced potential changes.

(ii) However, the rates of rise and fall of sodium conductance are much faster (usually ten to thirty times) than for potassium, and on depolarization the rise of potassium conductance has in addition a delayed onset.

(iii) If the membrane is held in a depolarized condition, the sodium conductance rapidly declines from its peak to a low value, while the potassium conductance is maintained indefinitely at its maximum.

B. THE IONIC HYPOTHESIS AND THE PROPAGATED ACTION POTENTIAL

On the basis of the quantitative determination of the effects of depolarization and repolarization on the sodium and potassium conductances of the nerve membrane, Hodgkin and Huxley (1952d, 1952e) have shown that a precise and complete explanation can be offered for the electrical events that occur during the propagated nerve impulse. Movements of other ions such as chloride can play no more than a negligible role. For example, there is no evidence for an increased permeability to Cl⁻ ions (Hodgkin and Katz, 1949; Keynes, 1951b, 1951c), and at most the net Cl⁻ ion flux during activity is small. Keynes and Lewis (1951b) found a small gain of chloride (about 0·6 $\mu\mu$mol. cm.$^{-2}$ per impulse) in squid axons, but concluded that this amount could have passively diffused into the axon along with sodium under the influence of the changed membrane potential that would occur in consequence of the loss of potassium during the prolonged repetitive stimulation.

It has been possible numerically to compute the action potential that would be propagated according to the ionic hypothesis, the computation being based entirely on quantitative determinations of the electrical properties of the axon and of the ionic permeabilities of its surface membrane (Hodgkin and Huxley, 1952d, 1952e). The broken line in Fig. 13 A shows this computed action potential, which is in excellent agreement with the action potential that is recorded as an impulse propagates along this axon, even in respect of the slopes of rise and decline of the action potential and of the rates of propagation which are respectively 18·8 and 21·2 metres a second. This result may be regarded as the ultimate confirmation of the ionic hypothesis.

Fig. 13 A also shows the computed time-courses of the sodium and potassium conductances during the propagated impulse. The rapid rise and decline of the sodium conductance contrasts with the slower rise and much more gradual decline for potassium (cf. Figs. 9, 10, 11, 12). The resting level of potassium conductance (about 0·3 to 0·4 m. mho/cm.^{2}) is barely detectable on that ordinate scale, and it rises to a maximum value about thirty times greater. This value is only about one-third of the maximum

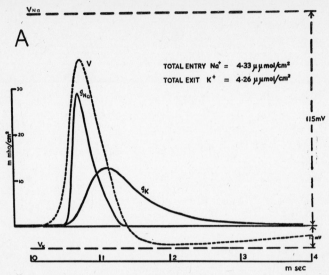

FIG. 13 A. Theoretical action potential (V) and conductance changes (see scale on left) for sodium g_{Na} and potassium g_K (continuous lines), which are obtained by solving numerically equations given by Hodgkin and Huxley (1952d, 1952e), and using values for the squid giant axon at 18·5° C. Depolarization in millivolts is plotted upwards. V_{Na} and V_K give respectively the equilibrium potentials for sodium and potassium, voltage scale being given on right (Hodgkin and Huxley, 1952d).

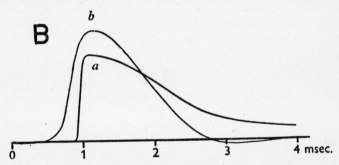

FIG. 13 B. Increase of membrane conductance a of a squid giant axon during an impulse which is shown monophasically b. Appropriate corrections have been made for electrode length and amplifier distortion (Cole and Curtis, 1939).

potassium conductance with maintained depolarization (Fig. 11). As calculated by the inward sodium flux (p. 16), the resting level of sodium conductance is much lower (about 0·02 to 0·05 m. mho/cm.[2]) and hence there is an enormous increase of about 1,000 times as it reaches its peak value of almost 30 m. mho/cm.[2] Thus, in contrast to potassium, the sodium conductance reaches a value almost as large as the maximum produced by depolarization (Fig. 11). This difference is of course attributable to the much faster rise of the sodium conductance with depolarization. By the time that the potassium conductance has reached its peak the repolarization phase of the action potential is already far advanced.

Since the conductance due to other ions is relatively negligible during the propagated impulse, the sum of the sodium and potassium conductances in Fig. 13 A should give the time-course of the membrane conductance during the propagated impulse. Cole and Curtis (1939) showed that, in the squid axon during the rising phase of the spike, there is a rapid increase in conductance to about forty times the resting level and a much slower decline, so that the membrane conductance is still high for some time after the spike (Fig. 13 B). A similar ratio was calculated by Hodgkin (1951) on the basis of the time-constant of decline of the spike potential in a Carcinus axon. The value of 0·2 msec. contrasts with the resting time-constant of about 9 msec. (cf. p. 27), and indicates an increase of about forty-five times in the ionic permeability of the membrane, which must be largely attributable to increased potassium permeability, i.e. to the operation of a special potassium-carrier mechanism.

Similar observations have been made on muscle (Katz, 1942; Fatt and Katz, 1951), and on the membrane at the nodes of medullated nerve (Tasaki and Mizuguchi, 1949). It is of particular interest that Fatt and Katz found a double peak on the conductance curve, one for the rising and one for the falling phase of the action potential, which would presumably be attributable to sodium and potassium conductances respectively. With cardiac muscle there is a long interval between the conductance peaks on the rising and falling phases, which may be correlated with the prolonged plateau of Fig. 14 D (Weidmann, 1951*b*). On the other hand, with the action potentials of giant fibres, the sodium and potassium conductance curves overlap so that little or no dip can be detected, the computed membrane conductance (Fig. 13 A) thus being in good agreement with observation (Fig. 13 B).

It is now possible to give a very complete description of the events occurring during the propagation of the action potential in the isolated giant axon. As shown in Fig. 13 A the equilibrium potentials for potassium and sodium are respectively 12 mV more positive and 115 mV more negative than the resting membrane potential (cf. Table 2). The initial depolarization at the foot of the action potential is attributable to the flow of local currents into the adjacent segment which is occupied by the impulse (cf. Fig. 2 A). This depolarization soon leads to a rise in the sodium conductance (i.e. activation of the sodium-carrier), which, by causing a rapid influx of sodium ions and so further depolarization, has a self-regenerative action on the sodium conductance. However, the sodium conductance soon reaches its peak and begins to decline (cf. Fig. 11), this decline being accelerated as soon as repolarization of the membrane begins, i.e. during the falling phase of the action potential (cf. Fig. 12 C). Meanwhile the potassium conductance has been rising along its delayed time-course. The simultaneous decline of the sodium conductance and rise of the potassium conductance not only prevent the action potential from attaining the equilibrium potential for sodium (V_{Na} in Fig. 13 A), but also bring about the rapid fall in the action potential (repolarization) due to the outward potassium flux exceeding the inward sodium flux. On account of the much slower decline that occurs on repolarization (Fig. 12 E), the potassium conductance remains high long after the sodium conductance has fallen to its low resting level; hence the membrane potential will cross the resting level and approach closely to the potassium equilibrium potential, thus giving the after-positivity of about 10 mV (cf. Figs. 7, 14 A). Finally the resting potential is restored as the potassium conductance slowly reverts to normal along its slow time-course (cf. Fig. 12 E). As shown in Table 2 Carcinus

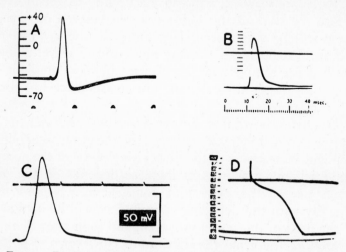

FIG. 14. Resting potentials and action potentials recorded with intracellular electrodes in a variety of excitable cells. The ordinate gives the potential of the internal electrode relative to that of the external solution. In A the zero potential is marked on the scale; in B, C, and D it is given by the horizontal line. Time marks, 2 msec. in A, 1 msec. in C, and 100 msec. in D. A is squid axon (Hodgkin and Huxley, 1945); B is frog muscle-fibre (Nastuk and Hodgkin, 1950); C is cat motoneurone (Brock *et al.*, 1952a); D is Purkinje fibre of dog heart (Draper and Weidmann, 1951).

nerve and frog muscle have resting potentials so close to the potassium equilibrium potential that the observed absence of a positive phase is to be expected (cf. Fig. 14 B).

The time-courses and magnitudes of the net sodium and potassium fluxes may also be calculated from the curves of Fig. 13 A. At any instant the magnitude of the flux will be given by a product of the conductance and the electrochemical gradient. In Fig. 13 A the sodium and potassium gradients may be immediately determined by measuring the potential differences between the actual potential and the respective equilibrium potentials, V_{Na} and V_K

The net inward sodium flux will rise sharply to a maximum as soon as the sodium conductance increases rapidly, but the diminishing electro-chemical gradient for sodium, as V_{Na} is approached, will cause a decline to set in even before the peak of the sodium conductance. Conversely there will be a low secondary hump in the net inward sodium flux during the falling phase of the action potential because temporarily the electro-chemical gradient is increasing faster than the sodium conductance is falling (cf. Fig. 13 A).

The net outward flux of potassium runs a simpler time-course. A small increase will occur as the electro-chemical gradient increases with the early rising phase of the action potential, but a significant increase depends on the delayed rise of the potassium conductance. Necessarily, equality with the declining sodium flux will be achieved at the peak of the action potential, and soon after there is a rapid decline from the maximum. However, the potassium flux remains above the resting level for the whole duration of the after-positivity, the high conductance more than compensating for the low electro-chemical gradient.

Finally, integration of the curves for net inward sodium flux and net outward potassium flux gives the total net flux of each, the values for the curves of Fig. 13 A being 4·33 and 4·26 $\mu\mu$mol./cm.^{2} respectively. These calculated values are in good agreement with values directly determined (cf. columns 7 and 8 of Table 5) for the giant axons of squid and sepia. As pointed out on p. 35 these values are considerably in excess of the ionic fluxes required to change the membrane capacity by the voltage of the action potential, but, as calculated from Fig. 13 A, this discrepancy is due to the considerable overlap in the phases of inward sodium flux and outward potassium flux.

C. EXPLANATIONS BASED ON THE IONIC HYPOTHESIS AND ELECTRICAL HYPOTHESIS OF IMPULSE

1. *Subthreshold activity and the threshold for excitation*

A stimulus that is too weak to generate a propagated impulse may produce at the region of the cathode a local graded response that resembles a miniature action potential (Katz, 1937; Hodgkin, 1938). Such subthreshold responses have now been shown to occur even when large areas of the membrane of giant axons are subjected to uniform depolarization (Marmont, 1949; Cole, 1949; Hodgkin *et al.*, 1949, 1952; cf. Fig. 9 A at −14 mV). As Hodgkin (1951) points out, the subthreshold response may be simply explained by the graded and reversible relation between membrane potential and sodium conductance (Fig. 11).

When, under the cathode, the membrane is depolarized by flow of current, there will be, of course, an increase in the electro-chemical gradient for potassium and chloride ions (cf. p. 26), and a consequent increased flux of these ions in a direction that tends to restore the resting potential, i.e. outward flux of potassium and inward flux of chloride. For brief stimuli there will be no significant alteration of potassium permeability. With a small depolarization there is only a small increase in sodium conductance, so that the inward sodium current is less than the outward potassium and chloride current. The inward sodium current will merely delay the repolarization of the membrane. There has been a local response.

Above a critical value of initial depolarization, the inward sodium current will be larger than the outward potassium and chloride current. Consequently the membrane will be depolarized still more and have regenerative action on the sodium-carrier, and so on until eventually the full-sized propagated impulse is generated, though at just critical conditions this process may take some time, even as much as a millisecond at room temperature

(Hodgkin, 1938; Hodgkin *et al.*, 1952). Thus the *membrane threshold* is defined by the potential of depolarization at which the inward sodium current exceeds the outward potassium and chloride current and so initiates a self-regenerative action. This critical voltage for excitation is about 15 mV in the squid axon (Marmont, 1949; Hodgkin *et al.*, 1949, 1952).

The all-or-nothing relationship of the *propagated* impulse to the initial generating agent immediately follows from this explanation.

2. *Refractory period*

The refractory period refers to a period after the setting up of a propagated impulse during which the nerve is refractory to stimulation. Normally the absolutely refractory period terminates about the end of the spike potential (Gasser, 1937; Grundfest, 1940), while the period of raised threshold or relative refractoriness continues with decrementing intensity for many milliseconds thereafter. The conditions causing this depressed state have been investigated by means of the voltage-clamp technique (Hodgkin and Huxley, 1952c).

After a brief depolarization by a square wave, such as in Fig. 12 B, a much smaller inward sodium current is generated by a second similar depolarization. There has been some inactivation of the sodium-carrier mechanism, and, by testing at various intervals, it is shown that regeneration occurs slowly with a time constant of about 10 msec. at 6° C. However, even immediately after a pulse such as that of Fig. 12 B, the inactivation is found to be far from complete, an observation that may be correlated with the fact that repolarization had been induced (by termination of the square wave) while there was still a considerable sodium conductance. After a longer depolarization there would have been a more complete inactivation.

The intense depolarization during the propagated impulse (cf. Figs. 13 A, 14) would largely inactivate the sodium-carrier and hence cause the subsequent refractory state. But a further factor is the high level of potassium conductance that continues after the action potential (Fig. 13 A). Both these factors will raise the threshold (cf. Hodgkin, 1951), i.e. the level of depolarization which is required in order that the inward sodium current due to the sodium-carrier is just larger than the outward current due to flux of potassium plus chloride ions.

3. *Accommodation*

When a constant current is passed through a nerve there is raised excitability under the cathodal electrode and depressed excitability at the anodal region. However, if the current is continued, both these changes decline towards normal over many milliseconds, an effect which is called accommodation (cf. Erlanger, 1937; Katz, 1939). Furthermore, after cessation of the current, there is a period of raised excitability at the anodal region and depressed excitability at the cathodal, post-anodal exaltation and post-cathodal depression respectively (Erlanger, 1937). The voltage-clamp experiment has also revealed the mechanism of these effects (Hodgkin and Huxley, 1952c).

A continued depolarization at a level too low to cause appreciable activation of the sodium-carrier, e.g. -8 mV, nevertheless brings about a relatively slow decline (time constant of milliseconds) of the effectiveness of a large testing depolarization, i.e. it causes a partial inactivation of the sodium-carrier. Conversely a continued hyperpolarization causes the development of an increased effectiveness of a large testing depolarization, i.e. it has a regenerative action on the sodium-carrier. In this way it is shown that at the resting potential only about 60 per cent. of the sodium-carrier is normally available for activation, the remaining 40 per cent. being available for regeneration by a sufficient hyperpolarization.

Clearly such observations will explain both accommodation and the subsequent states of post-cathodal depression and post-anodal exaltation, for after inactivation the sodium-carrier shows a slow recovery over several milliseconds (p. 54). The recovery of excitability after post-cathodal depression would thus be expected to have much the same time-course as the relatively refractory period, as is actually observed (cf. Erlanger, 1937).

4. *Axonal swelling with activity*

It has recently been shown (Hill, 1950; Tobias, 1952) that prolonged repetitive stimulation of giant non-medullated axons causes an extremely small transient swelling, which runs a time-course of development and subsidence that is measured in minutes. The average increase in diameter of a 200 μ axon was 0·22 μ for 10,000 impulses.

The ionic hypothesis seems to provide a satisfactory explanation. In the first place the swelling would be due to an inward movement of water, which is attributable to the increase in osmotic pressure within the fibre. Hill suggested that most of this increase is quantitatively accounted for by the inward transfer of sodium plus chloride ions (cf. p. 47), while about 10 per cent. would be attributed to the exchange of sodium for potassium ions during the nerve impulse. This latter effect is of significance because sodium ions are osmotically more active than potassium ions on account of their larger hydrosphere (cf. Hill, 1950). However, Keynes and Lewis (1951*b*) have been unable to find the relatively large chloride influx postulated by Hill, and suggest that some process other than inward ionic flux may be responsible for much of the uptake of water.

5. *Saltatory transmission in myelinated axons*

Vertebrate myelinated axons have a thick myelin sheath which is interrupted by nodes at distances of the order of a millimetre, so that for a few microns the surface membrane of the axon is unprotected by myelin. First Lillie (1925) and later the Japanese investigators, Kato (1936) and especially Tasaki (1939), and finally and conclusively Huxley and Stämpfli (1949, 1951*a*, 1951*b*) and Frankenhauser (1952) have shown that the active changes in impulse propagation are confined to the nodes, while the myelin sheath acts as an insulator, forcing the local circuits to act some distance ahead of the active region. An effective discussion of the criticisms of the saltatory theory is given by Hodgkin (1951).

In terms of the ionic hypothesis the following explanation may be developed, it being assumed that the events characteristic of activity in non-myelinated axons and muscle-fibres occur also at the nodal regions of the surface membrane, but not in the internodal regions, which are covered by myelin. Ahead of the active region the outwardly directed current will be largely restricted to the nodal membrane (cf. inset diagram to left of Fig. 15), which will consequently be rapidly depolarized to the critical potential for effective sodium-carrier activation. The rapid sodium entry at the node depolarizes the whole exterior of the internodal region by local circuit action, and of course also the nodes farther ahead. It is to be noted that on account of the thick (about $2 \cdot 5 \, \mu$) myelin sheath the internodal regions have a very low capacity ($0 \cdot 0025 \, \mu F$ cm.$^{-2}$). The falling phase of the action potential would be attributable to the usual process of sodium-carrier inactivation and outward flux of potassium, which presumably occurs largely at the nodal region, though internodal contribution is not yet excluded.

The crucial test of this explanation was provided by Huxley and Stämpfli (1949) and Frankenhauser (1952) who measured the radial current flow occurring in various short lengths of a single medullated fibre (Fig. 15). The radial current in the internodal regions is mainly outward, though some records show a trace of inward current during the falling phase of the action potential. But the inward current during the rising phase of the action potential is absolutely restricted to the nodal regions. There-

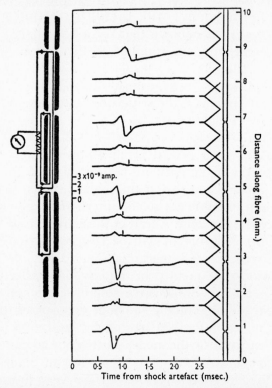

FIG. 15. Distribution and time-course of membrane current in a frog's myelinated nerve-fibre (Huxley and Stämpfli, 1949). Each curve shows the difference between the longitudinal currents at two points 0·75 mm. apart on the fibre. The position of these two points relative to the nodes on the fibre is indicated by the forked lines on the diagrammatic fibre to the right. The vertical mark above each graph shows the time when the membrane potential reaches its peak at that position on the fibre. Outward current is plotted upwards (note ampere scale). To the left is shown another diagrammatic fibre with lines of current flow indicated to illustrate outward and inward membrane current at nodes as impulse propagates upwards.

fore the activity of the nerve, i.e. the inward sodium flux, is restricted to the nodes. The myelin-covered areas thus contain no mechanism for generating action current, and, with respect to the action currents, act merely as a capacity and resistance in parallel. Just as with non-myelinated axons, the resting potential is logarithmically related to the external potassium concentration (Fig. 4 c), and the action potential is logarithmically related to the external sodium concentration (Fig. 8 c; Huxley and Stämpfli, 1951b). Propagation in a myelinated axon is likewise rapidly blocked by deficiency of external sodium. Thus the propagation is essentially similar in the two types of axons.

Evaluation of the electrical characteristics of the node and internode reveals that the device of intermittent myelination has made the myelinated axon an extremely efficient structure (cf. Hodgkin, 1951). According to the ionic hypothesis the smallest quantity of sodium that must enter unit area of the surface membrane during one impulse is given by dividing the Faraday (F) into the product of the capacity per unit area and the action potential (cf. p. 35). For a frog myelinated fibre 14 μ in outside diameter, the myelin sheath is about 2·5 μ thick, and the capacity is about 13 $\mu\mu$F per cm. length, while the non-myelinated axon of identical diameter (9 μ) the capacity would be about 2,800 $\mu\mu$F per cm. length. Thus, on account of the myelination, the amount of sodium inward flux that is required to produce the action potential is reduced to less than 0·5 per cent. and yet the velocity of the impulse is increased by five to ten times. Until the actually effective area of the active membrane at the nodes is known, it will not be possible to evaluate accurately the electrical and permeability properties of the surface membrane at the nodal region.

6. *Problems relating to size of nerve-fibres*

In non-myelinated axons made of similar materials, i.e. with identical properties of the surface membrane and of the axonal core, the conduction velocities of propagated impulses will be proportional to the space-constant, λ (p. 27). When *in situ* in the body, $\lambda = (r_m/r_i)^{\frac{1}{2}}$ (p. 28), and, since $r_m \propto D^{-1}$ and $r_i \propto D^{-2}$, $\lambda \propto D^{\frac{1}{2}}$, where D is the axonal diameter. Pumphrey and Young (1938) have observed that in non-myelinated nerves there is approximately this predicted relationship between D and the velocity of propagation V, i.e. that $V \propto D^{\frac{1}{2}}$.

In an important theoretical paper Rushton (1951) has shown that, if myelinated nerves are evolved to conduct impulses as fast as possible for any given diameters, they would be made of the same specific materials and have dimensional similarity of structure of the internodes. In every respect where it can be tested there is found to be this dimensional similarity of structure. For example, the axon diameter bears an approximately constant ratio of 0·6 to over-all fibre diameter, and the internodal length is approximately proportional to fibre diameter. However, there is as yet no reliable data on the size of the nodal clefts in the myelin sheath, which on the above postulate is predicted to have the same width for all fibre diameters. It is of particular interest that the ratio of axon diameter to fibre diameter should be close to the theoretical optimum for conduction velocity (0·6). Hence it seems likely that the conduction velocity of impulses has been an overriding factor in determining nerve structure.

The dimensional similarity of internodes leads to the prediction that all space relations of myelinated nerve-fibres are the same if scaled in units of internodal length, for example that the space constant and the conduction velocity of impulses are proportional to fibre diameter, D, which accords closely with experimental observations (Hursh, 1939). Since with non-myelinated fibres $V \propto D^{\frac{1}{2}}$ and with myelinated fibre $V \propto D$, it follows that, below a transitional over-all diameter, nerves will conduct fastest if non-myelinated, and above this size if myelinated. The general thesis that conduction velocity is of prime importance in nerve design (Rushton, 1951) is supported by the fact that vertebrate nerve-fibres are myelinated above this transitional size of 1 to 2 μ, and non-myelinated below this size.

Rushton (1951) has also considered the problem of the factors determining the size of the fibres employed for any given function. The importance of speed in the myotatic reflex will be evident from later considerations (p. 186), and the afferent nerve-fibres for this reflex are largest and conduct fastest (Lloyd, 1943b, c). With slower reflexes such as the flexor reflex, it becomes of less importance to save time in the afferent path, and correspondingly the afferent fibres are smaller and slower (Lloyd, 1943b). An extreme example is the small size of the fibres subserving the very slow reactions mediated by the sympathetic system. Thus it appears that economy prevails in determining fibre size, fibres being made as small as possible consistent with the required speed of the reactions that they mediate. An interesting example is considered on pp. 183–8.

D. CONCLUSIONS ON IONIC HYPOTHESIS

It may be concluded that so far the ionic hypothesis has given an extremely satisfactory explanation of the principal events that occur during the propagation of the nerve impulse in non-myelinated nerves, in muscle-fibres and in myelinated nerves. It has survived such a rigorous series of experimental tests that its essential validity seems no longer in doubt.

But much remains obscure. For example, the problems of the control and mode of operation of the sodium-pump have already been discussed (p. 22). Again, so little is known about the nature of the sodium- and potassium-carrier mechanisms that very little effective discussion is possible. Hodgkin *et al.* (1949) made an attempt to explain the relation of sodium-carrier activity to membrane potential by postulating a lipoid-soluble carrier bearing a large negative charge. Hodgkin (1951), however, concludes that 'in certain respects this hypothesis gave good agreement with experimental results; but subsequent work has shown that some of its predictions are in serious conflict with experiment'. There is as yet no modification of this carrier-hypothesis that brings it into line with experimental findings, but at least it would seem that the large increases in sodium and potassium permeability would have to be explained by some carrier mechanism that operates, as shown by the virtually unchanged capacitance, without any substantial molecular reorientation of the surface membrane. A further problem is the delayed onset of the potassium-carrier activation, an effect which is of vital importance in the genesis of the impulse, for otherwise the inward sodium flux would not so effectively depolarize the membrane.

Other outstanding problems are provided by the negative and positive after-potentials that follow single or repetitive activity in nerve-fibres. Lorente de Nó (1947a) has shown that the negative after-potential is explicable by the delayed repolarization of the L-fraction of the membrane potential. But there is as yet no explanation of the L-fraction in terms of the ionic hypothesis, so the genesis of the negative after-potential remains obscure. Likewise there is little to offer in explanation of the positive after-potential. Possibly, as Hodgkin and Huxley (1947) suggest, it is attributable to the increased activity of the sodium-pump, which in this way is eliminating the sodium that has been carried in during the impulse.

Finally the remarkable effects of high and low calcium concentrations are not yet accounted for by the ionic hypothesis (cf. Monnier, 1949). The original carrier hypothesis of Hodgkin et al (1949) attempted to do this by postulating that the Ca^{++} ion competed with the Na^+ ion for the carrier molecule.

Thus the ionic hypothesis evidently provides a great many problems for experimental investigation, and despite its amazing success it would still appear to be in an early stage of development. However, it forms an essential basis for the development of hypotheses relating to events at all other levels of the nervous system and will be used in this way in subsequent chapters.

E. SUMMARY

These first two chapters have been an attempt to review the whole story of the properties of nerve- and muscle-fibres that specifically concern the generation and propagation of impulses.

Essentially the fibre is a polarized cable-like structure so designed that potential changes in one segment are decrementally transmitted by local current flow to adjacent segments. The membrane is so constituted that, when depolarized to a critical level, a self-regenerative process of high sodium conductance, the sodium-carrier, is activated. By carrying sodium inwards the membrane is further depolarized, and so on to reversal of the membrane potential, and even almost to the equilibrium membrane potential for sodium. But this process quickly is inactivated and meanwhile is being succeeded by a potassium-carrier process that quickly restores the original potential by means of outward potassium movement.

While these events are in progress, the cable-like spread causes further segments to be invaded. Thus the cable structure, though very defective (cf. p. 28), i.e. heavily decremental, is able to ensure that each segment in turn is depolarized adequately for its own self-regenerative process to take over and lift the potential change to the full height, and so on all along the fibre.

With myelinated nerve this spreading activation is made much more efficient by the insulating myelin sheath that covers all but a fraction of a per cent. of the fibre, so that for large fibres the cable is much more efficient—about ten times—for the spread of depolarization in a given time.

Furthermore, because the ionic exchange (gain of sodium ions and loss of potassium ions) is restricted to the narrow nodal areas between the myelinated segments and the internodal regions have such a low capacity (p. 59), there is probably less than 1 per cent. of the ionic exchange that occurs with non-myelinated axons of similar size; hence there is an enormous gain in efficiency.

It is important to distinguish clearly between the carrier activities during the impulse and the sodium-pump activity that goes on between impulses. Thus carrier activity is merely a device for increasing selectively the sodium and potassium conductances of the membrane. The ions so carried move along electro-chemical gradients and do work, which is essentially the provision of the E.M.F. for the electric currents that ensure the further spread of the impulse. On the other hand the sodium-pump pushes sodium out against a heavy electro-chemical gradient and so requires a source of energy from metabolism within the fibre. Probably in the first instance this is provided by the activity of phosphorylating enzymes (cf. p. 23). However, the metabolism and the associated heat production of nerve at rest and during activity is beyond the scope of the present inquiry. The heat production of nerve has recently been reviewed by Hodgkin (1951).

III

TRANSMISSION ACROSS PERIPHERAL JUNCTIONAL REGIONS

In the preceding two chapters attention has been focused on the events in a single nerve- or muscle-fibre. We have seen how an impulse can propagate along such a fibre, and indeed that it can travel along the whole length of a fibre in an all-or-nothing manner. Moreover, it would invade all branches of that fibre in the same way. But eventually a nerve impulse comes to the end of the nerve-fibre, either to an ending in contact with a nerve-cell (a synaptic ending) or to an ending on a muscle-fibre or gland-cell. Transmission across such junctions occurs by a special mechanism, which will be first studied in the vertebrate neuro-muscular junction, where our information is most complete. For recent systematic treatments of transmission across peripheral junctional regions, reference may be made to the review by Fessard and Posternak (1950) and the monograph of Rosenblueth (1951).

A. NEURO-MUSCULAR JUNCTIONS IN VERTEBRATE SKELETAL MUSCLE

1. *Introduction*

It is generally agreed that essentially the same mechanism of transmission occurs at all neuro-muscular junctions in vertebrate skeletal muscle. So far as possible it will be convenient to concentrate on neuro-muscular transmission from large motor nerve-fibres in the frog, because it is the only situation where there has been investigation with intracellular electrodes (Fatt and Katz, 1950, 1951, 1952*b*; Nastuk, 1950). A general statement of the chemical hypothesis of neuro-muscular transmission is best preceded by a brief account of the structure of the junction (cf. Gutmann and Young, 1944; Couteaux, 1945, 1947).

A motor nerve-fibre branches extensively as it approaches its termination so that one fibre innervates usually more

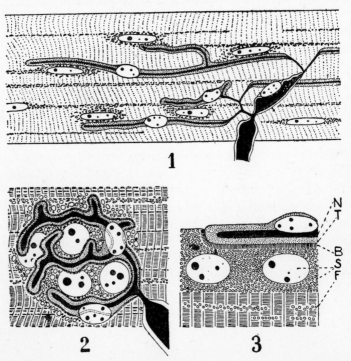

FIG. 16. Semi-schematic drawing by Couteaux (1945) showing motor-nerve endings on the surface of muscle-fibres in the frog (1) and mouse (2). (3) is drawing of section in order to show the relationships of nerve-fibre (N), teloglia (T), and the specialized end-plate membrane (B). S is the sarcoplasm of the end-plate and F the striated myofibrils. Similar conventions are adopted in drawings 1 and 2.

than one hundred muscle-fibres. The nerve branch to a muscle loses its myelin sheath before it penetrates the sarcolemna, a connective tissue sheath of the muscle-fibre, and then it terminates in a more or less complex ending, the detailed structure of which varies greatly in different species. For example in the frog the fine terminal nerve filaments extend for even 100 μ or more along the muscle-fibre, whereas in the mammal the ending is much more compact (Fig. 16).

There is no continuity between the nerve terminal and the muscle-fibre, but merely a close contact over an extensive area, the nerve terminals often lying in grooves indenting the muscle-fibre surface. Histologically the cytoplasms of the nerve- and muscle-fibres are separated as if each has a continuous bounding membrane. This discontinuity is confirmed by electrical recording, for an electrode in the muscle-fibre fails to disclose, before the muscle response, even a trace of the nerve-spike potential (Figs. 20, 24, 27). Furthermore, as shown in Fig. 16, there is evidence of special structural features not only in the narrow cleft at the junction, but also immediately under the surface membrane of the muscle-fibre at the junctional region. This specialized junctional region of the muscle is called the motor end-plate. Recording with an intracellular electrode reveals that the resting polarization of the end-plate membrane is virtually identical with that of the membrane elsewhere, as shown schematically in Fig. 17 A (Fatt and Katz, 1951).

2. The chemical hypothesis of neuro-muscular transmission

An enzyme system, choline-acetylase, in the motor nerve-fibre manufactures acetyl-choline, ACh, which is stored within the motor fibre at a relatively high concentration (Fig. 17 A, cf. Feldberg, 1945, 1950a, 1950b). When an impulse passes along the fibre, a brief jet of ACh is liberated. Presumably this liberation occurs particularly freely from the non-myelinated nerve terminals (cf. Fig. 17 B). The liberated ACh diffuses across the junctional region to become attached momentarily to special receptors on the surface membrane of the motor end-plate. At the same time it is being rapidly hydrolysed by the specific cholinesterase that is concentrated at the end-plate surface (Fig. 17 B) so that its complete destruction occurs in a few

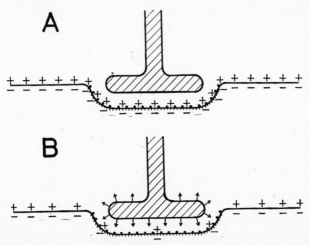

FIG. 17. Diagram of neuro-muscular junction to show, *A*, the normal resting state with uniform polarization of end-plate and muscle-fibre membrane, and *B*, the depolarization (but not reversal of potential) that occurs when a nerve impulse has released ACh. Electric currents (not shown) cause the depolarization to spread decrementally away from the motor end-plate. The region containing choline-acetylase and the store of acetyl-choline is hatched, i.e. it is restricted to the nerve-fibre. The arrows in *B* indicate diffusion of ACh when it is liberated. The special end-plate membrane is shown by a striated border (cf. Fig. 16), and the dots applied to its exterior represent the probable site of specific cholinesterase.

milliseconds. However, during the brief period of its attachment, it rapidly depolarizes the surface membrane of the motor end-plate (Fig. 17 B), thus giving rise to the end-plate potential, henceforth e.p.p. Adjacent regions of the membrane in turn become depolarized by discharging into this sink at the junctional region. If this depolarization reaches a critical level, i.e. if the inward sodium current due to sodium-carrier activation becomes greater than the outward current due to potassium and chloride ions (cf. p. 53), a muscle impulse is generated adjacent to the end-plate region and propagates in both directions along the muscle-fibre, causing it in turn to contract. Meanwhile even the acetyl-choline that acted on the surface membrane will have been destroyed by the cholinesterase.

Thus the postulated sequence of events may be written:

(i) ACh synthesis by choline-acetylase and storage in the nerve terminal;

(ii) ACh liberation by nerve impulse;

(iii) diffusion of ACh, its momentary combination with membrane receptors and generation of end-plate potential;

(iv) destruction of ACh by cholinesterase, which is largely concomitant with (iii);

(v) depolarization by end-plate potential of adjacent regions of muscle-fibre to critical level at which impulse is generated.

The experimental testing of this hypothesis has been going on since 1934 (cf. the reviews by Dale, 1937; Eccles, 1936, 1937; Brown, 1937b; Acheson, 1948; Kuffler, 1948, 1949 a; Hunt and Kuffler, 1950) and in some respects we are now in a position to develop the hypothesis quantitatively. In particular an extremely important quantitative study of the electrical and ionic events has recently been made by Fatt and Katz (1951). In discussion of the hypothesis particular attention will be paid to these quantitative investigations.

3. Testing and development of chemical hypothesis

(a) Initial experimental investigation

Originally this hypothesis was proposed on the basis of experiments which showed that, when motor nerve-fibres were stimulated, minute quantities of ACh were liberated into fluid perfused through the muscle (Dale, Feldberg, and Vogt, 1936), and that intra-arterial injection of very small amounts of ACh evoked impulses in muscle-fibres and hence caused their contraction (Brown, Dale, and Feldberg, 1936; Brown, 1937a). In addition there was evidence that curare-like substances blocked neuro-muscular transmission by depressing the response of muscle to injected ACh, and not by depressing the liberation of ACh. The action of inhibitors of cholinesterase (Brown, Dale, and Feldberg, 1936; Bacq and Brown, 1936; Brown, 1937a) provided further supporting evidence, for it would be predicted that under such conditions the ACh would be prolonged and intensified in its action, and this was observed. The excitatory effect of a single nerve volley was prolonged to give a brief waning tetanus of the muscle, and in curarized muscles there was restoration of neuromuscular transmission. The details of this work were discussed in contemporary reviews (Dale, 1937; Brown, 1937b; Eccles, 1936, 1937).

At that time the effectiveness of neuro-muscular transmission was studied by recording either the contraction of the muscle or the propagated impulses in the muscle-fibres. Much more rigorous tests became possible when the end-plate potential was discovered (Göpfert and Schaefer, 1938) and shown to be a depolarization of the end-plate by the transmitter mechanism, and to be an intermediary response which in turn generated a muscle impulse if it reached a critical size (Eccles, Katz, and Kuffler, 1941; Eccles and Kuffler, 1941a; Kuffler, 1942a). An exhaustive study of the end-plate potential has now been made by Fatt and Katz (1951) with intracellular electrodes in frog muscle (cf. Fig. 3 B), attention being concentrated particularly on its role in generating a muscle impulse (cf. pp. 82, 83).

But, before this very recent development, an important advance had been made by Kuffler (1943, 1945; cf. Buchthal and Lindhard, 1939) who showed that direct application of ACh in a relatively low concentration (10^{-6}) specifically depolarized the end-plate region and so caused it to generate muscle impulses (Fig. 18). Other regions of the muscle were at least 1,000 times less sensitive to the depolarizing action of ACh. Possibly the special histological structure of the end-plate membrane (Fig. 16) is related to this striking pharmacological specificity. By similar direct test, curare-like substances were shown to depress

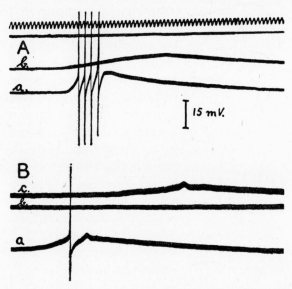

FIG. 18. Potentials recorded at site of application of ACh to the end-plate of a single nerve-muscle fibre (Kuffler, 1943). In A*a*, 10^{-6} ACh caused a sharp depolarization leading on to four impulses, while in A*b* a lower concentration of ACh gave only a prolonged depolarization. A similar response was given in B*c* by 10^{-6} ACh except that a small local response supervened, while in B*a* a stronger concentration evoked an impulse followed by a local response. Time, 1 d.v. = 10 msec.

the sensitivity of the end-plate to ACh by as much as 100 times. Furthermore, it has now been shown by histochemical methods that specific cholinesterase is concentrated at the neuro-muscular junction (Koelle, 1950, 1951; Couteaux, 1951), probably in the space between the nerve terminal and the end-plate, and even attached to the surface as shown schematically in Fig. 17 B.

(b) *End-plate potential in curarized muscle*

(i) *Time-course and spatial distribution of end-plate potential.* The end-plate potential (e.p.p.) can be recorded uncomplicated by a muscle spike when neuro-muscular transmission is depressed as, for example, by curarine in Fig. 19, where there is graded depression to complete blockage. Fig. 20 A shows a series of e.p.p.'s set up by a single nerve impulse and recorded by a micro-electrode in a muscle-fibre at progressively longer distances from the end-plate. At the end-plate there is a rapid depolarization of the membrane, reaching a maximum in about 1 msec., from which decline is at first very rapid and then progressively slower. The relationship of this e.p.p. to the transmitter action can be discovered by investigation of the e.p.p.'s at increasing distances away. The farther the micro-electrode is from the end-plate, the slower the rise, the later the summit and the slower the decline, as may be seen in the superimposed tracings of Fig. 21. The explanation is that local-circuit action is causing a redistribution of the charge (actually, the 'deficit of charge') over the membrane progressively farther from the end-plate in a manner described by the classical cable theory (cf. p. 27; Hodgkin and Rushton, 1946). In parenthesis it may be noted that strictly speaking the name end-plate potential is a misnomer, for, though arising at the end-plate, the

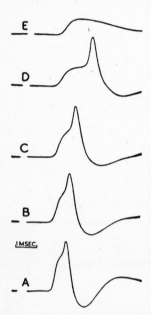

FIG. 19. Potentials generated by nerve impulse at the end-plate region of a single muscle-fibre, the recording being by an external electrode applied to the fibre immersed in saline: *A*, normal e.p.p. and spike response; *B* to *E*, progressive curarization causing blockage at *E* (Kuffler, 1942*a*).

potential is not restricted there, but spreads decrementally therefrom along the muscle membrane. According to the cable theory the *total charge* on the muscle membrane should decay exponentially once the transmitter action at

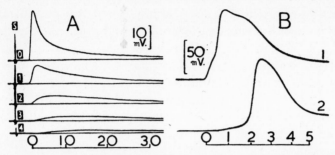

FIG. 20. Potentials set up by single nerve impulses and recorded from inside frog muscle-fibre (Fatt and Katz, 1950). *A*. End-plate potentials recorded in curarized muscle at indicated distances (in millimetres) from the nerve-muscle junction. *B*. Potentials in normal muscle-fibre at nerve-muscle junction (1) and 2·5 mm. away (2). Time scale in milliseconds.

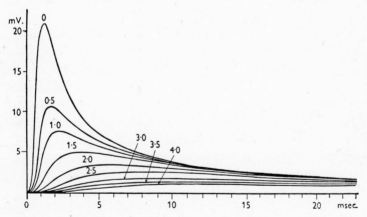

FIG. 21. Superimposed synchronized tracings of e.p.p.'s recorded as in Fig. 20 A at distances from end-plate centre indicated approximately in millimetres (Fatt and Katz, 1951).

the end-plate has ceased. This exponential decay is of course given by the normal resting ionic flux, largely potassium plus chloride current (cf. p. 26), which recharges the membrane capacitance, i.e. the time-constant of the decay would be expected to be identical with that already determined for the muscle membrane by electrical measurement (cf. Table 4, column 7). The total deficit of charge on the membrane at any instant is determined by plotting the spread of e.p.p. along the fibre at that instant, and computing the area under the curve (cf. Fig. 22 A).

It is seen in Fig. 22 B that the total deficit of charge decays exponentially from a maximum that is attained in less than 2 msec. The time-constant of decay averages 24 msec., which is within the range for frog muscle in Table 4. The important conclusion is that the active depolarization process at the end-plate has ceased within 2 msec. of the onset of the e.p.p., and thenceforth the potassium and chloride ion currents of the membrane along the length of the muscle-fibre are restoring the charge to the membrane with their characteristic time-constant. Necessarily at any point on the membrane the intensity of this current is proportional to the voltage of the depolarization. Increase of curarization merely depresses the size of the e.p.p. without otherwise affecting its spatial distribution or decay rate.

Thus the conclusion is that, at least in curarized frog muscle, the transmitter substance is extremely brief in its action (2 or at most 3 msec.), and thereafter the e.p.p. is decaying by virtue of the passive electrical properties of the muscle membrane. The early onset of exponential decay in Fig. 22 B indicates that the muscle membrane does not itself contribute any regenerative excitatory action by virtue of its own sodium-carrier activity.

A similar conclusion about the duration of the transmitter action had previously been reached by less satisfactory methods. For example, Kuffler (1942c) showed that the later exponentially decaying part of the e.p.p. was destroyed by a propagated muscle impulse, exactly as occurred with the catelectrotonus set up by an applied electrical pulse. He arrived at an approximate duration of

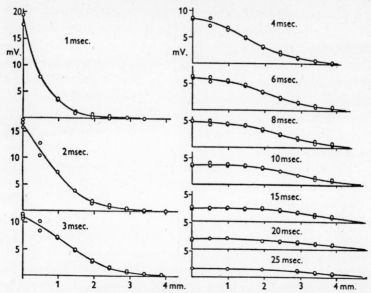

FIG. 22 A. Spatial distribution of e.p.p. for curves of Fig. 21 at indicated times after its onset (Fatt and Katz, 1951).

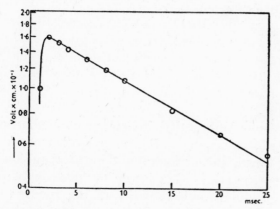

FIG. 22 B. The ordinate of each point is the measured area between the curve and base line in Fig. 22 A at that corresponding time interval (plotted as abscissae) after the onset of the e.p.p. (Fatt and Katz, 1951).

transmitter action (3 to 4 msec.) by observing the size of the e.p.p. that was rebuilt when the early phases of the e.p.p. were similarly subjected to the destructive influence of a muscle impulse. A similar duration was also estimated by analysis of the time-course of the e.p.p., it being assumed that the exponentially decaying phase was attributable to the passive repolarization of the muscle membrane (Eccles *et al.*, 1941; Katz, 1948). These methods are of interest because they are the only ones that can be applied to the analysis of post-synaptic potentials in the central nervous system (cf. pp. 138–42).

Time-courses and spatial distributions comparable with those of Fig. 20 A are observed when the e.p.p.'s of frog muscle are recorded with surface leads, the muscle-fibre or fibres being in air or paraffin (Eccles *et al.*, 1941; Kuffler, 1942*c*). However, e.p.p.'s of mammalian muscles have a much shorter time-constant of decay. The value of 4·5 msec. for cat's soleus (Eccles *et al.*, 1941) would be abbreviated because it was recorded in the volume of the surrounding inactive muscle (cf. also Fig. 19); but, with a strip of rat diaphragm suitably insulated, the e.p.p. decays with a time-constant as brief as 2 msec. (cf. Fig. 28 B; Jeffries, 1952; Ludbrook and Whyte, 1952). Such measurements are of course subject to considerable distortion by spread along the cable-like structure of the muscle-fibre (cf. Fig. 21), but partial compensation would be effected by the spatial dispersion of the end-plates (cf. Eccles *et al.*, 1941).

It is also of interest that, in lightly curarized mammalian muscle, local responses (cf. p. 53) often occur in the muscle membrane surrounding the end-plate (Eccles and O'Connor, 1941), i.e. in contrast to lightly curarized frog muscle, sodium-carrier activity of the adjacent muscle membrane may make a significant addition to the depolarization produced at the end-plate. Possibly the more compact structure of the mammalian end-plate (cf. Fig. 16) may account for this difference. However, local responses of the muscle membrane adjacent to the end-plate are even seen in frog muscle-fibres in response to a second nerve volley shortly after a conditioning volley (Kuffler, 1942*b*) and to locally applied ACh (cf. Fig. 18).

(ii) *Ionic fluxes and the end-plate potential* (Fatt and Katz, 1951). It is of great importance to study precisely the way in which the e.p.p. is produced because it might well provide the basis for understanding the local potentials at other junctional regions. Presumably the liberated ACh acts on the end-plate membrane and causes somehow a net inward flow of cations and also perhaps a net outward flow of anions. In the curarized frog muscle the sum of these net currents must be large enough to provide for the whole of the observed 'deficit of charge' on the membrane.

The total deficit of charge of the membrane is shown in Fig. 22 B to be twice (because Fig. 22 B is computed for one direction only from the end-plate) $1 \cdot 6 \times 10^{-3}$ V. cm. multiplied by the capacity per unit length of the fibre. Since the fibre of Fig. 22 B had a diameter of 135 μ and a capacity of 6 μF cm.$^{-2}$, the capacity per cm. length was $2 \cdot 55 \times 10^{-7}$ F. Thus $2 \times 1 \cdot 6 \times 10^{-3} \times 2 \cdot 55 \times 10^{-7} = 8 \times 10^{-10}$ coulombs of charge was transferred across the end-plate membrane and hence the net flux of univalent ions was about 8×10^{-15} mol. In the absence of curarine this calculated flux would have to be increased about 4 times, in order to allow for the depressant action of curarine on the e.p.p. (cf. Fig. 19). Thus the value of 3×10^{-14} mol. is the minimum quantity of ions which is caused to flow across the normal end-plate by the transmitter liberated by one impulse. This is an amazingly large amount in view of the small size of the end-plate. For example, assuming that the effect is restricted to the end-plate immediately under the nerve terminals, it would occur for an area certainly no larger than 10^{-4} cm.^{2} (cf. Fatt and Katz, 1951) and be virtually complete within 1 msec. (cf. Fig. 22 B). Thus the rate of flux would be 300,000 $\mu\mu$mol. cm.$^{-2}$ sec.$^{-1}$, which is about thirty times the maximum rate of sodium influx (9,600 $\mu\mu$mol. cm.$^{-2}$ sec.$^{-1}$) during the rising phase of the spike in sepia axon. Assuming that the rate of rise of the muscle spike is 450 V/sec. (Nastuk and Hodgkin, 1950; Fatt and Katz, 1951) and the membrane capacity 6 μF cm.$^{-2}$, the maximum rate of sodium flux through the muscle membrane during an impulse would be as large as 28,000 $\mu\mu$mol. cm.$^{-2}$ sec.$^{-1}$, which is still only a tenth of the minimal rate at the end-plate.

In view of the extremely large ionic flux at the end-plate, it is of interest to estimate the ionic content of the space between the nerve terminals and the end-plate membrane, i.e. the space of the neuroglia terminale (T) in Fig. 16. If it be assumed to have a concentration of cations of 0·1 M, then it would have 10^{-4} mol. per cc. and 10^{-8} mol. for a space of 1 μ thick and 1 cm.^{2} in area, which is about thirty times the calculated flux per cm.^{2} of end-plate membrane. Thus, even if the junctional space is somewhat less than 1 μ, the ionic reservoir immediately outside the end-plate is adequate for several impulses, and it would of course be reconstituted by diffusion in a few milliseconds. Diffusion of ACh in the junctional space will be discussed later (p. 93).

No estimate has been made of the ACh liberated by a single impulse in frog muscle, but the value of 20 $\mu\mu$g. was determined by Brown, Dale, and Feldberg (1936) for a single impulse in the cat's *Gastrocnemius*, and allowing for 200,000 muscle-fibres, and hence end-plates, in the muscle, there would be an output of 10^{-16} g. of ACh by the nerve terminals of one end-plate (cf. Acheson, 1948). However, there would be a considerable falling off in the liberation of ACh by the successive impulses during the long tetanus that necessarily had to be used in order to collect measurable quantities of ACh, hence this value of 10^{-16} g. should be increased say to 2×10^{-16} g., or 10^{-18} mol., it being remembered that at the low stimulus frequencies that were employed (5 to 15 a second) there would be much less decline than at the higher frequencies of Fig. 28 B. If 10^{-18} mol. is also assumed to give the order of magnitude of the ACh liberated on a frog's end-plate, each molecule of ACh would be responsible for the flux of some 30,000 ions across the end-plate membrane in 1 msec. Presumably the total ionic flux would be larger than this value, which merely gives the sum of the net inward cationic flux and the net outward anionic flux. It is evident that the ACh must initiate a very remarkable and efficient process for ion transport. The nature of this mechanism will be discussed in reference to the effect of the e.p.p. on the muscle spike (p. 82).

(iii) *Time-course and mode of liberation of ACh.* Even when measured so that a maximum allowance is made for the very brief conduction time of the nerve impulse, the latent period of the e.p.p. in frog muscle is at least 0·6 msec. (Kuffler, 1948, 1949 *a*). Presumably this latent period is in part due to diffusion time of ACh across the narrow cleft between the nerve terminal and the end-plate, and it is also possible that, on reaching the end-plate, the ACh molecules take a brief time to become attached thereto and cause the change that initiates the ionic flux. Further, it seems likely that, since ACh is a cation at the pH of body fluids, its liberation by the nerve impulse will follow much the same time-course as the efflux of potassium ions (cf. Fig. 13 A). Possibly this delayed liberation accounts for a considerable portion of the end-plate delay. The actual process of liberation of ACh raises a further problem as yet unsolved. Does it first diffuse out as a cation under the favourable electro-chemical gradient provided by the nerve action potential, or does it, as seems probable, require a special carrier mechanism to increase its diffusion rate? Whatever the mechanism of liberation, the brief duration of the depolarization process at the end-plate (about 2 msec. in Fig. 22 B) indicates that the period of liberation of ACh does not outlast the nerve impulse, or at least the potassium ion efflux.

(iv) *Action of anti-cholinesterases.* As shown in Fig. 23 A and B, anti-cholinesterases lengthen the duration of the rising phase of the e.p.p. and slow its decline. Under such conditions there has been no study of the total membrane charge as in Fig. 22, but there is clearly a large increase in the 'deficit of charge' which would be attributable to a more intense and a much more prolonged action of the

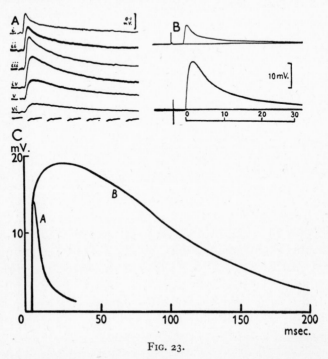

FIG. 23.

FIG. 23 A. E.p.p.'s set up by single nerve volleys in curarized (1/10,000 tubocurarine) frog's sartorius. (i) is control e.p.p. and from (ii) to (vi) a progressively increasing concentration of prostigmine is added. Time, 10 msec. (Eccles and Macfarlane, 1949).
FIG. 23 B. E.p.p.'s of curarized muscle recorded as in Fig. 20 A before and after addition 10^{-6} prostigmine. Time, msec. (Fatt and Katz, 1951).
FIG. 23 C. Superimposed tracings of e.p.p.'s recorded as in Fig. 23 B, but A for uncurarized muscle with transmission blocked by low sodium and B after addition 10^{-6} prostigmine (Fatt and Katz, 1951).

transmitter (cf. Eccles, Katz, and Kuffler, 1942; Eccles and Macfarlane, 1949; Fatt and Katz, 1951). With progressive increase in the anti-cholinesterase concentration the slowing of the e.p.p. reaches a maximum (cf. Fig. 23 A),

which presumably occurs when inactivation of cholinesterase becomes virtually complete, for example, at about
10^{-4} M for prostigmine on frog muscle (Eccles and Macfarlane, 1949). However, concomitantly, high anti-cholinesterase concentrations also depress the e.p.p., probably by
a curare-like action (cf. Fig. 23 A).

When neuro-muscular transmission is depressed by low
external sodium instead of curarine, an anti-cholinesterase
produces an enormous prolongation of the transmitter
action for 100 msec. or more (Fig. 23 C), an effect which
was also observed in the uncurarized preparation (Eccles
et al., 1942). It has been calculated that in Fig. 23 C the
anti-cholinesterase has increased by as much as fifty times
the charge that has been transferred across the end-plate
membrane to a value of about 10^{-7} coulomb (Fatt and
Katz, 1951, 1952b). Thus, according to the calculation on
p. 79 each molecule of acetyl-choline causes the flux of
over a million ions across the end-plate membrane when
it is protected by an anti-cholinesterase from immediate
enzymatic destruction. When cholinesterase action is completely suppressed, it may be assumed that ACh is removed
from the end-plate region solely by a process of diffusion,
for there is no other process for rapidly destroying ACh
in muscles (Fillenz and Hanafin, 1947; Eccles and Macfarlane, 1949).

(v) *Spontaneous local activity of nerve terminals.* Miniature randomly occurring end-plate potentials have been
recorded in frog muscles (Fatt and Katz, 1952a). As with
the e.p.p.'s they are diminished by tubocurarine and increased and prolonged by prostigmine. Presumably there
is a random activity (local responses) of small areas of the
terminal nerve-fibres, and minute jets of ACh are released
thereby. Thus the surface membrane of the nerve terminals would appear to be in an unstable state. Possibly this
instability is necessary in order that the nerve impulse can
invade with an adequate factor of safety the greatly expanded surface of the motor-nerve terminals (cf. p. 65).

(c) *The end-plate potential in normal muscle*

In the normal muscle-fibre the e.p.p. rises several times more steeply than in curarized muscle, and leads on to a propagating muscle spike (Eccles *et al.*, 1941; Kuffler, 1942*a*; Nastuk, 1950; Fatt and Katz, 1951). The records of Fig. 24 are action potentials set up by a nerve impulse

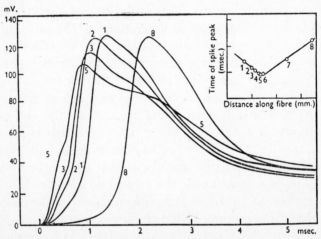

FIG. 24. Muscle potentials generated by single nerve volley and recorded intracellularly as in Fig. 20 B. Distances from end-plate (at position 5) being shown by the corresponding number in the inset diagram where time of spike peak is plotted against the distance along the fibre (Fatt and Katz, 1951).

in a muscle-fibre at various positions relative to the end-plate zone (see numbered positions in inset). Record 8 shows the muscle spike after it has propagated over 2 mm. from the end-plate zone and hence is virtually uncomplicated by the e.p.p. (cf. Fig. 20 B2). On the other hand, in record 5 at the end-plate zone (cf. Fig. 20 B1), there is a large initial e.p.p. step leading at about 50 mV to a muscle spike that was nearly 20 mV lower than at positions 8 or 1. Transitional records are seen at positions 2 and 3. The hump on the declining phase of the spike provides a third distinguishing feature of the end-plate zone. The significance of these three features will be discussed in turn.

(i) When an appropriate electrical stimulus is directly applied through a micro-electrode to any part of the muscle-fibre, an initial step of similar voltage and time-course is seen leading on to the muscle spike (Fig. 25). Thus an e.p.p. appears to initiate a muscle spike in the same way as does a depolarization by an electrical stimulus.

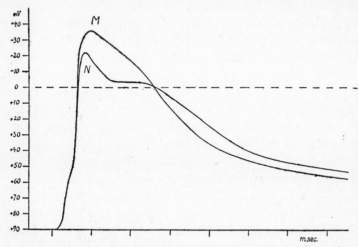

FIG. 25. Diagram showing electrical potentials recorded as in Fig. 20 B and evoked by a single nerve impulse (*N*), and a suitably adjusted direct current pulse (*M*), which was applied through another micro-electrode at the end-plate region (Fatt and Katz, 1952*b*).

In both the muscle spike would be initiated, when, in the adjacent muscle membrane, the inward sodium current due to sodium-carrier activation just exceeded the outward potassium and chloride current (see p. 53). There is no special problem in the generation of a muscle spike by the e.p.p., for the membrane adjacent to the end plate reacts to depolarization in precisely the same way as other regions of the membrane. There must be continuity of the end-plate membrane with the adjacent muscle membrane and there can be no transverse membranes to impede the flow of current from one region to the other. The spike usually arises when the e.p.p. is about 40 mV, a voltage which it attains at about 0·5 msec. after its onset.

(ii) On the other hand no simple explanation will account for the lowered spike height at the end-plate region (cf. Fig. 25). For example, Fatt and Katz (1951) excluded three possible explanations: recording at the point of origin of an impulse in contrast to the propagated impulse; continuous application of a depolarizing current during the spike, such as might be provided by the continuous depolarizing action of the e.p.p.; a special property of the end-plate region of the muscle-fibre. For example, this last suggestion was disproved by showing that muscle impulses propagating into the end-plate region, or directly set up there (Fig. 25), generated a full-sized spike. Hence they were led to formulate the important hypothesis that the transmitter (ACh) produces a drastic change of the end-plate membrane, whereby it becomes highly permeable to all ions and not merely sodium (cf. Fatt, 1950), i.e. that the end-plate membrane suffers a transient insulation breakdown, much as was originally postulated by Bernstein (1902) for the nerve impulse, and in contrast to the selective permeability changes to sodium and potassium that are now known to occur (cf. Chapter II). As a consequence, during the active phase of the e.p.p., the end-plate membrane acts as an effective short-circuit of the potential generated by the muscle spike in the adjacent muscle membrane. However, if the spike arises very late, the active phase of the e.p.p. may be virtually over; hence an explanation is available for the observed absence of any significant depression of the spike under such conditions.

As shown in Fig. 25 this postulated short-circuit effect reduces to almost half the active membrane potential of the spike, i.e. the reversal of potential at the spike summit. However, strictly, the zero potential for the postulated short-circuit would be the liquid-junction potential between the myoplasm and the external fluid, which would probably be about 14 mV below the zero line of Fig. 25 (Nastuk and Hodgkin, 1950; Fatt and Katz, 1951). Thus in Fig. 25 the effect of the short-circuit would be to reduce the active potential from about 49 mV to 35 mV, i.e. to about 70 per cent. In order to produce such an effect the short-circuiting resistance of the end-plate membrane must be approximately twice the effective resistance of the muscle membrane

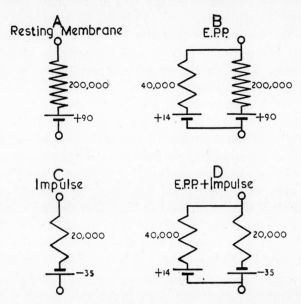

FIG. 26. Electric circuit diagram showing resistances and potentials across membrane of muscle-fibre and motor end-plate. *A* and *C* give conditions of muscle-fibre at rest and during impulse. Note reversal of potential from +90 to −35 mV, and diminution of 'cable resistance' (cf. Fatt and Katz, 1951) of fibre from 200,000 to 20,000 Ω. *B* and *D* give conditions of end-plate at height of transmitter activity, where its resistance is only 40,000 Ω and there is a series potential of about +14 mV due to liquid-junction potential between myoplasm and external solution. Ignoring time factors (reactances are omitted) the e.p.p. in *B* would be 63 mV, and in *D* the active membrane potential during the spike would be reduced from 35 mV (as in *C*) to 19 mV (cf. Fig. 25) by the shunting of the end-plate plus liquid-junction potential (modified from Fatt and Katz, 1952*b*).

at the spike summit. This latter value was directly determined, and shown to be about 20,000 Ω by measuring the potential added to the muscle spike when a known extrinsic current was passed outwards across the muscle membrane (Fatt and Katz, 1951). Thus it is postulated that, despite its minute size, the end-plate membrane has a resistance as low as 40,000 Ω during the end-plate potential and so acts as an effective short-circuit of the action potential developed in the adjacent muscle membrane, as is shown diagrammatically in Fig. 26 (Fatt and Katz, 1952*b*).

On the assumption that the end-plate membrane has an area of 10^{-4} cm.^{2} (cf. p. 77), the specific membrane resistance, Rm, for the end-plate membrane would be only 4 Ω cm.^{2}, i.e. about one-tenth of the specific resistance (40 Ω cm.^{2}) calculated for the active muscle membrane (Fatt and Katz, 1951). It may be noted that such an extremely high conductance of the active end-plate membrane has already been postulated in order to account for the ionic flux that must occur across it in generating the e.p.p., the calculated ionic flux being at least ten times greater than the net inward sodium flux during a spike in the muscle-fibre (cf. p. 78). It is pertinent to recall that Katz (1942) demonstrated that the neuro-muscular transmitter produced a brief phase of low resistance at the end-plate region and even suggested that ACh might act by rendering the membrane more permeable to other ions.

(iii) This postulated high conductance of the end-plate membrane also provides an explanation, without additional assumptions, of the hump that occurs on the falling phase of the spike (cf. Figs. 20 B1, 24, 25). The short-circuiting of the muscle membrane not only reduces the sodium potential of the active membrane (Fig. 26 D), but also causes it to discharge more quickly as the high sodium permeability fails. Likewise the restoration of the resting membrane potential by the outward potassium current will be delayed by the short-circuit. In other words the short-circuiting action of the highly conducting end-plate membrane will tend to maintain the membrane potential at about zero (or, more strictly, the liquid junction potential), an effect which would produce the hump, as may be seen in Fig. 25.

(d) *The end-plate permeability hypothesis*

Thus, in summary, the potentials which a nerve impulse generates at the end-plate region of normal muscle have been explained by the subsidiary hypothesis which postulates that it becomes very freely permeable to all ions (Fatt and Katz, 1951, 1952b). This same postulate of course would account also for the e.p.p. of curarized muscle, which would be thus attributable to a process that differs radically from the process giving the action potential of the nerve or muscle impulse. However, before accepting that interpretation of the genesis of the e.p.p., Fatt and Katz (1951) excluded experimentally two alternative explanations: that the transmitter mechanism in some way caused the transfer across the membrane of a fixed number of ions, as for example by extrinsic current flow from the motor-nerve terminals; or that there was a selective permeability to one species of ion, as for example occurs during the impulse. This was done by investigating the effect of a wide range of membrane potentials, as produced by applied extrinsic currents, on the e.p.p. (cf. Fig. 27 A, B, C). They found that under such conditions the size of the e.p.p. was approximately proportional to the initial membrane potential (Fig. 27 D), a result which would be expected if the e.p.p. is generated by the short-circuiting action of a non-specific ion permeability, but not on either of the other two explanations.

A sufficient degree of hyperpolarization prevents the e.p.p. from reaching that level of depolarization at which a muscle spike is generated. Hence the time-course of the e.p.p. and the maximum degree of its depolarization may be observed in the uncurarized muscle (Fig. 27 B). As in the curarized preparation (Figs. 20 A, 21), the maximum depolarization of the end-plate is reached in just over 1 msec., but it is much larger in size, usually about 70 per cent. of the resting potential (cf. Fig. 27 B). However, with different end-plates the size showed great variability and in a few the e.p.p. was so small that it normally failed to set up a muscle spike (Fig. 27 C), which would occur if it caused less than about 40 per cent. depolarization. On the other hand it was sometimes so large that anodic block was difficult to produce (Fig. 27 A). Presumably this varia-

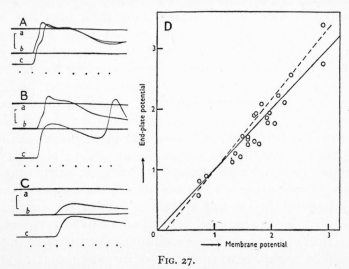

FIG. 27.

FIG. 27 A to C. Effect of artificially increased resting potential on size of e.p.p. in four separate end-plates. *b*, normal resting potential; *a*, zero membrane potential; *c*, increased resting potential. In B*c* late impulse arising at another end-plate. Potential scales, 50 mV; Time, msec.

FIG. 27 D. Relation between size of e.p.p. and initial membrane potential for series of records as in Fig. 27 A, B, C. Abscissae give resting potentials scaled to unity for normal value. Ordinates give e.p.p.'s measured relative to normal e.p.p. (the *b* records of Figs. 27 A to C). Continuous line gives predicted direct proportionality, while broken line gives prediction when allowance made for 14 mV liquid-junction potential (Fatt and Katz, 1951).

bility in size of e.p.p., and consequently in the safety factor of transmission, is determined by the size of the junctional contact area and by the quantity of liberated ACh.

Evidently, despite its extremely high intensity, the ionic flux across the end-plate is usually only two or three times above the critical value for transmission. Even at its maximum rate during the rising phase of the spike, the net inward sodium flux was calculated to be less than 10 per cent. of the ionic flux required to give the normal e.p.p. (p. 78). Thus a transmitter mechanism which merely activated the sodium-carrier would be inadequate for neuro-muscular transmission, and the special effect of membrane breakdown with non-specific ion permeability seems necessary for this purpose. Alternatively transmission could be ensured by increasing the area of contact of nerve terminals with the end-plate. But new difficulties would be created by this structural change, for the necessarily large expansion in the surface area of the nerve terminals would lower the safety factor for propagation into them, with a consequent danger of blockage at that stage of the transmission process (cf. Eccles, 1949). However, it would seem that this difficulty has been minimized by the great instability of the terminal nerve-fibres (Fatt and Katz, 1952a).

A very special problem is in fact created by the economic necessity of using an impulse in a relatively small nerve-fibre and ending to generate, with an adequate safety margin, an impulse in a very much larger muscle-fibre, especially as that fibre has an exceptionally large specific membrane capacity (cf. Table 4, column 6). It will now be appreciated that the only feasible solution appears to be the liberation by the nerve impulse of a chemical transmitter which causes a catastrophic breakdown in the ionic resistance of the subjacent muscle membrane.

4. *Special problems arising with repetitive stimulation*

(a) *Mobilization of ACh during repetitive stimulation*

At the onset of repetitive nerve stimulation there is in the frog a brief phase of potentiation during which the successive end-plate potentials are increased to several times the initial values. Then follows a decline to a subnormal size (Fig. 28 A*a*, *c*, *e*, *g*). There is good evidence that both the initial potentiation and the subsequent de-

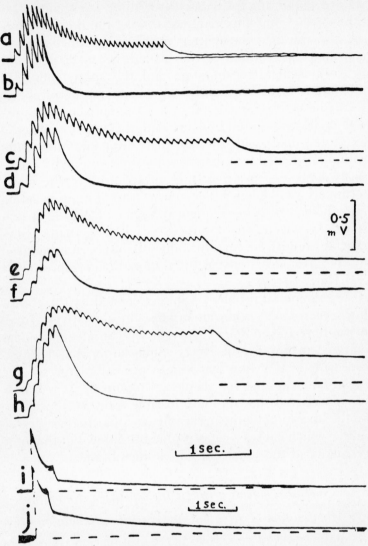

FIG. 28 A. E.p.p.'s recorded from frog's sartorius as in Fig. 23 A, but with repetitive nerve volleys at 100 a second. *a* and *b*, long and brief tetani with muscle curarized by 1/20,000 tubocurarine. *c* and *d*, *e* and *f*, *g* and *h*, similar pairs of tetani at progressively increasing doses of prostigmine. *a* and *b* at higher and *f* at lower amplification than scale shown. Records *i* and *j* are similar to *e* and *g* but at much slower time-scale (Eccles and Macfarlane, 1949).

cline are attributable to corresponding changes in the liberation of ACh by the successive impulses (Eccles, 1948; Eccles and Macfarlane, 1949). Possibly mobilization of a preformed store of ACh accounts for the potentiation,

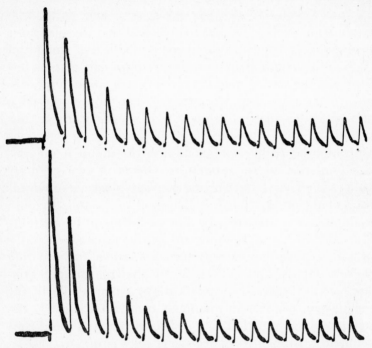

FIG. 28 B. E.p.p.'s recorded from an isolated and curarized strip of rat diaphragm in response to repetitive volleys in phrenic nerve at 180 a second. Lower record was taken at height of post-tetanic potentiation following stimulation of phrenic nerve at 300 a second for 15 seconds. Upper record is control response in absence of potentiation. Note that in lower record there is no potentiation after the first two responses, there being replacement by depression from the fourth response onwards. Temp. 39° C. (Liley and North, 1952).

though an alternative explanation is that the nerve impulse more completely invades the complex branching structure of the nerve terminal (cf. Fig. 16). Partial exhaustion of the stored ACh would account for the subsequent decline in output. As shown in the latter parts of the records of Fig. 28 A*a*, *c*, *e*, and *g*, the decline soon becomes stabilized at a plateau, the rate of manufacture of ACh then presumably balancing the rate of its liberation.

With mammalian neuro-muscular transmission, on the other hand, no initial phase of potentiation is observed. Decline of the successive e.p.p.'s begins at the outset (Fig. 28 B; cf. Eccles *et al.*, 1941, Fig. 17), and with rapid stimulation such a low level is reached that the plateau is negligible. It appears that there is much less storage of ACh in the mammalian motor nerve terminals. After a few impulses the rate of manufacture of ACh would appear to govern the rate of its liberation. Exhaustion of the ACh store and the relatively slow rate of its replacement thus would account for the rapid onset of neuro-muscular block with high frequency tetanization of the motor nerve.

Summation of the excitatory effects of two or more volleys is effective in relieving a curare blockage of neuro-muscular transmission (cf. Eccles *et al.*, 1941). In both mammals and frogs this facilitation seems to be attributable entirely to the building up by the successive e.p.p.'s of a membrane depolarization that is critical for initiating muscle impulses (cf. p. 83), but in the frog the potentiation of the successive e.p.p.'s plays a major role in the facilitation, whereas in mammals facilitation is solely dependent on summation of the successive e.p.p.'s and consequently is much less effective (Eccles *et al.*, 1941).

(b) *Removal of the liberated ACh from the end-plate region*

As shown in Fig. 28 Aa and b, the e.p.p. set up in curarized frog muscle by repetitive stimulation decays very rapidly to zero. However, progressive dosage with an anticholinesterase causes a two-stage decay to develop (Fig. 28 Ac to h). There is an initial quick phase with a half-time of about 20 msec. and a slow phase with a half-time of 1 to 3 seconds (Fig. 28 Ai, j). Apart from this striking difference in time-course, these two components have reacted similarly. For example, both are similarly diminished by soaking in stronger tubocurarine or in acetyl-choline (Eccles and Macfarlane, 1949; Fillenz and Hanafin, 1947). The double phase of decay is possibly attributable (cf. Eccles, 1948) to an initially rapid diffusion of ACh from the minute end-plate area to the surrounding relatively insensitive membrane. Diffusion away from this much larger area would be much slower and hence would account for the second phase of very slow decay. Some idea of the affectiveness of diffusion may be gained from the following calculation by Ogston (1952) for a cylinder approximating in size to the nerve endings on a frog muscle (Fig. 16). If a given quantity of ACh is liberated at zero time at the axis of a cylinder of 1 μ radius, all but 1/e will have diffused beyond the cylinder in 1·1 msec. and all but 10 per cent. in 4·7 msec. A more precise study with intracellular recording of the e.p.p. is needed in order to test the diffusional explanation of the double phase of e.p.p. decay. It may be concluded that normally the destruction of ACh by the cholinesterase concentrated at the end-plate (cf. p. 71) is so rapid that there is no significant accumulation even with rapid repetitive stimulation.

In the curarized mammalian preparation repetitive stimulation fails to build up any prolonged phase of the e.p.p. even when the cholinesterase is inactivated. Possibly the liberation of ACh is so depressed during rapid repetitive stimulation that diffusion is able to prevent significant accumulation at the end-plates.

(c) *Replenishment of transmitter after depletion*

During a sufficiently long tetanus the e.p.p. of the mammalian nerve-muscle preparation declines to a low value (Fig. 28 B), indicating presumably that the store of ACh is exhausted. If it be assumed that there is no significant change in the sensitivity of the end-plate to ACh and in the propagation of the impulses into the nerve terminals, the rate of replenishment of this store will be indicated by the sizes of the e.p.p.'s set up by a single test volley or by a short tetanus at various times after the end of the conditioning tetanus. Necessarily only one such test can be made after each conditioning tetanus. As shown in Fig. 29 B about 30 seconds are required for recovery to the initial size of e.p.p., but thereafter there is a prolonged

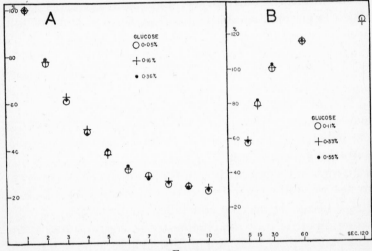

FIG. 29.

FIG. 29 A. Plotting of heights of successive e.p.p.'s of isolated and curarized strip of rat diaphragm during repetitive response at 180 a second as in upper record Fig. 28 B. Successive responses marked 1 to 10 on abscissae, ordinates percentage of initial e.p.p. Three series observed under identical conditions except that muscle equilibrated in glucose concentrations varying from 0·05 to 0·36 per cent. as indicated (Jeffries, 1952).

FIG. 29 B. As in Fig. 29 A, but to determine if variation of the glucose concentration affects the recovery of the e.p.p. after a tetanus at 180 a second for 1 minute. Note recovery from initial post-tetanic depression to post-tetanic potentiation after about 30 seconds (cf. Figs. 28 B, 69 D). Virtually same recovery for concentrations of glucose ranging from 0·11 to 0·55 per cent. (Jeffries, 1952).

supernormal response (cf. Fig. 69 D; Liley and North, 1952), which is an example of the so-called post-tetanic potentiation (cf. p. 194). Investigation in this way of the replenishment of the ACh store after depletion should be of value as an *in vivo* test of the various factors that play a part in ACh synthesis. It has already been shown (Fig. 29) that the glucose concentration of the external medium can be varied within wide limits (0·05 to 0·55 per cent.) without causing significant change in the development of depression of the e.p.p. during a tetanus (Fig. 29 A) and in post-tetanic recovery (Fig. 29 B), i.e. the glucose-brake that operates in the *in vitro* synthesis of ACh (Feldberg, 1945, 1950*a*) does not appear to be effective in motor nerve terminals in the *in vivo* state (Jeffries, 1952).

5. *Conclusions*

Neuro-muscular transmission to skeletal muscle has been more intensively investigated than any other junctional transmission. In fact we may say that it has set the pattern for investigations of other junctions both peripheral and central, and has led to the first quantitative formulation of some of the problems involved in any junctional transmission. The chemical (acetyl-choline) hypothesis has been able to offer satisfactory explanations of all the experimental findings, and moreover the calculated ion fluxes across the end-plate membrane are so large that the only possible explanation would seem to be that a chemical transmitter has actually broken down the high resistance of the surface membrane at the end-plate region so that all ions pass freely through. This subsidiary hypothesis has survived some crucial tests (see p. 87).

However, even in this developed form the chemical hypothesis is far from complete. For example, knowledge of the factors controlling the *in vivo* synthesis of ACh and its storage is still rudimentary, as is also the case with the liberation of ACh. Likewise it is assumed, but without any rigorous investigation, that ACh acts on the end-plate membrane by locking into appropriate steric configurations on the surface. This explanation satisfactorily accounts for the similar depolarizing action of chemically related compounds, and for the depolarizing and blocking action of decamethonium (Paton, 1951). It also accounts for the blocking action of various curariform compounds (cf. Ing, 1936; Taylor, 1951), which have related structure, and which presumably act as competitive inhibitors. An attractive hypothesis is that the steric configurations appropriate for ACh are produced on the surface of the end-plate membrane on account of the prevailing ACh 'atmosphere' there. The molecular structure of the surface membrane would in part be laid on templates provided by the ACh which is continuously being liberated from the nerve terminals, i.e. a process is envisaged of the same type as occurs in immunity reactions (cf. Landsteiner, 1945; Pauling, Campbell, and Pressman, 1943). This hypothesis accounts for the fact that the sensitivity of the end-plate membrane to ACh is thousands of times higher than the rest of the muscle membrane (Kuffler, 1943, 1945). It also would help to explain how regenerating nerve-fibres can make functional end-plates at new places on muscle-fibres (Gutmann and Young, 1944), for presumably at this new site the muscle membrane has to be changed to become highly sensitive to ACh.

Finally there is no explanation of the changes which ACh produces in the structure of the end-plate membrane, whereby it becomes so highly permeable to ions. Since an impulse directly set up in the muscle-fibre gives a full-sized action potential at the end-plate (cf. Fig. 25), there cannot then be the same catastrophic change in the end-plate membrane that occurs in neuro-muscular transmission. It is possible that the end-plate membrane is activated by the propagating impulse in the same way as other regions of the muscle membrane, i.e. that it has the same sodium-carrier mechanism. The membrane break-down under the influence of ACh would then be an additional special property. Alternatively, as suggested by Fatt and Katz (1951), the end-plate membrane may lack the sodium-carrier mechanism, and be inexcitable electrically, as, for example, by a propagating impulse. Its area is so small that there would be no detectable deficit in muscle-action potential, so these two alternatives cannot at present be experimentally distinguished.

B. OTHER TYPES OF NEURO-MUSCULAR TRANSMISSION

Very brief reference will be made to the diverse phenomena that occur at junctional regions with other muscles.
Not only is the experimental data inadequate, but it is not
particularly helpful in the present attempt at elucidating
the nature of the processes concerned in central transmission at synapses.

1. *The small motor-fibre system*

(a) *In the frog* (cf. Kuffler, 1949*b*; Hunt and Kuffler, 1950)

The small motor fibres innervate different muscle-fibres
from the large motor fibres, these fibres often being segre-
gated to form a special part of the muscle. As with the
large fibres, transmission is effected by ACh, and, so far
as it has been investigated, the pharmacology is similar.
Local potentials resembling e.p.p.'s are set up on the
muscle-fibres, but in contrast do not generate muscle impulses even when summed by rapid repetitive stimulation.
However, these summed potentials are very effective in
causing contracture of the muscle.

(b) *In the mammal*

The small motor fibres (Eccles and Sherrington, 1930)
innervate the polar regions of the intrafusal muscle-fibres
of the muscle-spindle (Barker, 1948). A local potential resembling the e.p.p. has been recorded, and the transmission is undoubtedly cholinergic (Hunt, 1952), but, in
contrast to the frog, it has been impossible to detect any
trace of tension development (Leksell, 1945; Kuffler,
Hunt, and Quilliam, 1951). However, indirect evidence
of contraction is given by the effect of repetitive small-
nerve stimulation in evoking a corresponding frequency
of afferent impulses from the muscle-spindle, exactly as
occurs with repetitive muscle stretches (Kuffler, 1949*b*;

Kuffler, Hunt, and Quilliam, 1951; Hunt and Kuffler, 1951a).

2. *Crustacean neuro-muscular transmission*
(*cf.* Katz, 1949).

Excitatory nerve impulses set up in the muscle-fibres local potentials that resemble end-plate potentials (Katz and Kuffler, 1946). With a few muscles the end-plate potential is large and may even generate a propagated muscle impulse as in vertebrate muscle. Most junctions resemble those of the frog's small motor-fibre system, and give merely local potentials which are potentiated by repetitive stimulation and may consequently build up to quite a large local potential with accompanying muscle contracture. It is of great interest that these transmissions are not cholinergic, i.e. not mediated by ACh. It may be assumed that some unknown chemical mediator is involved, for, on account of the very large membrane capacity (about 40 μF cm.$^{-2}$, Fatt and Katz, 1942c), the quantity of electrical charge that has to be transported across the membrane is even larger than with the frog neuro-muscular transmission, where it was seen that a special process of membrane break-down was required (p. 84).

The most interesting feature in crustacea is provided by the action of inhibitory nerve-fibres, there being two distinct types of inhibitory action (Kuffler and Katz, 1946). In its effect the alpha inhibition resembles curare action on the vertebrate e.p.p., causing a diminution of the local potential generated by excitatory impulses. Possibly this effect is produced by a transmitter substance that competitively blocks the effect of the excitatory transmitter by occupying the receptor areas of the membrane (Fatt and Katz, 1952c). Alternatively transmission could be blocked in the nerve terminals, much as botulinum toxin appears to do in vertebrates (Burgen, Dickens, and Zatman, 1949, but see Ambache, 1951). There is now evidence that under certain conditions inhibitory impulses cause a small slow hyperpolarization of the muscle-fibres (Fatt and Katz, 1952c). This effect is of great interest because it may resemble the hyperpolarization that occurs when neurones are subjected to inhibitory synaptic action (cf. p. 156). There is no evidence concerning the identity of the inhibitory transmitting substance.

C. SYNAPTIC TRANSMISSION IN THE SYMPATHETIC GANGLION

1. *Histology*

Usually all the nerve-fibres in the preganglionic trunk to the mammalian superior cervical ganglion end in synaptic relationship with the ganglion-cells therein, and there are believed to be no interneurones, so that ganglion is particularly favourable for investigations on synaptic transmission (de Castro, 1932, 1951). The cat's stellate ganglion provides an even more favourable preparation because, in addition to the monosynaptic relationship of preganglionic fibres to postganglionic fibres in the cardiac nerves, i.e. only one synaptic junction is interposed, there is only one main fibre type in contrast to the several for the superior cervical ganglion (Bronk, Tower, Solandt, and Larrabee, 1938; Larrabee and Posternak, 1952).

As with the neuro-muscular junction, there is no continuity between the preganglionic fibres and the ganglion-cells, but merely a close contact with likewise probably some slight separation by intercellular material (de Castro, 1942, 1951; Couteaux, 1947). Some of the preganglionic fibres have been described making specialized contacts with the bodies of the ganglion-cells (cf. Gibson, 1940), but such structures are so infrequent that it seems probable that effective junctional contacts occur without any histologically recognizable differentiation. This seems particularly to occur in the specialized glomerular structures (de Castro, 1932).

2. *Synaptic transmission by acetyl-choline*

The evidence for chemical mediation by ACh is almost as convincing as for neuro-muscular transmission, but the electrical investigation has not been so precise, for no intracellular records are available. However, there is much of value for our purpose because in many respects the synapses of sympathetic ganglia seem to occupy an intermediate position between the neuro-muscular junction and the central synapses. For detailed accounts of the older literature reference may be made to contemporary reviews (Brown, 1937b; Dale, 1937; Eccles, 1936).

As with neuro-muscular transmission, there is a liberation of ACh by the preganglionic impulses. It has now been shown that ACh liberation into a whole-blood perfusate occurs just as effectively as into a saline perfusate, but a much higher concentration of eserine is needed in order to prevent its destruction by the specific cholinesterase in the red blood-cells (Emmelin and MacIntosh, 1948). One preganglionic volley liberates as much as 10^{-10} g. (Emmelin and MacIntosh, 1952), which corresponds to an amount that is certainly larger than 5×10^{-16} g. per ganglion cell and under optimal conditions up to 10^{-15} g. per cell. It is not possible, nor does it seem of much value, to estimate the amount liberated at any one synaptic junction, for the significant effect is the over-all depolarization of the ganglion-cell, not the effect of any one synaptic junction. The amount of ACh per ganglion-cell appears to be considerably larger than the amount per motor end-plate (cf. p. 78), and the surface to be depolarized would undoubtedly be much smaller; hence a single ACh molecule is probably much less effective in causing ionic flux across the membrane of the ganglion-cell. However, in making such comparisons it should be remembered that the electrical capacitance of the ganglionic surface membrane is unknown, and it may be large, for its electric time-constant, as indicated by the decay of the latter part of the post-synaptic potential (Fig. 30), is about 60 to 80 msec. for the cat's stellate ganglion (Eccles, 1943).

ACh stimulates ganglion-cells to discharge impulses and this discharge continues for a long time when a steady

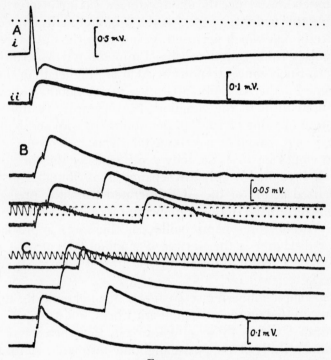

FIG. 30.

FIG. 30 A. Action potentials set up by single preganglionic volley in cat's stellate ganglion and recorded between ganglionic origin and distal end of cardiac nerve. (ii) Post-synaptic potential left after curarization which completely blocked the ganglionic discharge of impulses that gave the large initial spike in (i) before curarization. Time, 10 msec. throughout Fig. 30.

FIG. 30 B. Summation of post-synaptic potentials set up by two volleys at various intervals.

FIG. 30 C. Summation as in Fig. 30 B but at lower degree of curarization so that summation produced a post-synaptic potential sufficiently large to generate a discharge from some ganglion cells—note spikes (Eccles, 1943).

concentration is perfused through the ganglion. The higher the concentration within limits the higher is the frequency of discharge (Bronk, 1939). For example, increasing the concentration from 1 in 40,000 to 1 in 10,000 raised the frequency from about 1 to 3 per second. But the actual concentration of ACh acting on the ganglion-cell would be much lower since the cholinesterase was not inactivated. When this is done, 5×10^{-7} is the minimum effective concentration at which perfused ACh evokes the discharge of impulses from ganglion-cells (Emmelin and MacIntosh, 1952). Such concentrations of ACh are higher than those attained if the ACh liberated by a preganglionic volley is diffused through the ganglion. For example, assuming a maximum value of 10^{-10} g. per volley (p. 100) and half of the 20 mg. ganglion as extracellular space, the concentration would be 10^{-8}, i.e. only 2 per cent. of the threshold level. Presumably this discrepancy is attributable to the localized action of the ACh liberated from the preganglionic terminals. In this connexion it is of interest that only after twenty presynaptic volleys is there any appreciable after-discharge in the eserinized ganglion, and at least 100 volleys are required for an intense after-discharge (Eccles, 1944).

Specific cholinesterase is shown histo-chemically to be concentrated on the preganglionic fibres, but it is also concentrated within those ganglion-cells that themselves act cholinergically at the post-ganglionic terminals, as for example in the ciliary ganglion-cells (Koelle, 1951). Presumably its function within the ganglion-cell is to restrict the accumulation of the ACh that is being manufactured by the choline-acetylase system therein. Unless this accumulation is prevented, synaptic activation of the cholinergic ganglion-cells by ACh would cause them to liberate ACh and so re-excite themselves, and so on, i.e. there would be a self-re-exciting mechanism. On the other hand, with adrenergic ganglion-cells, such as form the bulk of the superior cervical and stellate ganglia, there is no such danger, nor is there any detectable content of specific cholinesterase (Koelle, 1951). Degeneration of the preganglionic fibres virtually clears such ganglia of specific cholinesterase.

Inactivation of cholinesterase has not given such striking results as with neuro-muscular transmission. For example, the eserinized ganglion does not discharge repetitively in response to a single preganglionic volley, nor is the time

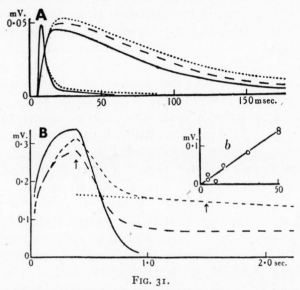

FIG. 31.

FIG. 31 A. Tracings of post-synaptic potentials of curarized ganglion set up as in Fig. 30, the continuous line before eserine, the broken and dotted lines after 0·5 and 6·5 mg./kg. eserine respectively. Potential scale for dotted curve 0·8 times that shown. The continuous 'peaked' line gives the time course of the synaptic transmitter action on the assumption that the latter part of the post-synaptic potential is due to passive recharging of the surface membrane. Dotted curve shows slight alteration by large dosage of eserine (Eccles, 1944).

FIG. 31 B. Tracings of post-synaptic potentials set up in curarized ganglion by repetitive preganglionic volleys—125 a sec. for 0·4 sec. Continuous line before eserine, long and short broken lines after 1·0 and 6·0 mg. per kg. eserine respectively. First arrow shows end of stimulation and second arrow site of measurement of slow after-negativity, which is plotted in inset against number of volleys (Eccles, 1944).

course of the slow potential waves much affected (Fig. 31 A). However, it has now been shown that repetitive preganglionic volleys (twenty or more) cause it to give a prolonged after-discharge (up to 10 seconds), which presumably is attributable to the accumulated ACh, for there is virtually no after-discharge when the cholinesterase is not inactivated (Eccles, 1944). Furthermore a prolonged depolarization of the ganglion-cells occurs under such conditions, and may also be seen under less complex conditions when the discharge of impulses from the ganglion-cells is suppressed by curarization (Fig. 31 B). Probably the diffusion of ACh from the small volume into which it is liberated from the minute nerve terminals is so rapid that its destruction by cholinesterase plays little part in the initial rate of its disappearance and in any case the cholinesterase, being on the preganglionic fibres, is unfavourably placed for destroying ACh acting on the ganglion-cells, which contrasts with the probable situation at the neuro-muscular junction (cf. Fig. 17).

It has been calculated that, if a given amount of ACh is liberated at a point source, all but $1/e$ of that amount will have diffused outside a sphere of radius $1\,\mu$ in 0·6 msec., and all but 10 per cent. in 1·7 msec. (Ogston, 1952). During repetitive stimulation, and in the absence of destruction by cholinesterase, there would be a progressively less steep diffusion gradient from the foci of liberation, and in addition there would be a generalized background concentration that would only slowly be removed by diffusion into the circulation. Some such concept seems necessary in order to explain the after-discharge that continues in an eserinized ganglion for at least 10 seconds after a tetanus of 20 or more preganglionic volleys (Eccles, 1944).

However, it was calculated above (p. 102) that perhaps a hundred volleys would be required to build up a general concentration of ACh in the ganglion that would generate a discharge of impulses in the same way as occurs during perfusion. Presumably the discrepancy in part arises because the focal action of ACh close to the site of its liberation, e.g. within the capsule surrounding the ganglion-cell, is of importance in the generation of impulses in ganglion-cells.

3. Post-synaptic potentials

Just as with muscle, blockage of junctional transmission is produced by relatively low concentrations of tubocurarine or related substances (Fig. 30 A), which presumably act likewise as competitive inhibitors of the depolarizing action of ACh. Under such conditions the ganglionic spike potential is replaced by a relatively prolonged local potential which is attributable to depolarization of the ganglion-cells by the synaptic transmitter (Figs. 30 A, B, 31 A, 32 Aa; Eccles, 1943; Laporte and Lorente de Nó, 1950; R. Eccles, 1952a). This post-synaptic potential appears in every respect to be homologous with an end-plate potential. It seems probable that there is likewise a brief depolarizing action of ACh and a slow phase of recovery due to the passive recharging of the surface membrane (cf. Fig. 31 A). As with the e.p.p., there is a critical level of depolarization at which a spike is initiated, and repetitive stimulation gives summation of synaptic potentials to this critical level and hence the discharge of impulses (Figs. 30 C, 32 Ba). It may be assumed also that curare blocks transmission by occupying specific steric configurations on the surface that act as post-synaptic receptors for ACh. However, there is as yet no evidence to suggest that ACh produces its depolarizing action by causing a break-down of the membrane in the way that appears to happen at the end-plate (p. 84). Such evidence may be forthcoming when intracellular recording is possible.

Reference has already been made to the effect of anti-cholinesterases in causing the appearance of a prolonged after-negativity after tetanization of the curarized ganglion (cf. Fig. 31 B), an effect undoubtedly due to ACh. However, there is still a fairly rapid initial decline at the end of the tetanus, while even heavy dosage with anti-cholinesterases causes little change in the post-synaptic potential set up by a single preganglionic volley (cf. Fig. 31 A with the e.p.p.'s in Figs. 23 A and B), or in the analysed transmitter-action curve (Fig. 31 A; Eccles, 1944). Presumably diffusion and not cholinesterase accounts for the removal of much of the liberated ACh (cf. p. 104).

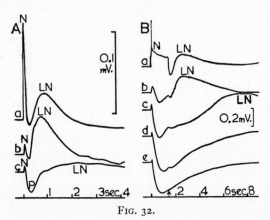

FIG. 32.

FIG. 32 A. Tracings of post-synaptic potentials set up by single preganglionic volley and recorded as in Fig. 30, but from isolated superior cervical ganglion of rabbit. *N* shows post-synaptic potential as in Fig. 30—note the very slow time-scale, and *LN*, the late negative wave. *a* and *b* in 2.5×10^{-5} *M*, and 8×10^{-5} *M* *d*-tubocurarine. *c* as in *b* but with 3×10^{-6} *M* prostigmine added (R. Eccles, 1952*b*).

FIG. 32 B. As in Fig. 32 A but with repetitive preganglionic volleys, 20 a second for 1·4 seconds (arrow marks end of tetanus) *a* and *b* in 1.6×10^{-5} *M* and 8×10^{-5} *M* *d*-tubocurarine respectively. Note small ganglionic spike in *a*. *c*, *d*, and *e*, as in *b*, but with progressive prostigmine concentration: 3×10^{-7} *M*, 3×10^{-6} *M*, and 6×10^{-6} *M* respectively. Note apparent increase of P wave and progressive delay and eventual abolition of LN wave (R. Eccles, 1952*b*).

Very slow recording reveals that the post-synaptic potential (*N* in Fig. 32 A*a*) is followed, after a slight positivity (P wave), by a prolonged late negative wave (*LN*) (R. Eccles, 1952*b*). With deeper curarization the post-synaptic potential is greatly depressed, but the LN wave is even increased (Fig. 32 A*b*, see similarly Figs. 32 B*a*, *b*) and the P wave is more prominent so that with still deeper curarization a large P wave may follow a negligible N wave (cf. Laporte and Lorente de Nó, 1950, on isolated turtle ganglia). Fig. 32 further shows the remarkable finding that anti-cholinesterases depress, delay, and eventually abolish the LN wave, and at the same time increase and greatly prolong the P wave (R. Eccles, 1952b). The difference between Fig. 32 B and Fig. 31 B is due to the much heavier curarization in Fig. 32 Bb to e.

Evidently the transmitter problem with the ganglion is much more complicated than with the neuro-muscular junction. It would seem that some transmitter other than ACh must be postulated for the LN wave, because it is increased by curarization and depressed by anti-cholinesterases. Since the P wave is increased and lengthened by anti-cholinesterases (Figs. 32 Ac and 32 Bc, d, e), it presumably is generated by the action of ACh. If that is so, heavy tubocurarine dosage would appear to have the remarkable effect of transforming the depolarizing action of ACh into a hyperpolarizing action, which is an effect of great interest in connexion with the mechanism of action of inhibitory synapses in the central nervous system (cf. p. 164). On the contrary Laporte and Lorente de Nó (1950) regard the hyperpolarization in the turtle's superior cervical ganglion as an action of special preganglionic fibres, which is revealed when the usually predominant depolarization is depressed by heavy tubocurarine dosage. They would further attribute to these fibres an inhibitory action on the ganglion-cells (Lorente de Nó and Laporte, 1950). But it may be doubted if a special inhibitory mechanism has yet been demonstrated in sympathetic ganglia (Job and Lundberg, 1952). The depressed response to a second preganglionic volley may be merely a result of a diminished post-synaptic potential (cf. Eccles, 1943) and attributable to temporary depletion of the transmitter substance, as occurs with the mammalian e.p.p. (p. 92) and is assumed to occur with synaptic transmission in the spinal cord (p. 138).

4. *Conclusions*

In many respects synaptic transmission in the sympathetic ganglion appears to be transitional between neuromuscular transmission and central synaptic transmission. It resembles the former because ACh undoubtedly plays the major role in the transmission, but it is difficult to account for all the post-synaptic actions, particularly the LN wave, without postulating another transmitter. On the other hand it resembles the latter because there are multiple minute foci of synaptic action, not the single large motor end-organ; hence summation, spatial and temporal, is necessary to generate impulses, which is exactly the situation with central synaptic transmission (Eccles, 1936). In the prominence of hyperpolarization effects, the sympathetic ganglion also resembles central synapses, and further investigation of the P wave might well be of great importance in understanding the way in which inhibitory impulses cause hyperpolarization of motoneurones (p. 164). Intracellular recording from sympathetic ganglion-cells will thus provide data of great interest.

IV

THE ELECTROPHYSIOLOGY OF THE NEURONE AND SYNAPTIC TRANSMISSION IN THE CENTRAL NERVOUS SYSTEM

A. INTRODUCTION

THE simplest responses of the central nervous system may be grouped under the collective title of reflexes. In a reflex some spatio-temporal combination of nerve impulses propagating into the central nervous system evokes a discharge therefrom of impulses to effector organs, whereby some simple and appropriate reaction is brought about. Reflexes, as it were, provide the basic functional units of the central nervous system, and Sherrington's *The Integrative Action of the Nervous System* (1906) may be regarded as giving the classical description of reflexes and their inter-relationships. The *Reflex Activity of the Spinal Cord* (Creed, Denny-Brown, Eccles, Liddell, and Sherrington, 1932) summarized the later analytical study of reflexes by the Sherrington school of neurophysiology at Oxford. Since that time new techniques have made it possible to develop a much more precise and detailed picture of the essential events that occur in the reflex (cf. the reviews by Fessard and Posternak, 1950, and Eccles, 1950). But it will be convenient to preface this detailed description by a brief preliminary account of those structural features of the reflex arc about which there is general agreement, and by an introductory statement of a hypothesis of synaptic transmission that has formed the framework, as it were, for the more recent developments.

B. THE STRUCTURE OF THE REFLEX ARC

Propagation of impulses in the central nervous system occurs along nerve-fibres that closely resemble the fibres in peripheral nerves. The tracts of white matter are composed of myelinated fibres that possess a nodal structure (Cajal, 1909; Huxley and Stämpfli, 1949). Since the velocity of impulse propagation corresponds approximately with that observed for peripheral nerve-fibres of comparable diameter (Lloyd, 1944; Lloyd and MacIntyre, 1950; Rudin and Eisenman, 1951), it may be assumed that the same kind of saltatory transmission (cf. p. 57) occurs there also. When nerve-fibres enter the grey matter, they lose their myelin sheaths some distance before their terminal arborization. Finally they make functional contact with nerve-cells by means of small swellings, synaptic knobs (Fig. 33 A), which may be either at the end of the fibre or along its course (Cajal, 1909, 1934; Lorente de Nó, 1938; Bodian, 1942). The name synapse is given to this functional structure, the synaptic knob plus the subsynaptic membrane. Thus the synapse is homologous with the motor end-organ, where there is likewise a functional contact, but not continuity, across the junctional region (p. 67). However, it has not been possible to establish the existence of a space between the pre- and post-synaptic membranes (cf. Fig. 16), and Bodian (1942) refers to them collectively as the 'synaptolemma'.

In the spinal cord the synaptic knobs have a diameter usually between 0·5 and 2 μ, the mean diameter being about 1·0 μ (Haggar and Barr, 1950). Any nerve-cell is closely encrusted by these knobs, it being estimated that up to 40 per cent. of the surface of the soma and large dendrites of a motoneurone is so covered (Fig. 33 B), and over 400 have been counted on the soma and dendritic stumps of one motoneurone. There is evidence that there is some histological specialization of the presynaptic terminals which contain mitochondria-like granules (Bodian, 1942), but no post-synaptic specialization as in Fig. 16 has been described. Any one presynaptic nerve-fibre branches profusely and establishes synaptic contact with many nerve-cells, and usually multiple contacts with any one

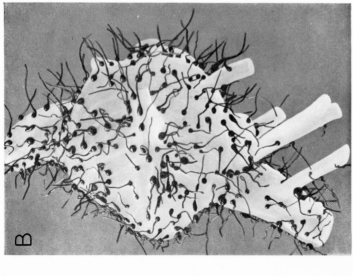

Fig. 33 A. Drawing of soma and large dendritic stumps of mammalian motoneurone showing various sizes of synaptic knobs, there being often several attached to one presynaptic fibre (Cajal, 1934).

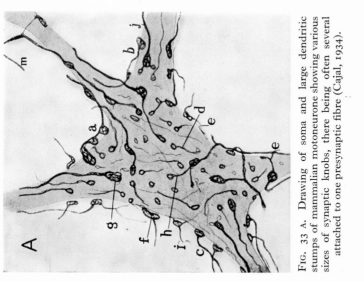

Fig. 33 B. Model of soma and large dendritic stumps of a mammalian motoneurone, showing dense population of synaptic knobs. Constructed from serial sections (Haggar and Barr, 1950).

nerve-cell (Cajal, 1909, 1934; Lorente de Nó, 1938). Thus a presynaptic impulse acts at varying degrees of intensity on many nerve-cells, the intensity presumably depending on the size and number of the activated synaptic knobs. Furthermore, any one nerve-cell receives synaptic contacts from the many presynaptic fibres that converge on it. If sufficiently excited by these synapses, a nerve-cell generates an impulse, and so on in serial sequence along the various neuronal links in the reflex path.

One type of reflex arc through the spinal cord is extremely important experimentally because there is only one synapse on the pathway, i.e. the afferent fibres entering the cord through the dorsal root send collateral branches, the reflexo-motor collaterals of Cajal (1909), directly to the motoneurones (Fig. 34 A). The afferent fibres that thus act monosynaptically are the largest entering the spinal cord, and arise in the annulospiral endings of the muscle spindles (Matthews, 1933; Lloyd, 1943b; Granit, 1950; Hunt, 1951; Hunt and Kuffler, 1951a, 1951b). As indicated in Fig. 34 A their distribution is restricted to the motoneurones belonging to their muscle of origin (the homonymous motoneurones) and to those of synergic muscles (Eccles, 1946; Lloyd, 1946 a, b). Thus the familiar myotatic reflex or tendon jerk (Lloyd, 1943c) is the only monosynaptic reflex in the spinal cord.

The nerve-cell typically has a central part (soma or body) from which branch long dendrites that usually terminate in a profuse arborization. The large dendritic processes resemble the soma and like it are thickly encrusted with synaptic knobs (cf. Fig. 33), but the 'synaptic scale' rapidly thins towards the smaller dendrites (Lorente de Nó, 1938). The axon of the cell (cf. Fig. 35) arises from a conical projection (the axon hillock) and usually but not always is devoid of synaptic knobs (Bodian, 1942). The axon of a motoneurone is non-myelinated for a considerable distance, usually 100 or more microns, but it assumes a myelin sheath some distance before it enters the white matter.

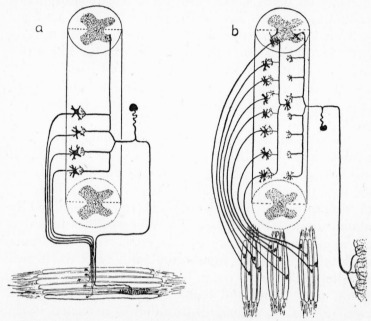

FIG. 34. Diagrams showing reflex pathways for monosynaptic reflex arc (*a*) with afferent fibre from annulo-spiral ending, and for polysynaptic flexor reflex (*b*) with cutaneous afferent fibre. The three muscles in *b* are supposed to represent flexors of hip, knee, and ankle (modified from Cajal, 1909).

C. STATEMENT OF HYPOTHESIS OF SYNAPTIC EXCITATORY ACTION

The presynaptic fibre and the neurone have each a surface membrane that has essentially the same properties as the membranes of peripheral nerve- and muscle-fibres (cf. Chapters I and II). For example, there is a resting membrane potential determined by the relative potassium (and chloride) activities inside and outside, and this potential is momentarily reversed during an impulse by activation of the sodium-carrier mechanism. As with the neuromuscular junction (cf. Figs. 16, 17) it is assumed that the presynaptic and post-synaptic membranes are separated by an extracellular space at the junctional region.

When a presynaptic impulse invades a synaptic knob it causes, by some synaptic transmission process, the subjacent post-synaptic membrane to become depolarized so that it is a 'sink' for current flowing externally from other regions of the post-synaptic membrane. In parenthesis it may be noted that no attempt will be made for the present to distinguish between the two explanations that have been offered for this synaptic transmission process: chemical transmission, as in the peripheral junctional regions; or electrical transmission by the flow of current generated by the presynaptic impulse. The surface membrane of the neurone (the post-synaptic membrane) becomes depolarized by current flowing into the subsynaptic sink, just as occurs with the generation of the end-plate potential (cf. Fig. 17 B). The spreading potential thus set up has been called the synaptic potential (Eccles, 1946), but more correctly it should be the post-synaptic potential, p.s.p. (cf. p. 130).

With the synaptic junctions in reflex pathways, the p.s.p. set up by a single presynaptic impulse is never large enough to generate an impulse, which is in striking contrast to the e.p.p. of skeletal muscle, but similar to the conditions obtaining in the sympathetic ganglion (p. 108). However, the spatial spread and the duration of the depolarizing influence of any one activated synapse ensures that there will be summation of the effects produced by any synapses on a neurone that are activated in a sufficiently close spatio-temporal relationship. When, by this summation, depolarization reaches a critical level, an impulse is generated in the post-synaptic membrane and propagates thence down the axon of the neurone by the usual local-circuit action. As in peripheral axons, the impulse would be expected to be generated at that level of depolarization at which the inward current due to sodium-carrier activation just exceeds the outward potassium and chloride current.

D. RECENT EXPERIMENTAL TESTING OF THE HYPOTHESIS

1. *Technique*

Recently (Brock, Coombs, and Eccles, 1951, 1952*a*, *b*, *c*) it has been possible to record electrically from motoneurones in the spinal cord of the anaesthetized cat by the same technique that has been used for isolated nerve- and

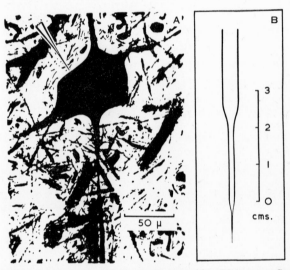

FIG. 35. Microphotograph of motoneurone together with its axon. Superimposed on it is a drawing of actual size and shape of micro-electrode, which is shown just before penetration. Inset shows drawing of main shaft of micro-electrode (Brock *et al.*, 1952*a*).

muscle-fibres (cf. Fig. 3 B), and so subject the above hypothesis to much more rigorous testing than has hitherto been possible (cf. also Woodbury and Patton, 1952; Alanis and Matthews, 1952). A fine glass tube filled with 3M-KCl and with a tip diameter of about 0·5 μ is used as a microelectrode. Necessarily it has to be inserted 'blindly' into a motoneurone lying some 2 mm. deep in the spinal cord (Fig. 35). However, the position of a pool of motoneurones belonging to any one muscle is now fairly well known

(Romanes, 1951), and the motoneurones are made to signal their position electrically during the process of insertion by firing impulses into them antidromically and also by monosynaptically activating them. The entry of a micro-electrode into a motoneurone is immediately and unambiguously signalled by two events: the development of the resting membrane potential; the inversion and large increase in the antidromic spike potential, i.e. the spike is then recorded as a relative positivity to the indifferent electrode exactly as occurs with intracellular recording from peripheral nerve- and muscle-fibres (p. 30).

2. *Properties of the resting membrane*

On account of the blind and random method of insertion it must be assumed that motoneurones are often seriously injured in the process of insertion, particularly as the branching dendritic structure is so vulnerable. Hence the values for the resting potential are likely to be lowered by flow of injury currents. The estimated value of 75 mV (Table 2) makes some allowance for such injury effects and values of 80 mV or more have been encountered several times. It would be expected that in the absence of injury the nerve-cells would be virtually in a steady state, for they are lying in their normal environment with an adequate blood-supply. Thus, according to the hypothesis, the resting potential is given by the equation,

$$E_r = 62 \log_{10} \frac{(K)_i}{(K)_0} \text{ millivolts} \qquad (11)$$

where 62 is substituted for 58 of Eq. 2 on account of the higher temperature. The values given for $(K)_0$ in the mammal vary considerably, but it appears that 5·5 mM is an average value for the cat (Davson, 1951; Krogh, 1946), while a $(K)_i$ value for muscle is perhaps 140 mM. Assuming a like value for the nerve-cell and equality of activity coefficients, the E_r value should be 87 mV, which is very little above the highest of our measured values (Fig. 36).

It thus appears that the resting potential approximates to the Donnan potential for potassium, and presumably also for chloride. In that case it may be assumed that the potential across the nerve-cell membrane does not differ significantly from that across the axonal membrane.

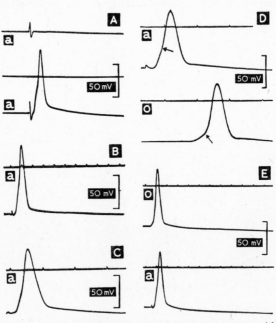

FIG. 36. Spike action potentials recorded from motoneurones with intra-cellular electrode, (a) indicating antidromic responses and (o) orthodromic responses evoked by a single afferent volley from the appropriate muscle nerve. Reference line gives zero membrane voltage and also time in msec.
(Brock et al., 1952a).

Consequently resting current flow between soma and axon would be negligible, as has been observed between the end-plate and other regions of a muscle-fibre (p. 67).

The only other data on the resting membrane is the time-constant, which is later (pp. 138–42) shown to be given by the decay of the post-synaptic potential, and to average about 4 msec. (extremes about 3 to 5 msec.). If a value of about 1·3 μF cm.$^{-2}$ be assumed for the membrane capa-city (the mean of the non-medullated nerve values in Table

4), then the membrane resistance would be 3,000 Ω cm.^{2}; but in the absence of direct measurements such estimated values for membrane capacity and resistance are liable to considerable error.

3. *The spike potentials of motoneurones*

When an antidromic impulse invades a motoneurone, it sets up a spike potential resembling that in a nerve or muscle-fibre. A similar spike potential is generated by a sufficiently large synaptic excitatory action. However, close inspection of Fig. 36 D, E reveals that differences (cf. below) occur in the early parts of the rising phases, but not subsequently, unless polysynaptic excitation is superimposed on the initial monosynaptic excitation. The mean voltage of the recorded spike potential was about 95 mV in motoneurones that showed little sign of injury, but it has been concluded that, when allowance is made for distortion by the recording system and for the external membrane potential (Brock *et al.*, 1952*a*), the membrane spike potential of a motoneurone would be at least 110 mV and the reversal of potential 35 mV, as shown in Table 2.

When measured from the inflexion on the rising phase to the termination in a small after-negativity (Fig. 36), the spike duration is about 1 msec., and thus has about twice the duration of the spike in the medullated axon of the motoneurone (Gasser and Grundfest, 1936; Grundfest, 1940). The measured slopes of the rising and falling phases are as high as 500 and 250 V/sec. respectively, but allowance for distortion would considerably increase such values, which would then be comparable with slopes of spikes in giant axons.

No attempt has been made to investigate the effects of alterations in the external sodium or potassium concentrations on the resting and action potentials of motoneurones, but the similarity between these potentials and those recorded in isolated nerve- and muscle-fibres under normal conditions (cf. pp. 30, 50, 51) makes it highly probable that the same sequences of ionic fluxes occur during the spike potential.

However, in contrast, the after-potentials following a spike (generated either by synaptic or antidromic excitatory action) are much larger in the motoneurones than in the axons that stem therefrom. With relatively uninjured motoneurones the spike terminated in an after-negativity

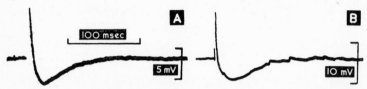

FIG. 37.   Intracellular action potentials evoked by single antidromic impulses in two motoneurones and recorded at high amplification to show positive after-potential (Brock *et al.*, 1952*a*).

of 5 to 10 mV (Fig. 36) which decayed over several milliseconds to a large positive after-potential that reached a maximum of about 5 mV in 10 to 15 msec. and finally disappeared at about 100 msec. (Fig. 37). The neuronal positive after-potential is thus about twenty times larger than for the peripheral mammalian axon (Gasser and Grundfest, 1936; Grundfest, 1940).

It is of interest that, when the resting potential of the motoneurone becomes depressed, presumably by the flow of injury currents, the spike potential immediately reverses to a large after-positivity of up to 10 mV. There is a similar immediate reversal after the spike of the isolated giant axon, which Hodgkin and Huxley (1952*d*, *e*) showed to be due to the continued high level of potassium conductance (Fig. 13 A). In this way the membrane potential would be made to approximate closer to the potassium (and chloride) potential as calculated for the steady state (cf. Table 2). For example, after the spike in the squid axon the membrane potential increased temporarily to about 10–13 mV more than the resting potential (cf. Figs. 7, 13 A). It may be assumed that after the spike in the deteriorating motoneurone a similar increase of the potassium relative to the sodium flux causes a temporary return of the membrane potential towards the value characteristic of the steady state. It may further be assumed that the absence of this effect in relatively uninjured motoneurones (cf. Fig. 36) indicates that their resting potential approximates closely to their steady-state potential, as has already been suggested. Thus at rest and during both activity and deterioration, there appears to be a general similarity between the neurone and the isolated giant axon.

4. *Antidromic responses of motoneurones*

Antidromic activation of neurones does not occur naturally, yet it is of great interest because it provides a method of studying the reactions of neurones to propagated impulses without the complications produced by synaptic excitation, and also because it can be employed as a test in the analysis of responses evoked synaptically. Hitherto, with antidromic volleys there has been some difficulty and uncertainty in interpreting the complex potential fields that are generated at all stages of antidromic invasion and subsequently. The antidromic volley would be propagating into thousands of motoneurones with dendrites arranged in random interlocking fashion. In contrast, when a micro-electrode is inserted into a motoneurone, it records the potentials generated by this motoneurone to the virtual exclusion of all other electrical potentials. Hence the action potentials set up by an antidromic volley are relatively simple and ideally suitable for experimental analysis (Brock *et al.*, 1952*c*). It may be claimed that the method of intracellular recording has settled most of the controversial issues of the antidromic responses (cf. Lorente de Nó, 1947*b*; Barakan, Downman, and Eccles, 1949; Brooks, Downman, and Eccles, 1950*a*; Eccles, 1950; Lloyd, 1951*a, b*).

Invariably there is a brief step or double inflexion on the rising phase of the antidromic spike at a voltage of about 40 per cent. of the spike potential (Figs. 36, the *a* records; 38 A, third record). Evidently this inflexion indicates that there has been some delay in the invasion process, which in different motoneurones varies from 0·05 to 0·3 msec. In the experiment that gave the longest delay (third record, Fig. 38 A), the large spike often failed to

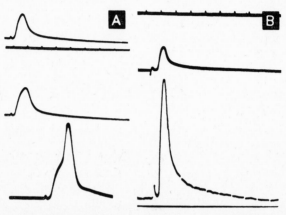

FIG. 38. Intracellular action potentials evoked by single antidromic impulses as in Fig. 36 A to c. Time, msec. *A* shows three responses at intervals of a few seconds from same motoneurone to illustrate NM spikes and an SD spike arising after a long delay. *B* shows, with another motoneurone, the same NM spike recorded at low and high amplification (Brock *et al.*, 1952*c*).

develop, and there was consequently only a simple brief spike having a potential equal to the height of the step (first and second records, Fig. 38 A). With some motoneurones an antidromic impulse always set up this small simple spike (Fig. 38 B).

Similar small spikes invariably are produced by an antidromic impulse a few milliseconds after a conditioning antidromic impulse, while at longer intervals the large spike is observed, though with a lengthening of the delay on the rising phase (Fig. 39). On the other hand conditioning by a preceding volley has never revealed a double inflexion on the rising phase of the small simple spikes. Both the small and the large spikes exhibit an all-or-nothing behaviour (cf. Fig. 36 A, where the first stimulus was just below threshold).

All the experimental evidence is in accord with the postulate that the small spike is set up by the antidromic impulse in the non-myelinated segment of the axon,

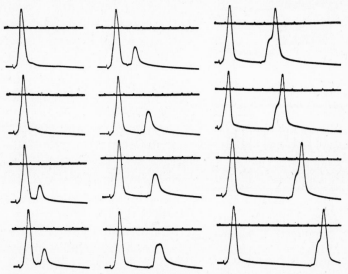

FIG. 39. Action potentials recorded as in Fig. 36, but set up by two antidromic impulses at various time intervals. Time in milliseconds on the reference potential line for zero membrane potential. Resting potential, 72 mV (Brock *et al.*, 1952*c*).

henceforth the NM spike. The large spike signals the invasion of the soma and dendrites, henceforth the SD spike, which has a duration of about 1 msec. The double inflexion between the NM and SD spikes is attributable to an axon-soma delay of 0·05 to 0·3 msec., which is virtually identical with the value assessed by Barakan *et al.* (1949). It may seem improbable that a micro-electrode in a neurone would record a spike as large as the NM spike from the relatively small area of the non-myelinated segment of the axon, which, with an assumed length of about 100 μ would be at most only a few per cent. of the surface mem-

brane of the soma and its large dendritic branches. However, if the antidromic impulse is blocked only after it has
spread some distance over the
expanded axon hillock, it
would be expected to pro-
duce an intracellular potential
change of that order because
the inward flux of sodium ions
through an activated mem-
brane is so intense. As a consequence there would be a
heavy outward current from
the membrane of the soma
and dendrites and within the
motoneurone an intense current from the axon hillock up
into the soma and dendrites.
The potential gradients due
to both of these currents
would contribute to the observed intracellular spike potential.

In contrast to the large
positive after-potential after
an SD spike, an NM spike is
followed by a very small positive after-potential, which is
no larger than with peri-
pheral axons (Fig. 38). Likewise repetitive activation of
NM spikes causes quite a
large positive after-potential
to be built up (Fig. 40 A). The
large positive after-potential
and the longer duration of

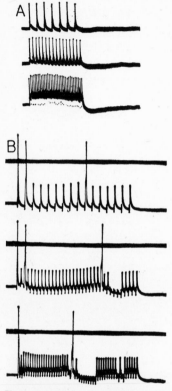

FIG. 40. Action potentials as in
Fig. 36, but set up by repetitive antidromic impulses. *A*. NM spike potentials as in Fig. 38 but at 100, 200,
and 450 a second. Note the positive
after-potential. *B*. Initially an SD
spike but mostly NM spikes and
even these failed periodically. Higher
amplification and faster recording
would then have revealed small M
spikes. Frequencies at about 150,
300, and 450 a second. Resting potential, 72 mV (Brock *et al.*, 1952*c*).

the spike reveal that the surface membrane of the soma
and dendrites differs characteristically from that of the

non-myelinated axon, which behaves very similarly to the axons in peripheral nerve (Gasser and Grundfest, 1936; Gasser, 1937; Grundfest, 1940). It is curious that in the ventral root the motor axons give very different after-potentials from those in peripheral nerve and in the non-myelinated axon, the negative and positive after-potentials being both abnormally large (Lloyd, 1951*b*).

According to the local-circuit theory of impulse propagation, there should be a low safety factor for propagation from the relatively small non-myelinated axon to the greatly expanded surface of the soma plus dendrites, for the inward sodium ion flux across the former has to depolarize a much larger surface area to the critical level at which the sodium-carrier is activated enough to continue with the depolarization process. The observed delay or blockage at the axon-soma junction is thus fully explained by the geometry. It is further of interest that, when the impulse in the non-myelinated axon fails to invade the soma, its NM spike is followed by a relatively large after-negativity (up to 10 mV) which decays with a time-constant that increases gradually from 2 msec. to 3 msec. or more (Fig. 38 B). Presumably under such conditions the surface membrane of the soma and dendrites has been subliminally depolarized by the currents flowing during the NM spike, and subsequently is being restored to the resting potential by its own potassium plus chloride current (cf. Hodgkin, 1951). The time-constant of decay of the after-negativity should thus be a measure of the electric time-constant of the soma-dendritic membrane. However, Lloyd (1951*b*) has shown that there is a large negative after-potential in the extra-medullary ventral root, so in part the after-negativity may be intrinsically produced in the NM segment.

Investigation of the external field of current flow during invasion of a motor nucleus by an antidromic volley has given evidence that antidromic propagation into the fine terminal dendrites of motoneurones is slow and that eventually blockage occurs (Lorente de Nó, 1947*b*; Barakan *et al.*, 1949; Lloyd, 1951*a*). On the local-circuit theory of propagation this blockage is to be expected in the profusely branched dendritic tree. On the contrary, with intracellular recording, there is no evidence that any antidromic spike potential persists beyond 1 msec. from the antidromic invasion of the soma, but possibly a spike in the dendritic terminals would have a negligible effect on the potential recorded in the soma.

Usually the NM and SD spikes each have an all-or-nothing character, but, at conditions just critical for antidromic invasion of the soma, the NM spike suffers a variable increase due to a late hump on its summit (cf. the second record of Fig. 38 A and eighth of Fig. 39). Apparently under such transitional conditions there is no sharp line of blockage at the axon-soma junction.

When propagation of the antidromic impulse into the non-myelinated segment is delayed or blocked by repetitive stimulation (cf. Fig. 40 B), a small (1 to 2 mV) all-or-nothing spike can be detected, which is probably generated by the antidromic impulse in the myelinated segment, and hence is called the M spike. The low safety factor for propagation from the myelinated to the non-myelinated axon would also be expected on the local-circuit theory of impulse propagation, for inward current flow through the small nodal regions adjacent to the junction has to depolarize to the critical degree the relatively large surface of the non-myelinated axon beyond the junction. Under physiological conditions propagation from a myelinated to a non-myelinated segment of an axon occurs after afferent fibres have entered the grey matter of the spinal cord and before the terminal arborization. A low safety factor for propagation would likewise be expected at this junction, and there is evidence for blockage in such fibres (Eccles and Malcolm, 1946).

Naturally the two regions of low safety factor for antidromic propagation would be regions of high safety factor for impulses discharged reflexly from motoneurones along their axons. In fact the whole path out from the moto-neurone and along the motor axon is very favourable for conduction.

As a conditioning antidromic stimulus is brought closer to the testing antidromic stimulus, there is firstly a failure of the SD spike, then at just over 1 msec. interval the NM spike also fails (Fig. 39, first two records), leaving a very small spike, which presumably is the M spike. Application of a third antidromic stimulus reveals that the second stimulus has made the axon of the motoneurone refractory, i.e. has set up an impulse in it, and this is observed until the test interval is shortened to about 0·6 msec. Thus the refractory period of the axon at the stimulated region (on the ventral root about 2 cm. from the spinal cord) is virtually the standard value for peripheral A fibres (Gasser, 1937; Grundfest, 1940), while there is a much longer refractory period for invasion of the non-myelinated segment and setting up the NM spike.

This lengthening would be expected in view of the low factor of safety for propagation from the myelinated to non-myelinated segments. But for the following reasons it is suggested that it is also in part attributable to the powerful catelectrotonic effect that is exerted on the NM segment by the current that flows during the SD spike: the refractory period following an NM spike is much briefer when it fails to generate an SD spike, i.e. when merely a small spike is recorded; with both peripheral nerve and muscle catelectrotonus has been shown to lengthen the refractory period (Blair and Erlanger, 1933; Eccles and Kuffler, 1941b).

The effect of a conditioning antidromic volley on the response to a testing volley at all intervals (cf. Fig. 39) may be explained in accordance with principles that have been found to obtain in simpler systems. As the testing interval is shortened from about 100 msec., there is firstly a progressive lengthening of the delay between the NM and

SD spikes, an effect which is attributable to the depressant action of the positive after-potential. When the delay has been lengthened to about 0·4 msec., further shortening of the test interval causes failure of the SD spike (cf. Fig. 39). As would be expected, the longer the delay normally obtaining, the longer the critical test interval at which the SD spike fails. When there is a relatively high safety factor for antidromic propagation into the soma plus dendrites, as shown by a very brief axon-soma delay in the control response, axon-soma transmission does not block until the test interval is very short. Critical intervals as brief as 2·5 msec. have been observed. For example, it is 4·0 to 4·3 msec. in Fig. 39. At such intervals the test volley arrives before the positive after-potential has developed, and the depression is attributable to the relative refractoriness of the soma and dendrites (cf. p. 146).

Thus, following a conditioning antidromic volley, blockage or impairment of axon-soma transmission appears to be attributable to two factors that operate in overlapping sequence. Refractoriness of the soma-dendritic membrane at short intervals overlaps at longer intervals with depression caused by the positive after-potential.

Similarly it has been possible to explain all the diverse responses to repetitive antidromic stimulation. If a single antidromic volley gives only an NM spike, then with repetitive stimulation there will be merely NM spikes which follow the highest testing frequency that has been used (450 a second) for a considerable time (Fig. 40 A). If the single antidromic volley gives an SD spike, much more complicated responses are observed, there being complex sequences of SD, NM, and M spikes (Fig. 40 B). During high frequency tetanus the SD spike is always followed by a transient failure of the NM spikes, an effect presumably attributable to hyperpolarization of the NM segment by current flow that is generated by the positive after-potential of the soma-dendritic membrane (cf. records 2 and 3, Fig. 40 B). But failure of the NM spikes

also occurs at other times and is presumably then attributable to the cumulative positive after-potentials in the NM

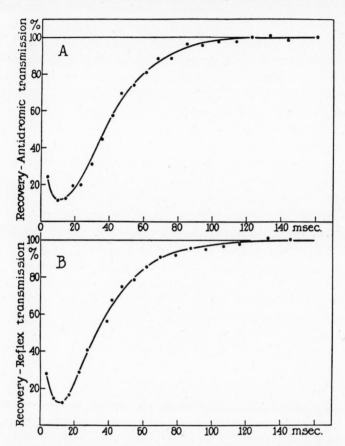

FIG. 41. Curves showing time-course of recovery of neuronal excitability
after conditioning by an antidromic volley (Lloyd, 1951a). *A*. Testing by
size of 'labile' spike recorded from motor nucleus and evoked by a second
antidromic volley, i.e. by number of neurones invaded antidromically as
a percentage of the normal control. *B*. Testing by monosynaptic reflex
as a percentage of normal control. Testing intervals as abscissae.

segment itself (cf. the after-potential in record 3, Fig.
40 A).

In conclusion it can be stated that the antidromic investigation is important because it indicates that, when

allowance is made for the special geometrical features and the after-potentials, the local-circuit theory will explain the propagation of impulses between the various components of the motoneurone, and hence presumably of any neurone. It may be concluded therefore that there is continuity of surface membrane over the whole neurone and all its appendages and that there are no significant transverse membranes. One further conclusion is that the surface membrane of the soma and dendrites differs from that of the axon in that the spike is longer in duration and is followed by a much larger positive after-potential, which has been shown by several methods to be associated with a deep depression of excitability (Brooks *et al.*, 1950*a*; Lloyd, 1951*a*). For example, as shown in Fig. 41, a conditioning antidromic volley causes a similar deep depression of the antidromic axon-soma transmission (cf. Fig. 39) and of the monosynaptic reflex response. The depression is very deep for more than 20 msec. and recovery is virtually complete in about 100 msec. A somewhat similar depression is observed after the reflex discharge set up by a conditioning orthodromic volley (cf. Fig. 46 A, B).

5. *Synaptic excitation of motoneurones*

(a) *The post-synaptic potential, p.s.p.*

The simplest conditions are provided by the monosynaptic excitatory action of the group Ia fibres from the muscle-spindle (cf. p. 111). A volley of impulses in these fibres (the orthodromic volley) produces electrical events in the motoneurone that have been studied accurately by intracellular recording. In this way it has been possible to subject the hypothesis of synaptic excitatory action (cf. p. 113) to crucial tests.

As shown in Figs. 36 D and E (*o* records) a large orthodromic volley may set up a spike potential in a motoneurone which closely resembles the SD antidromic spike. However, the two spikes differ at the start. Instead of the preliminary NM spike, an initial more gradual depolarization leads up to the spike. When the orthodromic volley is reduced in size, the spike fails altogether, being all-or-nothing, and the complete time-course of the initial de-

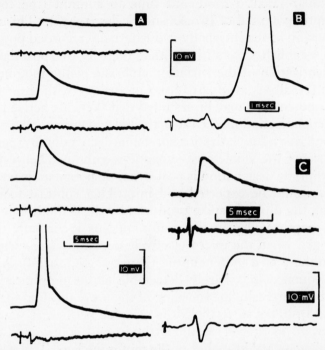

FIG. 42. *A*. Intracellular potentials set up in Biceps-Semitendinosus motoneurone by various sizes of volley in Biceps-Semitendinosus nerve. Note sizes of the dorsal root volley as recorded below each neuronal potential. The largest volley set up a p.s.p. large enough to generate a spike. The transition from the p.s.p. to the spike is marked by the arrow in the faster record (*B*). In *C* is a slow record of a p.s.p. in a Gastrocuemius motoneurone and a still faster record illustrating the latent period. Note dorsal root spike and also small presynaptic spike in intracellular record. Time spaces in milliseconds (Brock *et al.*, 1952*a*).

polarization is then revealed (Fig. 42 A). Further diminution of the orthodromic volley causes a corresponding diminution of the depolarization, but no significant change in its time-course.

It should be noted that the potential actually recorded

is an increasing positivity of the intracellular electrode against the indifferent external electrode. When the micro-electrode is just outside the motoneurone it picks up a much smaller potential in the reverse direction, but with a similar latent period and time to summit (the focal synaptic potential of Brooks and Eccles, 1947*b*). This relationship of the internally and externally recorded potentials establishes definitively that there is the postulated depolarization of the surface membrane of the motoneurone (cf. Brock *et al.*, 1952*a*). On analogy with the end-plate potential it may be assumed that there are active foci of depolarization under the activated synaptic knobs, and secondarily a depolarization spreading decrementally therefrom over the whole post-synaptic membrane; hence the appropriate designation is post-synaptic potential or p.s.p.

As would be expected and in striking contrast to the p.s.p., the diphasic spike produced by the orthodromic or presynaptic volley in the motor nucleus is virtually unchanged when the micro-electrode penetrates the surface membrane of a motoneurone (Brock *et al.*, 1952*a*). As a consequence it is barely detectable at the amplification used for intracellular recording of the p.s.p. (cf. Figs. 42 c, 48 A, B), but it nevertheless is of value because it signals the time of arrival of the orthodromic volley into the terminal axonal branches in the motor nucleus. The p.s.p. begins 0·3 to 0·4 msec. later and rises to its summit usually within 1 msec. (Fig. 42 c). Thereafter it exhibits a slow and virtually exponential decay, with a time-constant of 3 to 5 msec. (mean about 4 msec.). Subsequently there is a very small positive after-potential which runs a time-course resembling the much larger potential that follows the spike, and which is greatly increased after repetitive synaptic activation (Fig. 43).

Originally the evidence for the p.s.p. was derived by the more indirect procedure of recording the potential electrotonically transmitted along the motor axons to the ventral root as it emerges from the spinal cord (Barron and Matthews, 1938; Eccles, 1946). Necessarily the time-courses of such potentials were slowed by the intermediate membrane capacities. There was a distortion in the opposite direction when the p.s.p. was recorded focally by a micro-electrode in the motor nucleus (Brooks and Eccles,

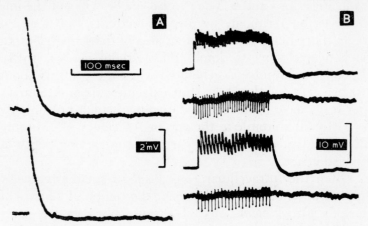

FIG. 43. Intracellularly recorded p.s.p.'s set up in Gastrocnemius moto-neurones by a Gastrocnemius afferent volley. *A*. Single orthodromic volley, the rapid rising phase of the post-synaptic potential being too fast to photograph. *B*. Repetitive orthodromic volleys in another Gastrocnemius motoneurone, the dorsal root spikes also shown below. Same time-scale as for *A* (Brock *et al.*, 1952*a*).

1947*b*). It has been suggested (Lloyd and McIntyre, 1949) that this latter potential was generated in the presynaptic terminals, but the intracellular recording of the p.s.p. has now established that at least a major fraction of the 'focal synaptic potential' is attributable to post-synaptic sinks on the motoneurones.

(b) *Summation and facilitation*

Since alteration in size of the orthodromic volley causes a corresponding change in size of the p.s.p. without appreciable alteration in time-course (Fig. 42 A), it may be concluded that each activated synaptic knob independently exerts a depolarizing action on the post-synaptic membrane, there being summation of these individual effects to give the observed p.s.p. This is the so-called spatial summation, which thus is attributable to the effect of local current flow in causing the spread and summation of the depolarizing action of each synaptic knob. If summation gives a critical degree of depolarization, an impulse is generated as in Figs. 42 A and B. The precise site of origin of the impulse is indeterminate by present methods, but it would seem more likely to occur in an area of dense distribution of activated synaptic knobs (cf. Lorente de Nó, 1938). Usually an impulse is generated when the p.s.p. is about 10 per cent. of the spike, but extreme values of 8 to 15 per cent. have been recorded, a range which presumably is partly attributable to the varying efficiency of grouping of the activated knobs and partly to the varying depth of anaesthesia.

Often the intracellular record shows small irregularly spaced potential waves that have the temporal courses of p.s.p.'s (Brock *et al.*, 1952*a*). Presumably they are generated by random synaptic bombardment of single orthodromic impulses. Of course each impulse would activate the several synaptic knobs of that fibre (cf. Fig. 33 A). The mean size is about 1 mV (range 0·5 to 1·5 mV); hence it can be concluded that usually about ten orthodromic impulses must converge on a motoneurone in order to produce a p.s.p. large enough to generate an impulse, i.e. about 10 mV.

As shown in Fig. 44 the p.s.p. produced by a second orthodromic volley sums with the residual p.s.p. of an earlier volley to give a depolarization that reaches the critical level for generating an impulse. By altering the volley interval it is possible to measure accurately this critical depolarization, e.g. it was 13·7 mV in Fig. 44. It is evident that, within limits imposed by the refractory period of the afferent nerve, this temporal summation gives a larger p.s.p. and hence is more effective in generating an impulse in a motoneurone, the shorter the volley interval.

When the conditioning and testing volleys are in synergic afferent nerves, i.e. nerves which act as excitors of the same motoneurones, this complication of refractoriness is eliminated. Under such conditions the test may be

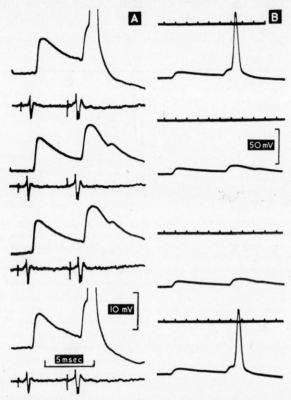

FIG. 44. Intracellular potentials set up in a Biceps-Semitendinosus motoneurone by two orthodromic volleys from Biceps-Semitendinosus nerve, the first stimulus being just submaximal for group I fibres, and the second supramaximal. Note that summation setting up a spike occurred at the shortest interval (first record), the equal intervals of the second and fourth being just critical. *A* and *B* show precisely the same responses but at high and low amplification respectively (Brock *et al.*, 1952*a*).

said to be heterosynaptic, as distinct from the homosynaptic testing of Fig. 44. It would be expected that heterosynaptically the most effective summation would occur with simultaneous volleys, and that, with progressive lengthening of the test interval, the summation would decline with a time-course given by the rate of decay of the conditioning p.s.p. The effectiveness of summation under these conditions is most simply shown when the test orthodromic volley causes the discharge of impulses by a considerable fraction of a uniform population of moto-neurones. In such circumstances the increase in size of the

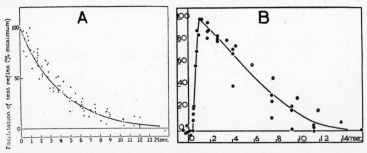

FIG. 45 A. Heterosynaptic facilitation curve drawn through plotted points which represent percentage increments of testing reflex spikes (monosynaptic) relative to maximum increment. Conditioning by sub-maximal group I afferent volley from a muscle nerve, which was reflexly subliminal, and testing by a maximal group I volley in a nerve to a synergic muscle. Test intervals as abscissae (Lloyd, 1946a).

FIG. 45 B. Facilitation curve plotted as in Fig. 45 A but testing by an antidromic volley. Ordinates show percentage increments of 'labile' spike recorded as in Fig. 41 A and measured relative to maximum increment as in Fig. 45 A. Test intervals as measured between arrival of orthodromic and antidromic volleys plotted as abscissae (Brooks and Eccles, 1947b).

test reflex, i.e. the number of additional motoneurones caused to discharge by facilitation, would be approximately proportional to the residual depolarization of the synergic conditioning volley. It is actually observed (Fig. 45 A) that optimum facilitation occurs at zero test interval and decays with a time-constant of about 4 msec. (Eccles, 1946; Lloyd, 1946a), which corresponds precisely to the effect predicted if facilitation is attributable to summation in each motoneurone of the p.s.p.'s to the critical level at which an impulse is generated. There appears to be no need to postulate that synaptic excitation has any direct action on a motoneurone other than the production of the p.s.p.

However, when facilitation between synergic volleys is investigated by a different method, a few experiments have revealed a different kind of facilitation which is not simply explicable by summation of p.s.p.'s to a critical level of depolarization (Brooks and Eccles, 1948a). It occurs when the conditioning volley alone generates impulses in many motoneurones, and hence excites a considerable number of others just short of threshold. At an interval of less than 1 msec. the testing volley may then cause a double reflex discharge. The second (β) corresponds to the ordinary facilitation due to summation of p.s.p.'s. The earlier α discharge is distinguished by the brevity of its latent period (measured from the testing volley) and its rapid decrement to extinction with lengthening of test interval beyond 1 msec. Possibly it is attributable to the effect of the initial subsynaptic depolarizations produced by the testing volley. Conceivably such areas, if produced soon enough and if strategically placed on a motoneurone, could aid in the generation of an impulse by a *conditioning* volley which alone was producing local responses in the post-synaptic membrane (cf. p. 142).

Facilitation by an orthodromic volley has also been tested by the electrical response which an antidromic volley evokes in a motor nucleus (Renshaw, 1942; Brooks and Eccles, 1947b). Depolarization of motoneurones by the p.s.p. relieves in many the axon-soma blockage of antidromic transmission (cf. p. 121). With intracellular recording it is observed that motoneurones which give only an NM spike can be caused in this way to respond by an SD spike in addition. With focal recording in the motor nucleus, this facilitation is revealed by an increase in the so-called labile or neuronal spike, which is actually the SD spike recorded extra-cellularly. As the testing antidromic volley is moved progressively later, this antidromic facilitation decays with a time-constant of about 4 msec. (Fig. 45 B). Necessarily the facilitation curves of Figs. 45 A and B deviate at short intervals, for optimum facilitation occurs when the conditioning and testing orthodromic volleys are synchronous (Fig. 45 A), whereas optimum facilitation of antidromic invasion of motoneurones occurs at about the time that the p.s.p. of the conditioning volley is at a maximum (Fig. 45 B).

Lastly facilitation by an orthodromic volley has been tested by direct electrical excitation of the motoneurones. The p.s.p. produces an increase in the number of motoneurones excited by a test stimulus, and this increase also decays with a time-constant of about 4 msec. (Brooks and Eccles, 1947b).

Thus, by all three methods of test, the facilitation produced by synaptic excitation is shown, by the time-course of its decay, to be attributable to the p.s.p. which is set up in the motoneurones.

(c) *Depression after orthodromic activation*

After a conditioning orthodromic volley there is a very prolonged depression of the reflex response to a homosynaptic testing volley (Bernhard, 1947; Brooks, Downman, and Eccles, 1950b; Eccles and Rall, 1951b; Schlapp and Jefferson, 1952). For example, in Fig. 46 A there is the brief initial facilitation of the subliminal-fringe motoneurones (cf. Fig. 44), then at 20 to 60 msec. deep depression with absent reflexes and eventually recovery by about 150 msec. to a plateau during which the testing reflex spike was still depressed almost to half the control value. As shown in Fig. 46 B the time-course of this phase of incomplete recovery corresponds closely with recovery after a conditioning antidromic activation (cf. Fig. 41 B) and presumably is likewise attributable to the passing off of the positive after-potential. The final recovery from this plateau of depressed response is a very slow process reaching completion in about 3 seconds (Fig. 46 c).

With heterosynaptic testing there is little or no depression after the initial facilitation (Fig. 45 A), an effect which requires two explanations corresponding to the two stages of recovery in Fig. 46. In the first place but little depres-

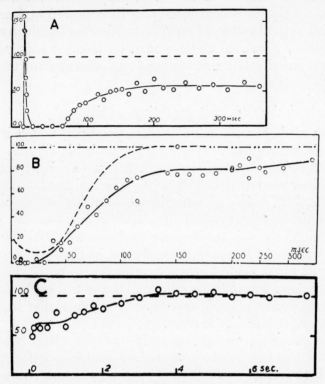

FIG. 46. Recovery curves after conditioning by a single orthodromic volley at zero time, the test being the size of the monosynaptic reflex response evoked by a similar orthodromic volley, i.e. homosynaptic testing using group I afferent fibres from muscle. Gastrocnemius nerve for A and B, Flexor longus digitorum nerve for C. In B the broken line shows the recovery curve in that experiment after conditioning by an antidromic volley (cf. Fig. 41 B). Ordinates, percentages of control monosynaptic reflex spike (Brooks, Downman, and Eccles, 1950b; Eccles and Rall, 1951b).

sion would be exerted by the positive after-potential of neurones that discharge in response to the conditioning volley, for in any case the heterosynaptic testing volley would be able to generate an impulse in few of those motoneurones (Lloyd, 1943*b*; Granit and Ström, 1951). In the second place the very prolonged depression is most probably attributable to a diminished presynaptic excitatory action and hence is strictly homosynaptic (cf. Eccles and Rall, 1951*b*). This depression may be observed to deepen during several volleys of repetitive activation (Schlapp and Jefferson, 1952), an effect which, on analogy with peripheral junctions (p. 91), suggests depletion of some transmitting agent (cf. pp. 166–7).

(d) *Analysis of the post-synaptic potential*

On analogy with the end-plate potential, which it so closely resembles, it seems highly probable (i) that the initial rising phase of the p.s.p. is due to a brief active depolarization that occurs under the activated synaptic knobs, but which spreads thence over the whole post-synaptic membrane, and (ii) that the much slower exponential decay is attributable to the resting ionic fluxes through this post-synaptic membrane, its time-constant of about 4 msec. being a probable value for the post-synaptic membrane. The only experimental test of this explanation that has been possible corresponds to the earlier test of Kuffler (1942*c*) on the e.p.p. (cf. p. 74).

As shown in Fig. 47, an antidromic impulse has been fired into a motoneurone at all time sequences before and during a p.s.p., and the resulting potential complex has been recorded intracellularly (Brock *et al.*, 1952*b*). As with the e.p.p. there is virtually complete destruction of the p.s.p. when it is set up before the antidromic impulse invades the motoneurone (records i to iii); and even when it would be set up during the invasion (record iv), i.e. subsequent to the antidromic spike, these records are virtually identical with the control antidromic response (xi). However, in record v, and progressively still more in records vi–x, a diminished p.s.p. is seen superimposed on the declining phase of the antidromic spike. These superimposed p.s.p.'s have a faster time-course than the control, as may be seen in the subtracted records of Fig. 48 A. The summit is earlier and the time-constant of decay much briefer. For example, the horizontal lines in Fig. 48 A show the time-constants at the respective times relative to the after-potential of the antidromic spike potential. The very low

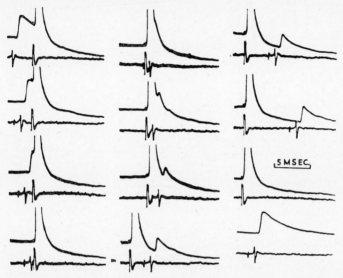

FIG. 47. Intracellular potentials evoked by an antidromic impulse and a group I orthodromic volley at all time sequences. The last two records in the third column show control antidromic and orthodromic (p.s.p.) responses respectively. Note dorsal root records below intracellular record. The antidromic stimulus set up a large artefact. Numbered consecutively downwards columns 1, 2, and 3 (Brock, Coombs, and Eccles, 1952*d*).

value (less than 1 msec.) immediately after the spike, and the progressive lengthening thereafter towards the control value of 3·5 msec., are precisely the effects which have been observed to occur after impulses in giant axons (p. 49), and which have been attributed to the slow decline of the raised potassium conductance to the resting level (Fig. 13 A).

Faster records than those of Fig. 47 have been used in determining the p.s.p. generated in a motoneurone immediately after an antidromic impulse has propagated

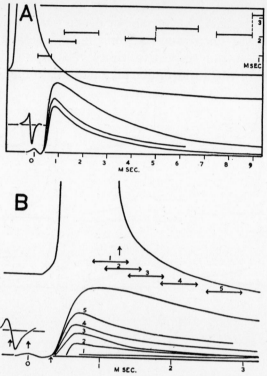

FIG. 48 A. Plotting from series partly shown in Fig. 47. In upper part is control antidromic response (spike truncated), and a series of horizontal lines whose ordinates give the membrane time-constant (see millisecond scale on right) and whose lengths give the time of measurement relative to the control antidromic curve. In lower part is control p.s.p. and two p.s.p.'s set up some milliseconds after the antidromic impulse and determined by subtraction of the antidromic control response from the combined response. Note dorsal root spike. Abscissal scale common to both parts of figure.

FIG. 48 B. Faster records from same experiment as Fig. 48 A, antidromic response being in upper part and in lower part p.s.p. records (also determined by subtraction) and control p.s.p. The horizontal lines numbered I to 5 show times of transmitter activities for the correspondingly numbered p.s.p.'s and are plotted relative to the antidromic response. Note dorsal root spike. Abscissal scale common to both figures (Brock *et al.*, 1952b, d).

over its surface. The subtracted records of Fig. 48 B show the progressive decline in size as the monosynaptic excitatory action is moved progressively earlier under the antidromic spike, until there is virtually none at the earliest position. The left ends of the horizontal lines 1 to 5 signal, relative to the antidromic spike potential, the times at which the p.s.p.'s would have been initiated in the absence of the conditioning spike (cf. arrow at start of p.s.p. records below). The actual p.s.p.'s produced are shown by the respective curves 1 to 5 that are plotted along with a control p.s.p. With position 1 it is evident that virtually no p.s.p. can be built up on the motoneurone by the orthodromic volley which reaches it in the later part of the declining phase of its antidromic spike potential, even at times when volleys at 3 and 4 positions are fairly effective. Thus it may be concluded that, within less than 1 msec. after it initiates a p.s.p., an orthodromic volley has already ceased to exert a depolarizing influence on the post-synaptic membrane. The later declining phase of the monosynaptic p.s.p. must therefore be attributable to the passive decay of the depolarization set up by a brief initial synaptic excitation, exactly as has been shown to occur for the e.p.p. (cf. p. 74). The very early summit and the early onset of the exponential decay are remarkable features in responses 2 to 5. These features indicate that all active depolarization is over within 0·5 msec.

The horizontal lines numbered 1 to 5 show for each test volley the maximum duration (0·5 msec.) of its active depolarizing action. One may assume that, somewhere at the end of the steep declining phase of the antidromic spike (cf. arrow in Fig. 48 B), it first becomes possible for the synaptic excitatory action to produce an effective depolarization of the post-synaptic membrane. Presumably it is ineffective earlier because the potassium conductance, and hence flux of potassium ions, is so high (cf. Fig. 13 A).

In Fig. 48 B the early summits of p.s.p.'s 3 to 5 contrast with the later and more rounded summit of the control p.s.p. If the above argument is sound, the synaptic excitatory action should have ceased before the summit of the control p.s.p., and yet some active depolarizing influence must be continuing. It seems unlikely that the duration of the synaptic transmitter action is altered by the state of the post-synaptic membrane; hence it may be supposed that, in the control p.s.p., a small self-regenerative depolarizing action is superimposed on the synaptic depolarization. Presumably there is a partial activation of the sodium-carrier mechanism in the post-synaptic membrane immediately around the synaptically excited regions, i.e. a type of local response such as has been observed around the mammalian e.p.p. (p. 76). When it is just below threshold for initiating an impulse, the summit of the p.s.p. is often considerably delayed and broadened, presumably by a further development of such local responses. Such an effect is also presupposed in the explanation of the α facilitatory effect (p. 135).

Thus, in conclusion, analysis of the monosynaptic p.s.p. has shown that it is caused by a very brief active depolarization process (presumably restricted to the subsynaptic membrane) and a subsequent passive exponential decay, with probably an intermediate phase of local response in the post-synaptic membrane when it is in a sufficiently excitable state. The electric time-constant of the membrane is given by the decay of the p.s.p., and normally averages about 4 msec. (extremes 3 to 5 msec.). Since synaptic facilitation is attributable simply to summation of p.s.p.'s, the time-constant of the decay of facilitation is also about 4 msec. However, as with giant axons and muscle-fibres, the time-constant of the post-synaptic membrane is much briefer immediately after a spike and progressively lengthens to normal over several milliseconds.

(e) *The action of the synaptic transmitter*

It was possible to estimate the amount of charge that was transferred across unit area of the end-plate membrane in producing the end-plate potential (p. 77). At the best it is possible with the p.s.p. to estimate only the order of magnitude of the transferred charge per unit area of subsynaptic membrane. For example, with the p.s.p. the maximum observed rate of depolarization was 50 V/sec. If the monosynaptically activated membrane is very generously estimated at 5 per cent. of the total, the ionic flux through it (estimated as 13,000 $\mu\mu$mol. cm.$^{-2}$ sec.$^{-1}$) would be considerably higher than during the steepest part of the rising phase of the spike (about 500 V/sec.). On the other hand, much greater ionic fluxes occur in the motor end-plate activated by a chemical transmitter. The striking contrast between the small presynaptic spike (cf. p. 130) and the large p.s.p. makes it highly improbable that the transynaptic flow of current generated by the former would be adequate to evoke the very large ionic flux required to give the latter. As concluded in the next chapter (p. 166), it seems that there is a chemical transmitter for synaptic excitatory action.

It would seem probable that, like the end-plate transmitter (p. 84), the synaptic transmitter would cause its intense depolarizing action by a large non-selective increase in the ion permeability of the subsynaptic membrane. But there was no sign of the predicted diminution in spike height during a synaptic potential (cf. Fig. 36 D, E), there being in contrast usually a slightly larger spike (about 1 mV) for orthodromic as compared with antidromic activation. However, since the p.s.p. was relatively much smaller (at most 25 per cent. of the resting potential) than the e.p.p. (about 70 per cent.), there would be expected to be a smaller increase in non-selective ion permeability, and consequently only a small diminution of spike height—no more than perhaps 2 mV as against 15 mV for the e.p.p. The observation of a small effect in the reverse direction might be attributable to the diminution of the antidromic spike by the forward shift of the NM spike relative to the SD spike (p. 121), and also to the increased dendritic invasion that might be expected to occur when the dendrites were partly depolarized by the p.s.p.

Clearly the nature of the synaptic depolarizing process is at present indeterminate.

(f) *Effect of repetitive synaptic bombardment*

In Fig. 44 there was summation of the monosynaptic p.s.p.'s produced by two successive volleys in the same afferent fibres. With repetitive volleys, summation causes

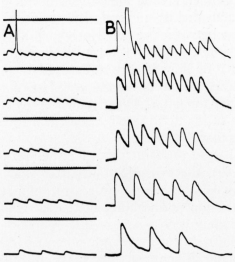

FIG. 49. Intracellular action potentials of motoneurone set up by repetitive orthodromic volleys in group I afferent fibres. Responses of *A* and *B* recorded simultaneously, *B* being at much higher amplification. Time marker in *A*, milliseconds on reference line for zero membrane potential. Approximate frequencies per second from above down, 300, 300, 200, 150, 100, (Brock *et al.*, 1952*d*).

little further increase in the height of the p.s.p., even at frequencies as high as 300 a second (Figs. 43 B, 49), and during the tetanus the successive p.s.p.'s reach approximately the height of the second or third responses.

The height to which the p.s.p. is thus built up by summation is limited by two factors (cf. Eccles and Rall, 1951*a*), which are both illustrated in Figs. 43 B and 49:

the size of the p.s.p. produced by a given orthodromic volley declines during the first few responses of a repetitive series; a positive after-potential develops progressively during a repetitive series, the successive p.s.p.'s of which are superimposed on this lowered base line. The last of the repetitive p.s.p.'s of Fig. 43 B is seen to decline into this positive after-potential, which runs a time-course comparable with that following an SD spike (Fig. 37).

The post-synaptic positive after-potential could be generated in the immediate subsynaptic areas of the membrane, though the postulated areas of local response (p. 142) would also be expected to contribute. Various explanations have been offered for the decline of the successive p.s.p.'s (cf. Eccles and Rall, 1951a); for example, the orthodromic volleys progressively decline in size; the subsynaptic membrane becomes less sensitive to the action of the synaptic transmitter, possibly on account of the cumulative positive after-potential; and finally, if transmission is due to liberation of a specific substance, there may be partial exhaustion of the store in the presynaptic terminals, as occurs in peripheral transmissions (cf. p. 91).

The initiation of impulses in a motoneurone by repetitive orthodromic volleys is of great interest because it leads to an understanding of the normal physiological situation where any neurone is subjected to random repetitive bombardment by impulses in many presynaptic fibres, the frequency of the discharge thus engendered being related to the intensity of the bombardment (cf. p. 177). Under such conditions the behaviour of a motoneurone conforms to the following two rules.

(i) If an impulse is not generated by either the first or second orthodromic volley, it is highly improbable that it will occur at all. Presumably this behaviour depends on the fact that with the third or subsequent volleys the height of the p.s.p. is little if at all greater than for the second volley. For example, in record i of Fig. 49, the second volley generated an impulse, while in record ii, with identical frequency and volley size, not only did the second volley fail, but so did all subsequent volleys; and their p.s.p.'s were never higher than that set up by the second volley.

(ii) Once an impulse has been generated, the generation of a second impulse is improbable for some time. There appear to be two explanations. The subsequent positive

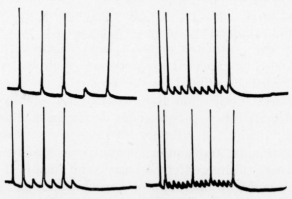

FIG. 50. As in Fig. 49 but in another experiment where single ortho-dromic volley generated a spike discharge. Note p.s.p.'s when spike failed. Approximate frequencies: 45, 100, 150, and 200 a second (Brock *et al.*, 1952*d*).

after-potential depresses the level of the summed p.s.p.'s (cf. Fig. 49, record i), hence generation of a second impulse becomes improbable until there has been some recovery from this hyperpolarization. Furthermore, after an impulse has traversed the surface of a motoneurone, the p.s.p. set up by a given orthodromic volley is considerably diminished in size and shortened in duration (Fig. 48), presumably on account of the high potassium permeability (cf. p. 139), and the lowered excitability of the surface membrane. This latter effect may be seen to operate during the whole remainder of the tetanus in Fig. 49 B, where record i may be compared with record ii.

When an orthodromic volley has a powerful stimulating action, as in Fig. 50, both the first and second orthodromic volleys may generate impulses even at fairly high frequencies, but subsequent discharges fail to follow the high stimulus frequency, presumably on account of the cumulative depressions outlined under rule ii above. Thus in Fig. 50 the first two volleys generate impulses even at 210 a second, but subsequently impulses are generated irregularly at about 40 to 50 a second.

At the other extreme are neurones that require summation of p.s.p.'s in order to generate an impulse. Usually no further impulses are generated by such neurones during that repetitive stimulation. For example, in Fig. 49, record i, it is highly improbable that further continuance of the stimulation would have evoked another impulse. This failure may be attributed to the smaller size of the later p.s.p.'s and to the accumulated positive after-potential (cf. p. 145).

These various behaviours of the individual motoneurones were inferred from the analysis of responses of a large population of neurones (Eccles and Rall, 1951a), hence the intracellular observations on a relatively few motoneurones may be regarded as applicable to the general population of motoneurones. In general it may be concluded that the generation by a neurone of impulses in response to repetitive orthodromic bombardment occurs whenever the depolarization reaches a critical level. There is no evidence of any accommodation process whereby during a tetanus a progressively greater depolarization would be required to generate an impulse. It is of importance to note that temporal summation is relatively ineffective in causing a motoneurone to discharge impulses. A frequency of afferent impulses as high as 150 a second is required in order that summation will build up a higher p.s.p. than the initial response and so be effective in generating an impulse. Such a frequency is above that often observed for discharges from mammalian muscle-spindles (Matthews, 1933; Hunt and Kuffler, 1951b) and indeed from many other receptor organs also.

(g) *Polysynaptic reflexes*

The polysynaptic reflex arc includes at least one inter-neurone and hence two synaptic relays in the path to the motoneurones. Usually, in such a polysynaptic reflex as the flexor reflex, there is a wide variety in the number of interneurones in the path, as indicated by the long dura-tion of the reflex discharge evoked by a single orthodromic volley (Lloyd, 1943*a*, *b*). Such flexor reflexes may be set up by volleys in the cutaneous afferent fibres (cf. Fig. 34 B) or in the group II and III muscle afferent fibres. It would be expected that the intracellular potentials would show evidence of prolonged and irregular synaptic bombard-ment, i.e. successive superimposed waves of depolariza-tion.

With strong stimulation of a muscle afferent nerve, the polysynaptic p.s.p.'s are superimposed on the declining phase of the initial monosynaptic p.s.p. that is seen in isolation when the stimulus is weaker (Fig. 51 A).

An afferent volley in a cutaneous nerve generates in a flexor motoneurone a prolonged and irregular polysynaptic p.s.p. with no monosynaptic component (Fig. 51 B). Here with the strongest stimulus a very late increment in the p.s.p. may be seen generating an impulse. It will be evident that the prolonged and irregular p.s.p.'s as in Fig. 51 B would generate the prolonged reflex discharges charac-teristic of the flexor reflex.

It may be concluded that no special problems are intro-duced by polysynaptic reflexes. Impulses in the axons of interneurones act on motoneurones by generating p.s.p.'s which appear to be similar to the p.s.p.'s generated by the monosynaptic impulses on which attention has hitherto been focused. Furthermore at other synapses in the spinal cord, e.g. on the dorsal horn-cells, there seems to be the same development of p.s.p.'s (the dorsal horn potential), which generate impulses if of sufficient intensity. Again a recent analysis of the potentials generated in synaptic transmission through the lateral geniculate body has revealed essentially the same sequences of events—a post-synaptic potential which has a time-course comparable to that in motoneurones and which generates the discharge

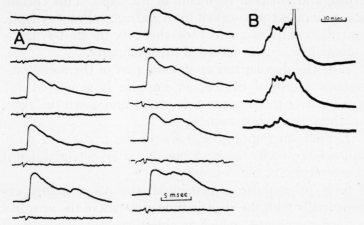

FIG. 51. Intracellular potentials generated in Biceps-Semitendinosus motoneurone. *A*. By orthodromic volley which was set up in Biceps-Semitendinosus nerve by stimuli of progressively increasing strength from top of left column to bottom of right column, the third record showing p.s.p. to maximum group Ia volley. Note humps due to poly-synaptically generated p.s.p. *B*. By orthodromic volley in a cutaneous nerve (Sural nerve). Stimulus progressively weakened from above downwards. Note truncated spike in top record (Brock *et al.*, 1952*d*).

of impulses if of sufficient intensity (Bishop, 1952). Thus it appears that essentially the same post-synaptic events occur generally at synapses in the central nervous system.

E. CONCLUSIONS

In synaptic excitatory action the following sequences of events occur when a presynaptic impulse propagates into a synaptic knob.

1. A brief delay of 0·3 to 0·4 msec.

2. The development of an intense brief depolarization of the subsynaptic membrane with a total duration of about 0·5 msec. This effect is attributable to a net inward

movement of cations, though possibly a net outward anion movement might contribute.

3. Due to local current flow into this 'sink' there is depolarization of the surface membrane of the soma, dendrites, and adjacent segments of the axon. This current also generates the so-called focal and ventral-root synaptic potentials. Effects 2 and 3 together give the post-synaptic potential (p.s.p.) as recorded intracellularly.

4. If the depolarization of some part of the membrane reaches a critical degree, an impulse is generated and spreads over the soma and dendrites and down the axon, i.e. there is a reflex discharge.

5. Such an impulse destroys all the preformed p.s.p. and is followed by the large positive after-potential that is characteristic of the neurone.

6. If no impulse is generated, the p.s.p. decays exponentially with the electric time-constant of the neuronal surface membrane, which is about 4 msec. However, it appears that the peak of the p.s.p. is usually slightly prolonged by the depolarizing action of local responses of the post-synaptic membrane.

Each presynaptic impulse independently produces its own p.s.p. Generation of an impulse is dependent on the summation of such unitary p.s.p.'s to give the critical level of depolarization. The nature of the synaptic transmission mechanism will be further considered in the next chapter, but already it has appeared improbable that the action currents of the presynaptic impulse could cause the very large ionic flux that gives rise to the post-synaptic potential; hence it may be postulated that there is a specific chemical transmitter as in peripheral junctions.

V

CENTRAL INHIBITION, CO-ORDINATION OF REFLEXES, AND TRANSMISSION OF INFORMATION

A. INTRODUCTION

IN the preceding chapter attention has been focused on a reflex in isolation—in particular on the process whereby impulses are generated in the motoneurones of a muscle by impulses in the group Ia afferent fibres of that muscle. For example, the stretch of an extensor muscle, as by the weight of the body in standing, would in this way reflexly cause that muscle to contract and support the weight. But, as particularly emphasized by Sherrington (1906), under normal physiological conditions reflexes are not elicited thus in isolation.

The spinal cord severed from the rest of the central nervous system gives the simplest situation for studying the competition that occurs between reflexes for the control of motoneurones and hence of movement. For example, if a flexor reflex is evoked by an orthodromic volley in some cutaneous afferent nerve (cf. p. 148), simultaneously with a reflex discharge from the flexor motoneurones, there is a depression or inhibition of the motoneurones of extensor muscles, whereby it becomes difficult or impossible to evoke reflex discharges from them. The significance of such inhibition for the co-ordination of reflexes has been extensively discussed (cf. Creed *et al.*, 1932).

B. DIRECT INHIBITION

Inhibition can be studied in a still simpler situation in the so-called 'direct inhibition', where the central delay of the inhibitory effect on a motoneurone is no longer than with monosynaptic excitation (Lloyd, 1941, 1946*a*). An orthodromic volley in the group Ia fibres of a synergic group of muscles directly inhibits the generation of impulses by the motoneurones of antagonist muscles. For example, in Fig. 52 A an orthodromic volley in the nerve to Quadriceps muscle inhibits the reflex response of many motoneurones of the antagonist muscles, Biceps-Semitendinosus. The inhibition can be detected when the conditioning 'inhibitory volley' enters the spinal cord only a fraction of a millisecond before the excitatory, it characteristically reaches its maximum with a testing interval of about one millisecond, and progressively diminishes with further lengthening of the test interval. Since a considerable fraction of the Biceps-Semitendinosus motoneurones reflexly respond to the test volley at all intervals in Fig. 52 A, it may be assumed that at any testing interval the depression of the reflex spike, i.e. the proportion of motoneurones prevented from discharging, gives an approximate measure of the intensity of inhibitory action (cf. p. 134).

Thus, as shown in Fig. 52 B, the measured inhibitions in a series of experiments often approximate to a curve that exponentially decays with a time-constant of about 4 msec. In such experiments the decay rates of the synaptic excitatory and inhibitory processes are virtually identical when they are examined in the simplest situations (monosynaptically). But in many experiments the inhibitory curve deviates widely from an exponential decay, an initial very rapid decay eventually becoming very much slower (Bradley, Easton, and Eccles, 1952). For example, with the weakest inhibition in Fig. 52 C (cf. Fig. 52 A) the time-constant of decay was initially less than 1 msec., and in its latter part more than 5 msec., while in the latter part of the other two curves the time-constant was at least 7 msec. Laporte and Lloyd (1951) have shown that in some experiments this deviation from the 'standard decay' curve (time-constant about 4 msec. throughout, cf. Fig. 52 B) is attributable to a superimposed disynaptic excita-

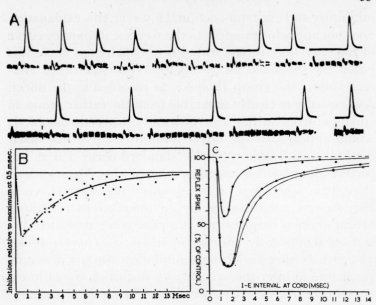

FIG. 52 A. Inhibition by an afferent volley in Quadriceps nerve of the monosynaptic reflex discharge evoked by a volley in nerve to Biceps-Semitendinosus. First, eighth, and last records show reflex spike to Biceps-Semitendinosus volley alone. Other records show effect of preceding Quadriceps volley. Volley intervals as recorded from the dorsal roots close to cord entry are shown below the spike records. Note gaps at millisecond intervals. Stimulus to Quadriceps nerve so weak that subliminal for group Ib and only set up impulses in 30 per cent. of group Ia. Each record is due to superimposed very faint traces of 20 sweeps at intervals of about 3 seconds in order that random variations may be smoothed out (Bradley *et al.*, 1952).

FIG. 52 B. Points and curve of direct inhibition plotted from four experiments with scaling of ordinates so that there is identical inhibition at an interval of 0·5 msec. The points show monosynaptic reflex spike heights at the respective volley intervals of abscissae (cf. Fig. 52 A). The upper horizontal line gives size of control reflex spike (Lloyd, 1946a).

FIG. 52 C. Plotting as in Fig. 52 B, but for series partly shown in Fig. 52 A. Each point represents mean of twenty superimposed records. The three inhibitory curves as shown are for inhibitory volleys; 30 per cent. maximal for group Ia (filled circles); maximal for group Ia and submaximal for Ib (open circles), and maximal for both Ia and Ib (dots in circles) respectively (Bradley *et al.*, 1952).

tory action of group I*b* afferent fibres from the muscle tendon organs (cf. Granit, 1950; Granit and Ström, 1951). The conditioning group I volley would thus have a mixed inhibitory and excitatory action. However, this explanation does not apply for example to the weakest inhibitory curve of Fig. 52 C because the stimulus to Quadriceps nerve was below the threshold for group Ib. With Quadriceps afferent volleys the group Ib spike, as recorded in the dorsal root, usually is clearly separable from the earlier group Ia spike, which also has a considerably lower threshold. It would appear that the direct inhibitory curve may itself deviate considerably from the 'standard decay' curve, but further discussion is postponed to p. 165. Meanwhile it should be noted that, if the weakest inhibitory curve of Fig. 52 C is not distorted by an intercurrent excitatory action, there is no justification for assuming that such distortion significantly affects the other two curves of Fig. 52 C, where there is stronger inhibition. In fact it is only justifiable to infer the existence of distortion by an intercurrent disynaptic excitatory effect when a weaker inhibition exhibits the 'standard decay', and this has not often been possible (cf. Laporte and Lloyd, 1951).

The nature of the processes occurring in direct inhibition will be studied before proceeding to discuss the role that it plays in reflex co-ordination. Already it appears that in the functioning of the central nervous system inhibition is as fundamental a process as synaptic excitation. Only two illustrative examples of inhibition have so far been given, but examples are found almost everywhere in the central nervous system and even in the retinal nervous system (Granit, 1952), probable exceptions being certain relay stations on afferent pathways, e.g. in the gracile and cuneate nuclei and in the lateral geniculate body.

C. THE NATURE OF THE INHIBITORY PROCESS

1. *The electrical events associated with inhibition*

(a) *Direct inhibition*

Since the problem of inhibition in the central nervous system has been completely changed by the technique of

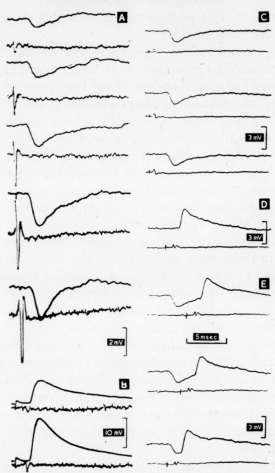

FIG. 53. *A* and *C*. Intracellular potentials set up in Biceps-Semitendinosus motoneurones by single afferent volleys in Quadriceps nerve of increasing size from above downwards. Note the sizes of dorsal root spikes in *A* particularly. *B* and *D*. p.s.p.'s set up by an afferent volley in Biceps-Semitendinosus nerve in same neurones as *A* and *C* respectively. *E*. Intracellular potentials set up by Quadriceps and Biceps-Semitendinosus afferent volleys combined at various intervals, the respective controls being seen in first record of *C* and in *D* (Brock *et al.*, 1952*a*).

intracellular recording, no attempt will be made to discuss previous attempts at explanation of direct inhibition, such as the Golgi-cell hypothesis (Brooks and Eccles, 1947*a*) and the presynaptic interference hypothesis (Renshaw, 1946).

It will be sufficient to demonstrate later that these hypotheses have been falsified.

Figs. 53 A and C show typically the potentials recorded by an intracellular electrode in a Biceps-Semitendinosus (knee flexor) motoneurone by group Ia afferent volleys in the nerve to Quadriceps (knee extensor). In their time courses the potentials are virtually mirror images of the p.s.p.'s set up in those same motoneurones by monosynaptic excitatory volleys (Figs. 53 B, D). The inhibitory potential signals an increase in the internal negativity of the motoneurone, and, since the external potential change is, if anything, in the direction of positivity (Brooks and Eccles, 1948b), it can be concluded that the 'inhibitory volley' in some way causes an active hyperpolarization process in the surface membrane of the motoneurone.

In Figs. 53 A and C the hyperpolarization begins about 1·5 msec. after the inhibitory volley is recorded in the dorsal root, reaches a maximum in about 1 msec. and decays therefrom with time-constants of 2·9 and 2·3 msec. respectively. The latent periods and summit times show little variation in our experiments in contrast to the time-constant of decay which varies from 2·2 to 7 msec. in different motoneurones. However, the hyperpolarization has always been small—usually 1 to 2 mV, so noise would cause considerable error in these estimates of the time-constant.

It would be expected that the over-all hyperpolarization of the neuronal surface membrane would depress its excitability, and thus directly explain the inhibitory effect. In other words, during this hyperpolarization a larger p.s.p. would be required in order to attain the critical level at which a self-regenerating sodium-carrier activity is initiated. Fig. 54 A gives support to this simple explanation of the inhibitory effect. For example, the generation of an impulse by the test volley is inhibited only at the three shortest test intervals (11·5, 9·5, and 5·5 msec.), where there is an appreciable residuum of hyperpolariza-

tion. Admittedly the hyperpolarization is small relative to
the p.s.p., but in the control response the p.s.p. of the test

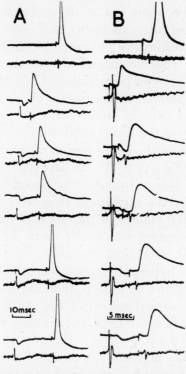

FIG. 54. Intracellular potentials generated in Biceps-
Semitendinosus motoneurone by inhibitory and excitatory volleys as in Fig. 53, but the excitatory volley
alone set up the discharge of an impulse, as shown
by the truncated spikes in control (upper) records of
A and *B*, and also in the two lowest records of *A*. In
all other records the excitatory volley set up only a
p.s.p., the spike being inhibited. Note records of dorsal
root spikes below the intracellular records, but in
slower records of *A* the inhibitory afferent spike was
too faint to print (Brock *et al.*, 1952*d*).

volley is only just above the threshold for initiating an
impulse. For example, in another experiment where the
p.s.p. of the test volley was considerably above the threshold,
inhibition was effective only with test intervals of 0·5 to

2 msec. It is evident that the inhibitory curves of Figs. 52
B and C are built up from the responses of a population
of motoneurones, some of which were inhibited over a
very brief range, some not at all, and some over various
durations of test intervals up to, and even beyond, those
of Fig. 54 A. Presumably the range of inhibition is determined by the relative magnitudes of the post-synaptic
potential and the hyperpolarization. Thus a hyperpolarization with the observed time-constant of decay (mean about
4 msec.) would explain satisfactorily the observed time-
course of decay of the direct inhibitory curve in Fig. 52 B.

The problem of the latent period of inhibitory action is
illustrated by Fig. 54 B. At the shortest interval the inhibitory volley was recorded in the dorsal root only about
0·5 msec. before the excitatory. However, from the times
of the respective volleys in the dorsal root, the onset of
the hyperpolarization was much more delayed than the
p.s.p., 1·4 msec. as against 0·5 msec., i.e. 0·9 msec. more
delay. Thus the hyperpolarization was inhibiting the generation of an impulse by a p.s.p. that had started 0·4 msec.
earlier. In the second record of Fig. 54 B it is seen that
this occurs because the hyperpolarization exerts its effect
just before the p.s.p. generates the impulse, i.e. the relatively long delay between the onset of the p.s.p. and its
generation of an impulse compensates for the longer central
latency of the hyperpolarization. If these two factors are
taken into account, the time-course of the incrementing
phase of inhibition in Figs. 52 B and C is adequately explained. When on the other hand the inhibitory and excitatory volleys enter the spinal cord at approximately the
same segmental level, inhibition begins with approximately
synchronous volleys (Fig. 52 B; Lloyd, 1946a) and not at
an interval of about 0·5 msec. as in Figs. 52 A and C.

The long central delay of the hyperpolarization in Figs.
53 and 54 (usually about 1·3 msec.) might suggest that a
synaptic relay is interpolated between the group Ia dorsal
root-fibres and the events producing the hyperpolarization

of the motoneurone. However, in Figs. 53 and 54 the group Ia afferent fibres from Quadriceps muscle will be entering the spinal cord at least 1·5 cm. farther rostrally than the motoneurone of Biceps-Semitendinosus muscle on which they are acting (cf. Fig. 58 A; Romanes, 1951, Fig. 18). Nothing is known about the size or myelination of the inhibitory collaterals that pass caudally from these group Ia fibres, but the delay of 0·7 msec. over and above the central delay for the monosynaptic depolarization (usually about 0·6 msec.) could probably be occupied in conduction over the additional 1·5 cm. of intramedullary path. Certainly, in view of this additional intramedullary conduction distance, there is no time for an interpolated synaptic relay. In addition such a relay is contra-indicated by two experimental findings with direct inhibition: the approximate direct proportionality of inhibition to size of group Ia volley, even down to a very small volley (Lloyd, 1943a; Bradley et al., 1952); the failure to block direct inhibition by deep anaesthesia (Brooks and Eccles, 1948b). A final possibility is that, even when the nerve impulses have reached the respective loci of action, more time is required to initiate the hyperpolarization process than the 0·3 msec. synaptic delay for depolarization (p. 130).

(b) *Polysynaptic or indirect inhibition*

The more complex and prolonged inhibition of extensor motoneurones by a cutaneous afferent volley is also attributable to a hyperpolarization process. For example, Figs. 55 A and B show respectively the potentials generated inside and immediately outside a Gastrocnemius motoneurone by a cutaneous afferent volley that was progressively increased in size from above downwards. The differences between the respective records give approximately the time-courses of the membrane potentials. Particularly with the larger volleys, the hyperpolarization is much more prolonged than with direct inhibition. Presumably, as with the p.s.p. of the flexor reflex (Fig. 51 B), this prolongation is attributable partly to delay of inhibitory influences by passage through polysynaptic paths, and partly to the longer conduction time of afferent fibres with higher threshold (Lloyd, 1943*b*), but accumulation of an inhibitory transmitter substance is also likely (cf. p. 168). The

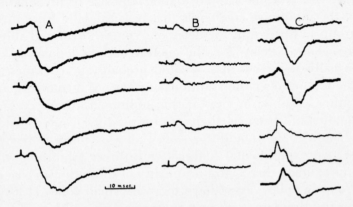

FIG. 55 A. Intracellular potentials evoked in Gastrocnemius motoneurone by single volleys in Sural nerve of increasing size from above downwards.

FIG. 55 B. Potentials recorded under identical conditions, just outside that same motoneurone.

FIG. 55 C. As in Fig. 55 A, but for another Gastrocnemius motoneurone and single volleys in Sural (upper three) and Superficial Peroneal (lower three) nerves. Same time-scale throughout (Brock *et al.*, 1952*d*).

small initial upward deflexion in the intracellular records is approximately matched in the extracellular records, and hence is attributable to the potential field produced by extrinsic currents which are generated, for example, by synaptic activation in the dorsal horn (cf. Campbell, 1945; Brooks and Eccles, 1948*b*). However, cutaneous volleys have often been observed to produce mixed depolarizing and hyperpolarizing actions on extensor motoneurones. Different afferent nerves often have very different actions on the same motoneurone (Fig. 55 C). This observation corresponds to the mixed excitatory and inhibitory actions that afferent impulses from the skin often exert on extensor motoneurones (Hagbarth, 1952). We have not systematically investigated the effect of cutaneous afferent volleys on flexor motoneurones.

(c) *Conclusions*

It may be concluded that both the direct and the indirect or polysynaptic inhibitory actions on a motoneurone are brought about by a hyperpolarization of its surface membrane. The experimental observations on both direct and indirect inhibition are at present adequately explained by the consequent increase in the p.s.p. that is required to generate an impulse.

2. *The mechanism causing inhibitory hyperpolarization*

(a) *Discussion of existing hypotheses*

Until the intracellular potential was recorded during inhibition of motoneurones, the Golgi-cell hypothesis (Brooks and Eccles, 1947*a*) satisfactorily explained all the experimental evidence. In particular there was much evidence that inhibition was attributable to foci of hyperpolarization on the motoneurone (Brooks and Eccles, 1948*b*, 1948*c*; Brooks, Eccles, and Malcolm, 1948), which acted by preventing the spread and fusion of the excitatory foci. But, according to the Golgi-cell hypothesis of inhibition, these hyperpolarized foci are caused by the inward flow of current that is generated extrinsically by the p.s.p. of Golgi-cells (neurones with short axis cylinders) and specifically applied to the motoneurone through synaptic knobs. Hence the effect of these foci of hyperpolarization on the potential recorded inside the motoneurone would be balanced by the equivalent amount of depolarization produced elsewhere on the motoneurone where the current flows outward. The observed increased negativity of the intracellular electrode relative to the indifferent earth lead (Figs. 53, 54, 55) would not be predicted from the Golgi-cell hypothesis, which indeed would predict a small potential in the reverse direction due to the extrinsic field of the

Golgi-cell p.s.p. (Brock, Coombs, and Eccles, 1952*a*); hence this hypothesis may be regarded as falsified.

The presynaptic interference hypothesis postulates that inhibition is caused by the inhibitory volley blocking some, at least, of the presynaptic excitatory impulses (Renshaw, 1946). This hypothesis completely fails to account for the observed hyperpolarization of the inhibited neurone. Furthermore it is directly disproved, for during the inhibition there is no diminution of the p.s.p. produced by the excitatory volley, at least in its initial rising phase, it being merely superimposed on the base line of hyperpolarization (Figs. 53 E, 54; cf. Brooks, Eccles, and Malcolm, 1948).

(b) *The hyperpolarization hypothesis of inhibition*

Since the latent period of the hyperpolarization is too brief to allow for a synaptic relay (p. 158), it must be assumed that impulses in collaterals of the group Ia fibres of the antagonist muscles cause a reaction of hyperpolarization in the surface membrane of the motoneurone. Immediately this hypothesis is confronted by an important problem: why do some impulses (the excitatory) set up a depolarization process of the motoneurone and others (the inhibitory) a hyperpolarization process?

Histological investigation as yet does not give any indication of an answer. Though synaptic knobs vary considerably in size, structure, and form (Fig. 33; Cajal, 1934; Haggar and Barr, 1950), there is no evidence relating any type to any function. Furthermore, the postulate of location of excitatory and inhibitory endings on specific areas of the motoneurone (cf. Gerard, 1941; Gesell and Hansen, 1945; Gesell, Hansen, and Siskel, 1947) provides no answer to the problem, because, with all positions of the micro-electrode in the motoneurone (as may be assumed with our method of insertion), excitatory and inhibitory effects are always associated with their characteristic potentials.

Any attempt to develop an electrical explanation for the production of hyperpolarization by an 'inhibitory impulse' must recognize that there is no evidence that the surface membranes of nerve- or muscle-fibres ever give active anelectrotonic reactions to inward currents (cf. Hodgkin, 1938; Cole and Curtis, 1941; Hodgkin and Rushton, 1946; Katz, 1948; Hodgkin, Huxley, and Katz, 1949) for the 'anelectrotonic local responses' described by Arvanitaki (1943) are otherwise explicable (Eccles, 1948). By making special assumptions it is possible to show how a flow of electric current from an activated synaptic knob could cause a general hyperpolarization after a brief initial depolarization of the neuronal membrane. But an inhibitory volley produces hyperpolarization and inhibition from the outset (Figs. 53, 54), hence an electrical explanation of inhibitory synaptic transmission seems most improbable. It would demand the postulate of special electrical properties qualitatively very different from those revealed by exhaustive investigations of surface membranes.

It may therefore be concluded that inhibitory synaptic action is probably mediated by a specific transmitter substance that is liberated from the inhibitory synaptic knobs, and causes an active hyperpolarization process in the subjacent membrane of the motoneurone. If it be assumed that the resting motoneurone is in a steady state for potassium and chloride (cf. p. 116), any alteration in the permeability to these ions would have no effect on the membrane potential (p. 22). It would thus appear that the simplest explanation of the hyperpolarization produced by the inhibitory transmitter substance would be that it caused an increased net outward flux of sodium ions. This effect could be brought about either by a decrease in the inward diffusion rate below the resting level (the sodium-pump continuing to pump sodium outwards at the resting rate), or by an increase in the activity of the sodium-pump.

On the contrary Burgen and Terroux (1952) suggest that

the inhibitory hyperpolarization that ACh produces on heart-muscle is most probably explained by an increase in potassium conductance. Since the measured resting potential of the heart-muscle (about 60 mV) is far below the calculated potassium equilibrium potential (87 mV), this explanation is attractive. It appears that the inhibitory hyperpolarization of crab muscle (p. 99) may also be explained in this way, for it is largest when the resting membrane potential is lowest, i.e. farthest off the potassium equilibrium potential (Fatt and Katz, 1952c). This relationship is not observed in the motoneurone, where large inhibitory hyperpolarizations have been observed when the resting potential is high; hence the sodium hypothesis appears more probable.

The observed maximum rate of rise of the hyperpolarization (7 V/sec.) would require a net outward flux of about 90 $\mu\mu$mol. cm.$^{-2}$ sec.$^{-1}$, on the assumption of a membrane capacity of 1·3 μF cm.$^{-2}$. But this is the average flux for the whole membrane, and if, for example, the monosynaptic inhibitory knobs covered only 5 per cent. of the neuronal surface, which seems a generous estimate for one special variety of inhibitory knob, the sodium-pump in the inhibitory subsynaptic areas would be working at the high rate of 1,800 $\mu\mu$mol. cm.$^{-2}$ sec.$^{-1}$. This value seems far too high for a resting sodium flux across the membrane (Table 3, columns 5 and 6), hence more probably the inhibitory transmitter exerts its action by increasing the activity of the sodium-pump. A pumping-rate of this magnitude may seem extraordinarily high, but the very large positive after-potential of the soma-dendritic membrane (cf. Figs. 37, 40 B, 47) presumably also indicates that the sodium-pump is much more highly developed than in the axon. However, the initial rate of development of this large positive after-potential indicates a much lower rate of activity for the sodium-pump. For example, with several motoneurones the slope of the developing positive after-potential was as high as 4 V/sec., but this would require that a sodium-pump activity of only 50 $\mu\mu$mol. cm.$^{-2}$ sec.$^{-1}$ be distributed uniformly over the membrane.

Since the time-course of the hyperpolarization of direct inhibition so closely resembles that of the monosynaptic p.s.p. (compare Figs. 53 A with B, and C with D), it may likewise be assumed to be due to an initial brief effect of the inhibitory transmitter substance, and a subsequent return to the resting potential by virtue of the inward current due to the net fluxes of potassium and chloride ions (cf. p. 138). Thus the time constant of decay of the direct inhibitory effect is also to be attributed to the electric time-constant of the resting membrane, and this common dependence explains the virtual identity often observed for the monosynaptic excitatory and inhibitory curves (cf. Figs. 45 A, 52 B). If it be assumed that the inhibitory synaptic knobs are randomly scattered over the surface of the soma and large dendrites of a motoneurone, local current flow would cause a very rapid spread of the hyperpolarization over the membrane, just as was assumed for the excitatory depolarization. Thus it would be more accurate to consider the inhibitory effect as due to a generalized hyperpolarization of the motoneurone rather than, as the Golgi-cell hypothesis must assume, to hyperpolarized foci which act by preventing the spread and fusion of excitatory foci.

It remains now to consider how the observed hyperpolarization could account for the initially fast decline that is characteristic of many inhibitory curves (Fig. 52 C). Such curves immediately recall the end-plate potentials that are recorded close to the end-plate (Figs. 20 A, 21). If the inhibitory synaptic knobs are concentrated on some region of a motoneurone, they would be expected to cause a hyperpolarization of that region which would run a time-course resembling the depolarization close to the end-plate (Figs. 20 A, 21). If at the same time the strategic grouping of the monosynaptic excitatory knobs made that same region the site at which they generated an impulse, then an inhibitory curve of the time-course of Fig. 52 C would be expected. Thus any segregation of the monosynaptic excitatory and inhibitory knobs to the same areas of the motoneurones would tend to give inhibitory curves of the type of Fig. 52 C, while, with completely random distribution, the curve of Fig. 52 B would be obtained, i.e. the time-course of decay would correspond to the electric time-constant of the membrane.

D. CHEMICAL TRANSMITTER SUBSTANCES IN THE CENTRAL NERVOUS SYSTEM

1. *The excitatory synapse*

Since the experimental evidence has falsified the Golgi-cell hypothesis of inhibition and left the chemical transmitter hypothesis as the only likely explanation, it suggests further that excitatory synaptic action in the central nervous system conforms with the pattern of chemical transmission that seems to obtain with all other junctions —at least in vertebrates. The alternative hypothesis of electrical synaptic action would have great difficulty in accounting for the high rate of net ionic flux that has been calculated to occur through the activated subsynaptic membrane (p. 143), whereas much greater fluxes occur in the end-plate membrane activated by a chemical transmitter (p. 77). Furthermore, since the presynaptic potentials recorded by the intracellular electrode are no larger than those recorded extracellularly (Brock *et al.*, 1952*a*), the synaptic knobs have no special method of injecting current across the post-synaptic membrane. The striking contrast between the small presynaptic spike and the large p.s.p. (Figs. 42, 48) also makes it appear improbable that the transynaptic flow of current would be adequate to evoke that large p.s.p. On the electrical theory of transmission it does not seem possible to provide an explanation for the great amplification observed. It has already (p. 138) been suggested that the prolonged depression of synaptic transmission (as tested homosynaptically, cf.

Fig. 46) is probably attributable to depletion of a chemical transmitter substance.

With the monosynaptic reflex the nature of the synaptic excitatory transmitter, however, remains obscure. It is improbable that it is acetyl-choline, not only because the dorsal root-fibres have such a low acetyl-choline and choline-acetylase content (Loewi and Hellauer, 1938; MacIntosh, 1941; Loewi, 1945; Feldberg, 1945, 1950a), but also (Eccles, 1946, 1947) because (i) even high concentrations of anti-cholinesterases have a negligible effect on synaptic potentials set up by repetitive stimulation, and (ii) synaptic transmission is but little depressed by soaking the isolated frog spinal cord in relatively high concentrations (10^{-3}) of acetyl-choline plus anti-cholinesterase. It should be noted, however, that the first of these observations does not necessarily exclude acetyl-choline as a transmitter, for Ogston (1952) (cf. p. 104) has shown that diffusion would account for a sufficiently rapid rate of dissipation of the acetyl-choline liberated from a synaptic knob of average size, approximately a sphere of radius $0.5\ \mu$ (Haggar and Barr, 1950). But with repetitive stimulation diffusion would be considerably slowed by the diminishing diffusion gradient, yet anti-cholinesterases still do not prolong the p.s.p. (Eccles, 1947), even when this is recorded intracellularly (Brock *et al.*, 1952d), which contrasts with the sympathetic ganglion (Fig. 31 B).

It has been suggested that the transmitter substance which is liberated at the peripheral ends of sensory nerve-fibres and causes antidromic vaso-dilatation is the same as the synaptic transmitter at the central synapses of those nerve-fibres (Feldberg, 1945, 1950a, 1950b). Recent work (Holton and Perry, 1951) indicates that this substance is neither acetyl-choline nor histamine, and, further, it throws doubt on the suggestion of Hellauer and Umrath (1948) that the substance liberated by sensory nerve terminals is destroyed by an enzyme that is inhibited by strychnine.

However, the high concentrations of acetyl-choline in

various parts of the central nervous system as well as the profound effects of anti-cholinesterases on the activity of higher centres suggest that acetyl-choline is the transmitter substance at synapses in many regions of the central nervous system (cf. Feldberg, 1945, 1950*a*, 1950*b*). More precise investigation is needed on the same pattern that showed the role which acetyl-choline plays at peripheral junctions (cf. p. 69). Already such work on the perfused spinal cord has indicated that acetyl-choline is the transmitter substance for some polysynaptic reflexes (Feldberg, Gray, and Perry, 1952).

2. *The inhibitory transmitter substance*

Some direct experimental evidence for an inhibitory transmitter substance is given by the action of repetitive inhibitory volleys and by the action of strychnine on direct inhibition. There is, however, no evidence relating to the nature of the inhibitory substance.

In contradistinction to synaptic excitation, a relatively prolonged inhibitory state follows a repetitive series of direct inhibitory volleys (Bradley *et al.*, 1952). For example, in Fig. 56 A, following two and four inhibitory volleys, the initially deep inhibition declined with the standard time-constant of about 4 msec., but at about 10 to 15 msec. a further inhibitory effect developed which ran such a slow time-course that it was still considerable at 80 msec. After a brief tetanus of ten volleys the prolonged inhibition became very prominent (Fig. 56 B) so that it virtually continued on from the depth of the primary inhibition. Since these prolonged inhibitions were observed with inhibitory volleys set up by stimuli too weak to excite group II or III afferent fibres, they presumably are attributable to group Ia afferent fibres, for the group Ib would be excitatory to the antagonist motoneurones (Laporte and Lloyd, 1951). There is even a suggestion of a small delayed phase of inhibition after single inhibitory volleys in Fig. 52 C but the observations were not made at a sufficiently long testing interval. Possibly these two phases of direct inhibitory action are attributable to the same transmitter substance, the double character being given by its rate of

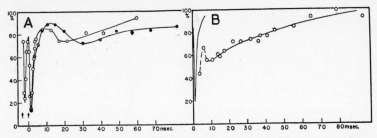

FIG. 56 A. Inhibitory curves plotted as in Fig. 52 C, but subsequent to 2 (open circles) and 4 (filled circles) volleys at 3·6 msec. apart. Each point represents the mean of 20 superimposed records, and with the 2-volley series the points are also shown for the inhibitory effect of the first of the two volleys at times shown by arrows. As in Fig. 52 A these inhibitory volleys in Quadriceps nerve were only 30 per cent. of maximum for group Ia and had no group Ib components. Ordinates: percentages of mean control reflex spike evoked by a maximum volley in Biceps-Semitendinosus nerve.

FIG. 56 B. Same series as in Fig. 56 A, but for single inhibitory volley (curve drawn without any points) and ten inhibitory volleys respectively, each point being the mean of 20 superimposed records (Bradley et al., 1952).

dissipation, as is observed with the repetitive e.p.p. of eserinized frog muscle (Fig. 28 A) and the repetitive postsynaptic potentials of ganglia (Fig. 31 B). However, it does not seem possible to explain in this way the incrementing phase that begins at 10 to 15 msec. (cf. Fig. 56). It may still be assumed that the initial rate of decay of the inhibitory transmitter is so rapid that the time-constant of the membrane governs the first rate of decay, just as occurs with the e.p.p. in Fig. 28 A. In preliminary experiments with intracellular electrodes, the hyperpolarization likewise showed a slowly decaying phase after an inhibitory tetanus, and the delayed phase of hyperpolarization in the polysynaptically inhibited motoneurone of Fig. 55 A also suggests the prolonged action of an accumulated transmitter substance.

Progressive dosage with strychnine shortens and diminishes the direct inhibitory action of a group Ia volley.

For example, in Fig. 57 a dose of about 0·08 mg. per Kg. greatly diminished the inhibition, and at the same time apparently enhanced the disynaptic excitatory action.

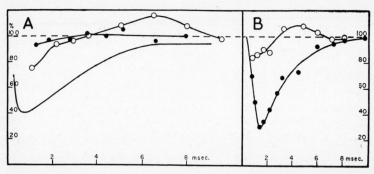

FIG. 57 A. Inhibitory curves to single inhibitory volley plotted as in Fig. 52 C. Control inhibitory curve is shown by continuous line without plotted points and after injection of 0·08 mg. strychnine per kg. the inhibitory curve is given by the open circles. Inhibitory volley in Deep Peroneal nerve and testing reflex spike evoked by maximum group I volley in Gastrocnemius nerve. Note smaller initial inhibition and later facilitation. When the inhibitory volley was set up by a similar stimulus applied to the nerve to Tibialis Anticus and Extensor Digitorum muscles (filled circles), there was no significant phase of facilitation and the initial inhibition was also slight.
FIG. 57 B. As in Fig. 57 A, but for another pair of antagonist muscles, the inhibitory volley in Quadriceps nerve and excitatory in nerve to Biceps-Semitendinosus. Filled circles, inhibitory curve before strychnine, and open circles after injection of 0·08 mg. per kg. of strychnine (Bradley *et al*, 1952).

Possibly strychnine blocks the action of the inhibitory transmitter substance just as curare blocks the action of acetyl-choline at the neuro-muscular junction. Alternatively strychnine may, for example, indirectly affect inhibition by depressing the sodium-pump. There has been no intracellular recording from preparations under strychnine.

3. *Problem of specificity of action of excitatory and inhibitory substances*

The group Ia afferent fibres from the muscle-spindles of a muscle monosynaptically excite the motoneurones of that muscle and its synergists, and monosynaptically inhibit the motoneurones of the antagonistic muscles. On the basis of chemical transmission at both types of synapses, there are two alternative structural arrangements by which this could occur: (i) two independent sets of muscle-spindles in a muscle, one discharging into afferent fibres having an excitatory action, and the other into inhibitory afferent fibres, i.e. the respective afferent fibres would be chemically specific; (ii) after it enters the spinal cord, an afferent fibre from the muscle-spindle gives off two sets of collateral branches, one set being excitatory, the other inhibitory on the appropriate motoneurones as shown in Figs. 58 A and B. The first alternative seems improbable and will not be further considered, but it has its own peculiar difficulties; for example, identical receptor organs in a muscle innervated by afferent fibres having antagonistic central chemical actions.

The second alternative is seemingly more probable, and gives economy of receptor organs and afferent fibres, yet it raises very difficult problems. Hitherto it has been accepted as a general rule that a chemical transmitter substance is manufactured along the whole length of the nerve-fibre and in the cell of origin, e.g. that choline-acetylase manufactures ACh along the whole length of the motor axon and also in the motoneurone (cf. Feldberg, 1950a, 1952). As a consequence the same transmitter substance will be liberated at all the terminal branches of a nerve-fibre. For example, it is assumed that the transmitter substance, which causes antidromic vaso-dilatation, is also probably concerned in central synaptic transmission from these same fibres (cf. p. 167). According to this rule the same substance or substances will be liberated at both the excitatory and inhibitory terminals of a group Ia fibre.

There are three ways in which such a system could operate (Fig. 58 B).

(i) The group Ia afferent fibres of flexor muscles liberate a substance (Y in Fig. 58 Bi) which depolarizes flexor and hyperpolarizes extensor motoneurones, while the group Ia fibres of extensor muscles liberate a different substance

(X) having the reverse actions. This suggestion might help to explain the specificity of monosynaptic connexions in the spinal cord. For example, the chemical specificity

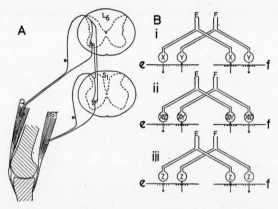

FIG. 58 A. Diagram showing probable pathways for reciprocal innervation for the extensor (Quadriceps) and flexor (Biceps-Semitendinosus) muscles of the knee-joint. One annulo-spiral ending and its group Ia afferent fibre is shown for each muscle, and it divides in the spinal cord into an excitatory and inhibitory branch which form synaptic knobs on an homonymous and antagonist motoneurone respectively. As shown, the Quadriceps afferent and efferent innervation arises from the spinal cord about two segments rostral to that for Biceps-Semitendinosus (Brock *et al.*, 1952*b*).

FIG. 58 B. Diagrammatic representation of possible modes of monosynaptic excitatory and inhibitory action, i, ii, and iii corresponding to the three situations described in the text. E and F are respectively group Ia afferent fibres from extensor and flexor muscles, and e and f respectively the surfaces of the extensor and flexor motoneurones. The synaptic knobs are shown containing the respective transmitter substances which they secrete, those ringed in ii being assumed to be inactive on the adjacent subsynaptic membrane. The striated and dotted borders on the subsynaptic membrane signify patches with specific sensitivity. The arrows indicate current flow due to the net cationic-anionic flux across the subsynaptic membrane. Hence an inward arrow gives depolarization and excitation, an outward hyperpolarization and inhibition.

could control the growth and connexions of the afferent fibre, or, if aberrant connexions were made, they would be functionless because the effective chemical transmitter was lacking. But there are grave difficulties in this concept. For example, it would imply that there was a different chemical transmitter for the group Ia fibres from each synergic group of muscles in a limb. And further it appears that hopeless difficulties and contradictions would arise in attempting to account in this way for all the wealth of interneuronal excitatory and inhibitory actions on motoneurones.

(ii) The group Ia fibres of a muscle liberate two substances (X and Y in Fig. 58 Bii), one of which (X) acts as an excitatory and the other (Y) as an inhibitory transmitter. There must, in addition (as represented in Fig. 58 Bii) be a specialization of the subsynaptic areas of the motoneurones whereby the appropriate motoneurones react only to the excitatory or inhibitory transmitter.

(iii) The group Ia fibres of a muscle liberate the same substance (Z in Fig. 58 Biii) at both excitatory and inhibitory terminals, but the subsynaptic areas are specialized so that this substance hyperpolarizes the motoneurones of the antagonist muscles, and depolarizes the homonymous and synergic motoneurones.

Both ii and iii involve the postulate of specialized subsynaptic areas, but such specialization certainly occurs at the end-plate of a muscle (Kuffler, 1943). The additional postulates with both are that the same motoneurone has subsynaptic areas not only specialized for opposite functions but also reacting differently to a particular substance (X and Y in Fig. 58 Bii and Z in Fig. 58 Biii). This latter postulate certainly involves a degree of specialization that has hitherto not been assumed for the surface of a single cell. However, a somewhat related postulate has been made for smooth muscle; for example that acetyl-choline acts as the excitatory transmitter substance for the detrusor of the bladder and as an inhibitory transmitter to the internal sphincter, and also in respect of the sphincters and general musculature of the alimentary canal. It would seem that a decision between those various alternatives will not be possible until the chemical transmitting substance or substances have been identified.

E. RHYTHMIC RESPONSES OF MOTONEURONES

The foregoing concepts of the excitatory and inhibitory properties of motoneurones may be used in outlining an hypothesis to account for the rhythmic discharges (Fig. 59), usually at 10 to 50 per second, of motoneurones that are subjected to continuous synaptic bombardment of a sufficient excitatory intensity (cf. Adrian and Bronk, 1929; Denny Brown, 1929). Temporal summation of the p.s.p.'s produced by repetitive bombardment of synaptic knobs, has usually been assumed to explain the build-up of an excitatory state, but it has been shown (p. 147) that this is ineffective at the repetitive frequencies that usually obtain, i.e. below 100 to 150 a second. However, spatial summation between the excitatory effects set up under different synaptic knobs on a motoneurone is effective for the duration of the individual p.s.p.'s (about 15 msec., cf. Fig. 45 A). The normal randomly distributed bombardment of the various knobs on the surface of a motoneurone will therefore, if intense enough, give rise to combinations of p.s.p.'s sufficiently close together in time and space to attain the threshold level for generating an impulse. This impulse will propagate over the surface of the motoneurone and cause complete destruction of the p.s.p. (cf. Figs. 47, 48 B), and also depression of the excitability of the motoneurone, this latter effect being attributable to the refractory period and the large positive after-potential (Figs. 37, 39, 41, 49).

In Fig. 60 A an attempt has been made to show diagrammatically the sequences of events during the rhythmic responses of a motoneurone to a continued synaptic bombardment. This explanation is essentially the same as that developed many years ago (Eccles, 1936), and more recently a similar explanation has been developed by Pitts (1943) for the rhythmic responses of phrenic motoneurones. The plotted curves show potential records that would be given by an intracellular electrode. The broken

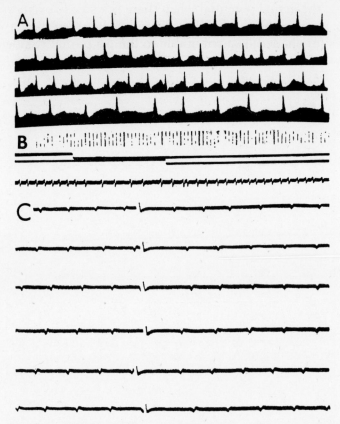

FIG. 59A. Rhythmic discharges of impulses from a motoneurone as recorded in Gastrocnemius muscle during crossed extensor reflexes of varying intensities. Frequencies from above downwards 16, 14, 18, and 11 a second (Adrian and Bronk, 1929).

FIG. 59B. Rhythmic discharge of extensor motoneurone recorded as in Fig. 59A. Between signals an ipselateral inhibitory nerve was tetanized with a consequent slowing of the rhythm. Time, 20 msec. (Creed *et al.*, 1932).

FIG. 59C. As in Fig. 59A, but in Soleus muscle, and the rhythm was interrupted by an antidromic impulse that was fired into the moto-neurone at various phases of its rhythmic cycle. Note the varying length of the subsequent compensatory pause (Eccles and Hoff, 1932).

lines show in each case the positive after-potential that would be recorded in the absence of an excitatory synaptic bombardment (cf. Fig. 37), while the continuous lines show the actual potential when there is a steady excitatory synaptic bombardment. The difference between these two lines (as shaded) is attributable to the p.s.p. that has been

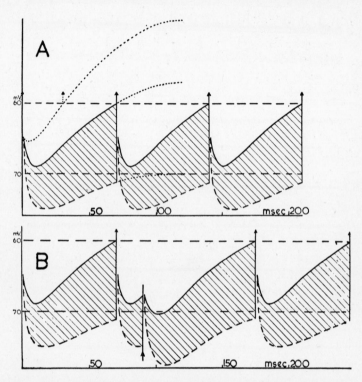

FIG. 60 A. Diagram illustrating suggested mechanism for generating rhythmic discharges of motoneurones. Full description in text.
FIG. 60 B. Diagram illustrating manner in which an antidromic impulse interrupts a rhythmic cycle and is followed by a partially compensatory pause (cf. Fig. 59 C). See text.

built up (cf. Fig. 49). At zero time an impulse is generated and the existing p.s.p. destroyed. The subsequent rebuilding of p.s.p. by the synaptic bombardment is governed by several factors: no p.s.p. is set up within a millisecond of the initiation of an impulse (Fig. 48 B); even several milliseconds after the impulse the p.s.p. production is depressed to about half its control value, being smaller in size and shorter in duration (Figs. 47, 48); the full recovery of p.s.p. size does not occur until the positive after-potential has passed off; the p.s.p. generated by any single pre-synaptic impulse has the standard time-course of Fig. 42 A, and hence will contribute in decrementing degree to the aggregate p.s.p. recorded up to 15 msec. or so later. As shown in Fig. 60 A, when the p.s.p. reaches the assumed (cf. p. 132) critical level of 10 mV depolarization (i.e. membrane potential reduced to 60 mV), an impulse is again generated (see arrow) and the cycle repeated, and so on, giving in this way a rhythmic discharge with a frequency of about 14 a second.

It is evident from Fig. 60 A that a more intense synaptic bombardment will give a higher frequency of response. For example, a p.s.p. building up to the much higher intensity shown by the dotted line in Fig. 60 A would give a discharge every 30 msec., i.e. 33 a second. However, instead of the assumed steady p.s.p. production, the random synaptic bombardment will give at times combinations of excitatory foci which are particularly effective by virtue of their close spatial and temporal relationship. Thus the curve for the summed p.s.p. should be drawn as an irregular wavy line rather than the smooth continuous line of Fig. 60 A. The recovery from the positive after-potential would account for the fairly regular rhythmic frequencies observed at any adequate intensity of continued synaptic bombardment (Fig. 59 A). But if the bombardment falls to such a low intensity that it rarely gives threshold combinations of excitatory foci (i.e. 10 mV. depolarization) even for the fully recovered motoneurone, the discharges will be conditioned only by the random factor and will loose all semblance of regularity, as is actually observed.

Since the hyperpolarization process produced by 'inhibitory impulses' has virtually the same time-curve as the depolarizing p.s.p. (Fig. 53), the superposition of a random

N

inhibitory bombardment on to the pure excitatory bombardment will merely be equivalent to a lowered intensity of the latter and hence give a correspondingly lowered frequency of discharge (Fig. 59 B) or cessation of all discharge. The well-known effects of inhibition (Liddell and Sherrington, 1924, 1925; Denny Brown, 1929; Creed *et al.*, 1932) are therefore simply explicable.

Two decades ago (Eccles and Hoff, 1932) it was shown that invasion of a rhythmically responding motoneurone by an antidromic impulse was followed by a lengthened cycle, there being thus a partial compensation for the induced early response of the neurone (Fig. 59 C). A similar effect was produced when the discharge to the motoneurone was brought about by an orthodromic volley (Hoff, Hoff and Sheehan, 1934). As shown in Fig. 59 B, the present hypothesis of rhythmic discharge provides an explanation for these experimental observations. The arrow pointing upwards shows the antidromic invasion of the motoneurone which destroys the existent p.s.p. and gives by summation an increased positive after-potential. It is seen that, as a consequence, the development of the critical level of depolarization takes a considerably longer time than with the normal cycles. The earlier the antidromic volley, the more effective the summation of the positive after-potentials, and hence the longer the subsequent cycle, as is actually observed (Fig. 59 C; Eccles and Hoff, 1932). Essentially the same explanation will account for the lengthened cycle following a discharge evoked by an intercurrent orthodromic volley (Hoff *et al.*, 1934), for the impulse generated by the orthodromic volley will destroy all the existent p.s.p. (Figs. 47, 48 B), hence the subsequent events will be identical with those following an antidromic impulse in Fig. 60 B.

Thus the explanation of rhythm here presented accounts very satisfactorily for the experimental observations on rhythmic motoneurones and is based upon actual observations on the intracellular potentials of motoneurones.

F. RHYTHMIC RESPONSES OF RECEPTOR ORGANS

In essential features the rhythmic discharge of a receptor organ so closely resembles that of a motoneurone that it is convenient to make a brief reference to it in the following sections.

1. In response to a continuous stimulus a receptor organ gives a rhythmic response in much the same way as does a motoneurone (Fig. 63 A), and the more intense the stimulus, within limits, the higher the frequency of discharge of impulses (Adrian, 1935; Matthews, 1933; Hartline, 1941; Hunt and Kuffler, 1951a, b). The frequency has approximately the same lower limit as the motoneurone (5 to 10 a second), but the upper range is much higher, being even over 200 a second with intense stimulation.

2. There is good evidence that the generation of nerve impulses is attributable to depolarization of the nerve terminals in the receptor organ, i.e. to a local potential that resembles the p.s.p. With the stretch-receptors of frog muscle it has been shown (Katz, 1950b) that stretching sets up a local potential (depolarization) of the afferent nerve terminals, which if adequate generates the discharge of an impulse, and is destroyed thereby. The local potential is then rebuilt to give the next discharge and so on (Figs. 61 A, B). There is also evidence that depolarization of the nerve terminals causes the discharge of impulses from the eyes of Limulus and Dytiscus (Hartline and Graham, 1932; Bernhard, 1942; Granit, 1947). More indirect evidence indicates that in the nerve terminals of the Pacinian corpuscle some enduring potential likewise mediates the discharge of impulses (Gray and Malcolm, 1950). However, many receptor organs are unsuitable for this investigation. For example, in the vertebrate retina complicating potentials are produced by synaptic action in the nervous layers (Granit, 1947, 1952).

3. As with the motoneurone, an antidromic impulse breaks the rhythm of the discharge and is followed by a

cycle (the subsequent cycle) that is longer than a normal cycle but not long enough to restore the original phase of the rhythm. With the mammalian stretch-receptor (Matthews, 1933) the effect is virtually identical with that given

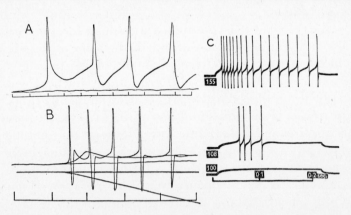

FIG. 61 A. Monophasic recording of electrical responses in sensory axon of M. extensor longus dig. IV of the frog during stretch of the muscle. Note the four impulses, each being preceded by a slow depolarization that is electrotonically propagated from the nerve terminal. Stretch begins at extreme left of figure. Time, msec. Note control base line in absence of stretch (Katz, 1950*b*).

FIG. 61 B. As in A but with diphasic registration of nerve impulses. The time-course of the muscle stretch is also shown as the downward sloping line. After application of procaine (0·35 per cent.) the same stretch fails to evoke the discharge of an impulse, there being merely a slow wave of depolarization. Time, 10 msec. (Katz, 1950*b*).

FIG. 61 C. Rhythmic discharge of impulses evoked in *carcinus* axon by application of direct currents at indicated relative intensities. Note rebuilding of depolarization after each spike and the effect of intensity in increasing frequency (Katz, 1950*b*).

by a mammalian motoneurone (Fig. 59 C), but with the frog stretch-receptor there is very little lengthening (at most 10 per cent.) of the cycle subsequent to an antidromic impulse (Matthews, 1931). It should be noted that no appreciable positive after-potential can be detected following activation of the nerve terminal of a frog's stretch-receptor either by an antidromic impulse, or by the normal discharge of an impulse (Katz, 1950*a*), though with both there is a large negative after-potential of the nerve terminal. Similarly with frog's motoneurones the positive after-potential was inconspicuous (Eccles, 1946). Fig. 60 B showed how summation of positive after-potentials explained the considerable lengthening of the cycle subsequent to the action of an antidromic impulse early in the rhythmic cycle of a mammalian motoneurone. With the frog stretch-receptors the small lengthening of the subsequent cycle may be accounted for by the absence of a large positive after-potential. On the other hand, with the mammalian stretch-receptors, the considerable lengthening of the subsequent cycle would indicate that the positive afterpotential of the afferent nerve terminals has the same order of magnitude as in mammalian motoneurones (Fig. 37).

4. The similarity of the effects produced by antidromic impulses makes it probable that the rhythmic discharge of mammalian stretch-receptors is generated by the same essential mechanism as with motoneurones (Fig. 60 A): depolarization to a critical level (the local potential); generation of impulse and destruction of the local potential thereby; positive after-potential; rebuilding of local potential and recovery from positive after-potential until an impulse is again generated as the critical degree of depolarization is attained. It would appear (Katz, 1950b) that the positive after-potential is much less important in the frog's nerve terminals, and that the rhythmic discharge must largely be determined by the time taken to rebuild the local potential after its destruction by the discharge of an impulse, and by the recovery from refractoriness (raised potassium and lowered sodium permeability). Hodgkin (1948) showed that a rhythmic discharge of impulses was generated in this way when a continuous current was applied to a *carcinus* axon (Fig. 61 c), which thus provided an interesting model of a receptor organ.

It may be concluded that a receptor organ is a mechanism for converting an appropriate stimulus to a rhythmic discharge of impulses, in which frequency signals the intensity

of the applied stimulus. It appears that, as with motoneurones, the rhythmic discharge is generated by a continuously acting depolarizing process.

G. THE CO-ORDINATION OF REFLEXES

A full treatment of this subject is beyond the scope of
these lectures. It is proposed merely to illustrate the principles of co-ordination by considering some of the simpler
situations that arise in the reflex responses of a limb. Any
given input of afferent impulses exerts a similar excitatory
or inhibitory effect on the motoneurones of any synergic
group, even in monosynaptic reflexes. Evidently this rule
of co-ordination is dependent on a structural counterpart,
the grouping together of motoneurones belonging to
synergic muscles (Romanes, 1951).

1. *The flexor and crossed extensor reflexes*
(Sherrington, 1906; Creed *et al.*, 1932)

Reference has already been made to one of the simplest
examples of reflex co-ordination; the flexor reflex that is
produced by impulses in afferent fibres from skin and the
slower afferent fibres from muscle. By polysynaptic action
there is on the ipselateral side excitation of flexor motoneurones and inhibition of extensors. But reciprocally on
the contralateral side there is polysynaptic excitation of
extensor motoneurones and inhibition of flexor motoneurones. The purposive character of the reflex is evident:
flexion and withdrawal of the injured limb and extension
of the contralateral limb which has to bear the additional
weight.

However, in the ordinary methods of eliciting the flexor
reflex, very complex interactions would be occurring in
the spinal cord. It has long been recognized that electrical
stimulation of a nerve trunk sets up an afferent volley in
nerve-fibres of the most diverse functions (cf. Creed *et al.*,
1932). The apparently simple reflex response is a tribute

to the efficiency of the spinal cord in integrating the conflicting afferent input. For example, on the ipselateral side, stimulation of a cutaneous nerve usually gives a pure flexor reflex, because the inhibition of extensor motoneurones is adequate to prevent the reflex discharges that would otherwise be evoked by the action of excitatory impulses on them. But it has now been shown that even the stimulation of the receptor organs of a small area of skin has often a mixed excitatory and inhibitory effect on both the extensor and flexor motoneurones on the ipselateral side (Hagbarth, 1952). Moreover as soon as a muscle begins to contract, there will be a change in the afferent barrage of proprioceptor impulses into the spinal cord. Thus the apparently simple flexor reflex presents extremely complex problems of reflex co-ordination, which may be more advantageously studied in the simpler proprioceptor reflexes.

2. *The function in the mammal of the muscle-spindle system in the co-ordination of reflex function*

The muscle-spindle system is a convenient term for a functional unit comprising not only the muscle-spindle but also the small motoneurones and the small motor fibres which innervate it and the group Ia afferent fibres from its annulo-spiral ending. The reflex effects of the group Ia impulses have already been fully treated. They are unique in that they act monosynaptically on motoneurones, exciting the motoneurones of the homonymous and synergic muscles and inhibiting the motoneurones of the antagonist muscles. These effects achieve special significance for the co-ordination of limb movements when considered in relationship to the three factors that control the response of the muscle-spindle as shown diagrammatically in Fig. 62.

(i) Longitudinal traction on a relaxed muscle is a powerful stimulant, evoking sustained discharges in the afferent fibres at frequencies as high as 200 a second (Fig. 63 A; Matthews, 1933; Hunt and Kuffler, 1951*a, b*).

(ii) The muscle-spindle is located in the muscle mass in parallel with the large muscle-fibres, hence contraction of the latter relieves the muscle-spindle of its longitudinal

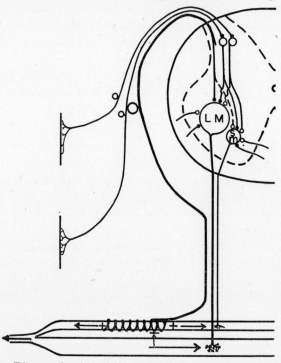

FIG. 62. Diagram showing schematically a large and a small motoneurone (*LM* and *SM*) in the spinal cord with axons innervating respectively a large muscle-fibre, and the polar region of a small muscle-fibre of a muscle-spindle which is in parallel with the large muscle-fibre. The group Ia fibre of the annulo-spiral ending ends monosynaptically on LM and probably (broken line) also on SM (see text). Throughout the convention is that filled knobs are excitatory, the open being inhibitory. The polysynaptic connexions of cutaneous afferents from two skin areas are shown to both motoneurones, one being excitatory, the other inhibitory. Note also excitatory and inhibitory endings from fibres stemming from the ventro-lateral tracts. The plus and minus signs show excitatory and depressant effects on the annulo-spiral ending, while the longitudinal arrows indicate stretch (when pointing to tendon) or contraction (when pointing towards the motor nerve endings) of the muscle-fibres.

tension, and so diminishes, or abolishes the discharge of impulses (Fig. 63 D; Matthews, 1933; Hunt and Kuffler, 1951*a, b*).

(iii) The muscle-spindle is caused to contract by the small motor fibres that innervate its polar regions. As a consequence the discharge of afferent impulses is evoked or intensified (Fig. 63 B), and it may continue even during

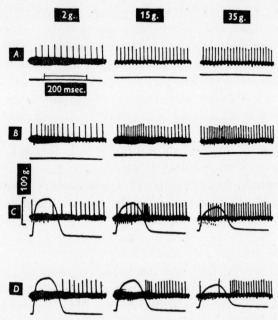

FIG. 63. Records of impulses discharged from an annulo-spiral ending of Flexor Longus Digitorum muscle at tensions of 2, 15, and 35 g. Note level of second beam operated by strain gauge. *A* is control discharge to stretches only. In *B* there is in addition stimulation of an isolated small-nerve fibre (9 stimuli at 10 msec. intervals at beginning of sweep). Note increase in frequency of discharge. In *D* there is a similar stimulation of several large-nerve fibres. Note cessation of discharge during the contraction which is shown by strain gauge record. In *C* there is a combination of both small- and large-nerve stimulations. Note cessation of discharge at lowest tension, but increasing effectiveness of small-nerve stimulation at the higher tensions (Hunt and Kuffler, 1951a).

contractions of the large muscle-fibres (Fig. 63 c), for the shortening of the muscle-spindle maintains its tension despite the shortening of the large fibres (Leksell, 1945; Kuffler *et al.*, 1951; Hunt and Kuffler, 1951a, b). As would be expected (cf. Fig. 62), the more the muscle is allowed to shorten, the less effective is contraction of the muscle-spindle in maintaining the discharge of afferent impulses.

If a muscle is stretched, e.g. the knee extensor (Quadriceps) by the weight of the body tending to flex the knee, the muscle-spindles of that muscle will be excited to discharge rhythmically along the group Ia fibres (Fig. 63 A). Such impulses will tend by monosynaptic action to cause reflex contraction of the Quadriceps muscle, so preventing the flexion of the limb and relieving the tension of the muscle-spindles. Consequently there will be a lowering of the frequency of discharge of the group Ia impulses. Thus there is an automatic negative feed-back mechanism which limits the intensity of the myotatic reflex, or at least the degree of muscle shortening which this reflex produces. The level at which this servo-mechanism operates is determined by the activity of two factors which play upon it (cf. Fig. 62); the net balance of excitatory and inhibitory synaptic influences on the large-motoneurones; the intensity of the reflex discharge along the small motor fibres (Fig. 64 A).

There is a background discharge of most small-motoneurones to a resting muscle, and this background is readily modified reflexly as indicated by the fibres converging on the small-motoneurone in Fig. 62 (Hunt, 1951). In such reflexes as the flexor and the crossed extensor, excitation of the large-motoneurones is accompanied by an increase in the small-motoneurone discharge to that muscle (Figs. 64 A2, C2); and, reciprocally, inhibition of the large- and small-motoneurones also occurs concurrently (Fig. 64 A3). For example, in the flexor reflex the small-motoneurones to flexor muscles are excited, while those to extensors are inhibited. The increased small-motoneurone discharge during activity may be expected to compensate for the reduction of stretch on muscle-spindles during reflex shortening, and thus maintain the discharge of some facilitatory group Ia afferent impulses during a reflex contraction. The small-motoneurone discharge is further

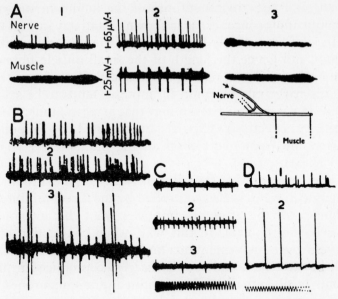

FIG. 64 A. Spinal cat. Simultaneous recording, as shown in inset, from central end of cut upper nerve branch to Tenuissimus and from lower end of muscle with intact innervation. In 1 are spikes of small motor nerve-fibres only, while in 2 squeezing of ipselateral foot evoked an increased small-nerve discharge and in addition large-nerve discharges which each give a muscle spike potential (the flexor reflex). In 3 squeezing of contralateral foot completely inhibited background small-nerve discharge (Hunt, 1951).

FIG. 64 B. Recording from a small branch of Gastrocnemius nerve in decerebrate cat. In 1 are small-nerve spikes and in 2 their frequency is increased by relaxing the tension on the muscle. In 3 an increase in tension reduces small-nerve discharges, but evokes discharges in large-nerve fibres (the myotatic reflex). Time, 100 cyc. a second (Hunt, 1951).

FIG. 64 C. Recording from small-nerve fibre to an extensor muscle. In 2 touching contralateral foot increases discharge while in 3 it is inhibited by stretching Gastrocnemius (Hunt, 1951).

FIG. 64 D. Recording from small and large fibre to an extensor muscle. In 2 stretching Gastrocnemius inhibits the small-nerve discharge and evokes a large-nerve discharge (Hunt, 1951).

regulated by stretch of the homonymous muscle, increasing stretch giving inhibition (Figs. 64 B3, C3, D2), and with decreasing stretch there is excitation (Fig. 64 B2). The effectiveness of very small stretches (Hunt, 1951) indicates that this action is due to the group Ia fibres from muscle-spindles, which would thus act reciprocally on the small- and large-motoneurones of the homonymous and synergic motoneurones, as is shown tentatively in Fig. 62.

In summary it may be stated that the intensity of discharge and hence the length of the small muscle-fibres is adjusted to different resting lengths of the muscle, so that the discharge rate of group Ia impulses tends to be stabilized. It has further been found that small-motoneurones are very effectively excited or inhibited by impulses descending from many areas in the brain-stem (Granit and Kaada, 1952b).

The level of the servo-mechanism in one group of synergic muscles is also controlled by the direct inhibitory influence of the group Ia impulses from the antagonist muscles (cf. p. 152). In this way, when contraction of a muscle causes movement of a limb, the antagonist muscles will be stretched, and the discharges so produced in the group Ia fibres will tend to inhibit the motoneurones of the contracting muscle, and hence limit its contraction. Thus an additional negative feed-back mechanism is provided.

3. *Reciprocal action of impulses in afferent fibres from tendon organs*

Stretching a muscle evokes the discharge of impulses from the Golgi tendon organs along the group Ib afferent fibres (Matthews, 1933; Hunt and Kuffler, 1951b). These impulses by disynaptic action inhibit the homonymous and synergic motoneurones and excite the antagonist motoneurones (Laporte and Lloyd, 1951; cf. also Granit, 1950; Granit and Ström, 1951). The threshold of these receptors is higher than the annulo-spiral endings, but they are excited both by contraction and stretch (Matthews, 1933; Hunt and Kuffler, 1951b).

Presumably their function is to limit by reflex inhibition powerful muscle contractions, i.e. to give the so-called lengthening reaction (cf. Creed *et al.*, 1932). This inhibition is distributed to the motoneurones of muscles other than synergists (Laporte and Lloyd, 1951), but the significance of this distribution is not understood. There is also no simple explanation of the significance of the disynaptic excitatory action on the antagonist muscles.

4. *Conclusion*

The general story that emerges from this study of the interplay of muscle contraction and reflex function is that of elaborate interlocking servo-mechanisms for the regulation of movement. Even at the segmental level of the spinal cord, there is check and counter-check that would serve to make movements smooth, and to follow up initial contractions with a steady maintained contraction. It is not possible to give such detailed descriptions of the co-ordination of reflex responses and reactions of other levels of the central nervous system, but there are general indications that the pattern of activity generally is built up from interlocking servo-mechanisms of the same type, though, doubtless, of much greater complexity in the higher levels of the nervous system. In particular the special function of the cerebellum appears to be servo-control.

H. THE TRANSMISSION OF INFORMATION IN THE NERVOUS SYSTEM

We have now completed a survey of the essential features of all the known mechanisms which are concerned in the transmission of information in the nervous system. On a crude analogy the nervous system may be likened to a telephone system with lines (the nerve-fibres) and exchanges (the synaptic components). All messages are conveyed in the form of a code, which is much simpler than the Morse code in that it consists of only one uniform type of signal, the all-or-nothing nerve impulses, i.e. it is a code of dots only. Nevertheless in principle it is possible to appreciate that all the complex transmission of information is handled by this very simple system.

Intensity of stimulation of a receptor organ is transmuted to frequency of discharge of impulses along its afferent fibre (p. 179), and this temporal pattern of impulses generates a post-synaptic potential by summation on any one neurone of the individual p.s.p.'s produced by each incident impulse (p. 131). If the p.s.p. reaches an adequate intensity, it will in turn evoke a discharge of impulses from that neurone and so on (p. 132). Inevitably there will be distortion of the original intensity-time course of the applied stimulus with each transmutation to frequency and back to intensity. Some indication of this distortion is given in Fig. 65 for the monosynaptic stretch reflex.

An assumed intensity-time course (A) for stretch of a muscle gives the discharge of group Ia impulses in B and this in turn generates on a motoneurone the summed p.s.p. (C). It is further assumed that there will be much the same bombardment of this motoneurone by impulses in several other group Ia afferent fibres that converge upon it, thus giving the aggregate p.s.p. of D, which in its intensity-time course bears a not-seriously distorted resemblance to A. If D is sufficiently intense, it will in turn generate discharges of the motoneurone as shown in E, and these in turn the contraction, F, of the muscle, which in its intensity-time course is appropriately related to the stretch which evoked it.

The significance of the transmutation from intensity to frequency and vice-versa can be appreciated only when account is taken of the integrative function of the nervous system. The most elementary level of integration is illustrated in Fig. 65, where stage D was derived from C by summation of the p.s.p.'s produced by impulses converging from different receptors. In this way intensity is transmitted by spatial as well as by temporal summation. Increase in the intensity of a given stimulus will not only increase the frequency of discharge of a single receptor organ, but also will cause other receptors to discharge and to increase the frequency of their discharge (Adrian, 1935, 1947).

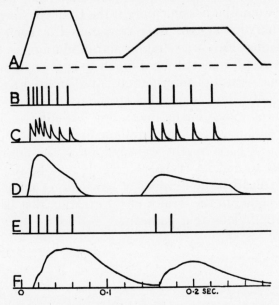

FIG. 65. *A* shows the time-course of a stretch that is applied to a muscle. *B* gives a probable discharge of impulses in a group Ia afferent fibre, and *C* shows the p.s.p. that those impulses would generate on a moto-neurone. The aggregate p.s.p. produced by all the group Ia impulses converging on that motoneurone is shown in *D*, the effect of the discharge of impulses on the neuronal potential being neglected. Finally, *E* gives a probable sequence of discharge of impulses by that motoneurone and *F* the resulting muscle contraction.

But in addition to this simple summation there is integration by inhibition. It has been shown (p. 156) that inhibition acts by direct antagonism of the depolarization produced by excitatory impulses, there being in Sherrington's terminology an algebraic summation of the excitatory and inhibitory effects on the motoneurone, and presumably on most other neurones. In fact the present concepts may be regarded as a development of his hypothesis of *E* and *I* effects (Sherrington, 1925), and of the later c.e.s. and c.i.s. (Creed *et al.*, 1932). All these concepts share the important postulate that excitatory and inhibitory effects are exerted by convergence on to a common locus, the neurone, and there integrated. It is evident that such integration would be possible only if the frequency signalling of the nervous system were transmuted at such loci to graded intensities of excitation and inhibition.

However, it may still be difficult to appreciate how the enormous wealth of information is transmitted by a code of dots only. The answer lies in the use of an enormous number of independent lines. For example, each optic nerve contains over half a million fibres, which provide a structural basis for the transmission of the information that goes to make a visual picture. It may be stated, as a general rule, that the number of nerve-fibres in any pathway is related to the wealth of information that has to be transmitted along that pathway.

VI

PROLONGED FUNCTIONAL CHANGES (PLASTICITY) IN THE NERVOUS SYSTEM

A. INTRODUCTION

OUR investigation, so far, has been restricted to events which occur in relatively simple neuronal systems and which have a time-scale measured in milliseconds. Neurophysiologists have frequently been criticized because they have failed to interest themselves in the functional changes that must form the basis of such enduring reactions as occur in learning, conditioning, and memory. For example, Young (1951) in his Croonian Lecture states: 'The most obvious failure of current neurophysiological theory is in providing an account of the changing potentialities or plasticity of the nervous system.' That failure, for example, can be seen in the severe handicap that Konorski (1948, 1950) encounters when he attempts to develop a coherent neurophysiological theory of conditioned reflexes.

Investigations into the long-term effects of such procedures as nerve or muscle transposition have on the whole provided little evidence of plastic changes in simple reflex systems. On the contrary, the balance of evidence indicates a remarkable stability of reflex patterns in the spinal cord (Sperry, 1945). However, the very nature of these experiments precluded the possibility of observing subtle changes in reflex function. As described below, more recent investigations have shown that relatively enduring enhancement of reflex function occurs after a burst of repetitive stimulation (post-tetanic potentiation) and on the contrary prolonged disuse leads to defectiveness of synaptic function, which, however, can be partially restored, at least for many hours, by repetitive activation.

Finally, on the basis of experimental evidence it will be argued that repetitive stimulation is necessary for maintenance of synaptic function and that increased activity leads to enhanced function. In the light of this evidence an attempt will be made to develop an explanation of the simplest type of conditioned reflex, and on such a basis to account in principle for the phenomena of learning. However, these are only the first stages in a programme that must extend to reactions of almost infinite variety and complexity, as may be realized after study, for example, of Tinbergen's (1951) recent book on instinctive behaviour. He also is handicapped by the meagreness of the neurophysiological contribution to this vast subject.

B. POST-TETANIC POTENTIATION

This name has been applied to the relatively prolonged increase in response that occurs after a junctional region has been subjected to repetitive orthodromic activation. It appears in all junctional regions that have been studied, but it will be convenient to describe it in detail in the monosynaptic reflex where it has been most intensively investigated.

1. *Monosynaptic reflexes*

After repetitive stimulation of the group Ia fibres of a muscle there is a large and prolonged potentiation of all the reflex effects (excitatory as in Figs. 66, 71 A, and also inhibitory) which are directly produced by impulses in those fibres (Lloyd, 1949; Eccles and Rall, 1951*b*). This post-tetanic potentiation was not observed for the reflex effect of impulses in afferent fibres other than those stimulated, i.e. it was restricted to the 'homosynaptic' reflex path as distinct from the 'heterosynaptic' synergic paths (cf. p. 133). Furthermore, post-tetanic potentiation is not associated with an increased excitability of motoneurones as tested antidromically; hence there is general agreement that it is attributable to some change restricted to the specific presynaptic pathway that has been tetanized (Lloyd, 1949; Eccles and Rall, 1951b).

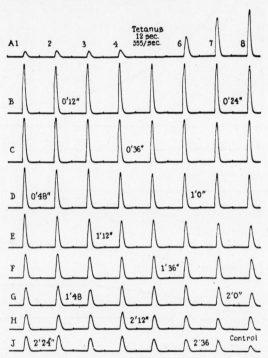

FIG. 66. Monosynaptic reflex spikes discharged from Gastrocnemius motoneurones in response to a maximum group I afferent volley from Gastrocnemius nerve. After the first four control responses the Gastrocnemius nerve is tetanized as shown, and subsequent tests at 2·4 seconds interval reveal the slow development and subsidence of a large post-tetanic potentiation (Lloyd, 1949).

In Fig. 67 A the time-course of the post-tetanic potentiation is shown for a wide range of tetani. The curves plot the size of the monosynaptic reflex spike evoked by the standard test volley at successive intervals of 2·4 seconds after the conditioning tetanus (cf. Fig. 66). Hence, by the familiar argument of sampling a population of motoneurones, the curves will represent approximately the time-course of the potentiated action of any one presynaptic

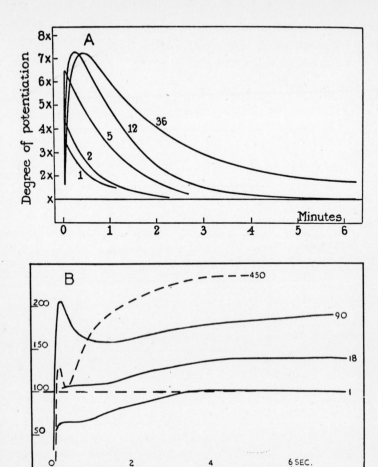

FIG. 67 A. Plotting of time-courses of post-tetanic potentiations, i.e. reflex spike sizes as in Fig. 66, after conditioning tetani of various durations (marked in seconds on the curves) at a constant frequency of about 500 per second. Note progressive slowing of post-tetanic potentiation as conditioning tetanus is made more severe (Lloyd, 1949).

FIG. 67 B. Plotting as in Fig. 67 A, but after less severe conditioning tetani and over a much briefer time-scale in order to show, after a moderate tetanus (90 volleys), the separation of the early brief potentiation from the later; whereas after 450 volleys the early potentiation is negligible, and in the 18-volley record there is a transition to the depression observed after 1 volley. All stimulations applied to nerve to Flexor Longus Digitorum and all tetani at 300 a second. Horizontal broken line shows potential of control reflex spike (Eccles and Rall, 1951*b*).

impulse. When briefer tetani are tested at shorter intervals post-tetanically, an early brief phase of potentiation precedes the main potentiation, for example after 90 volleys in Fig. 67 B. But on the contrary, after a single or very few impulses in Fig. 67 B, the test response is depressed for as long as 3 seconds (cf. Fig. 46 C; Eccles and Rall, 1951b; Schlapp and Jefferson, 1952).

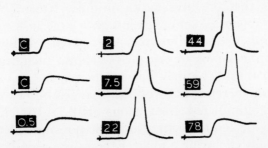

FIG. 68. Intracellular potentials recorded as in Fig. 42 from Biceps-Semitendinosus motoneurone and generated by a single volley in Biceps-Semitendinosus nerve. Initial control responses marked *C* are typical p.s.p.'s. Subsequent to a conditioning tetanus of 450 a second for 15 seconds the p.s.p. is depressed at the 0·5 second test, but then potentiated and generates the discharge of an impulse at five of the testing intervals (marked in seconds), being still considerably potentiated at the longest testing interval, 78 seconds (Brock *et al*, 1952d).

By recording focally and from the ventral root it has been shown that during post-tetanic potentiation the presynaptic volley sets up a larger post-synaptic potential and this has been confirmed by intracellular recording (Fig. 68). It is possible to account for the potentiation by this increase in post-synaptic potential, which amounts to 30 to 40 per cent. in Fig. 68, there being no diminution in the critical level of depolarization at which the motoneurone generates an impulse. Under certain conditions an increase in the size of the presynaptic spike potential is associated with the post-tetanic potentiation (Lloyd, 1949; Eccles and Rall, 1951b). However, after the briefer tetani the presynaptic spike, as actually recorded in the motor nucleus, is usually diminished during the initial phase of potentiation and not significantly modified during the later phase. There are also significant discrepancies for the longer tetani. Potentiation of the spike potential of the presynaptic volley thus gives at the best but a partial explanation of post-tetanic potentiation (Eccles and Rall, 1951b).

The most probable postulate for post-tetanic potentiation is that the presynaptic impulse becomes a more effective synaptic excitor (or inhibitor), because repetitive stimulation temporarily alters the spatial relationship of the synaptic knobs to the post-synaptic membrane; for example, the knobs may become larger and/or in closer apposition thereto. The volume changes observed in repetitively stimulated giant axons (Hill, 1950; cf. p. 56) may be expected to occur also in the non-medullated presynaptic fibres during and after repetitive stimulation, for the uptake of water in considerable part at least is determined by the flux of ions that is associated with the nerve impulse. The relatively large surface to volume ratio associated with the very small diameter of these fibres (probably no more than 0.2 to 0.3 μ) would lead one to expect a relatively greater swelling and possibly a more rapid time-course of the swelling and recovery therefrom. Furthermore, given uniform elastic properties of the membrane, the synaptic knob, having a larger radius of curvature than its attached fibre, would be expected to swell more readily than this fibre in response to an increase in turgor of the system, i.e. there would be a flow of axoplasm from the swollen fibre to increase further the swelling of the knob.

If it is assumed that the uptake of water per sq. cm. of surface is the same as in the giant fibre (cf. p. 56, where it is rather more than 10^{-5} cc. per sq. cm. of membrane for 10,000 impulses), then there is a surprisingly large swelling of the fine presynaptic fibre and knob. A 0.3 μ diameter fibre would more than double its volume, swelling to 0·46 μ diameter, and a 1·0 μ diameter (spherical) knob would swell to 1·2 μ. If there is a further knob swelling due to fluid flowing from fibre into knob, a very plausible explanation is available for the great increase that occurs in synaptic efficacy during post-tetanic potentiation. For example, a doubling of the surface area of the knob might well occur, which would certainly be adequate to account for the observed increase in post-synaptic potential (Fig. 68; cf. Eccles and Rall, 1951b).

An increased effectiveness of transmission by a swollen knob would be expected on either an electrical or chemical mode of action, but the effect of fairly rapidly repeated test volleys favours a chemical explanation. With a testing tetanus at 400 a second, no post-tetanic potentiation was observed after the first one or two volleys (Ström, 1951), but this failure was also observed at testing rates as low as 10 a second (Eccles and Rall, 1952). The most plausible explanation of a similar observation on the potentiated end-plate potential was that potentiation was associated with an increased output of transmitter substance (acetyl-choline) from the swollen nerve terminals; hence a more rapid depletion of transmitter occurred with repetitive stimulation (Fig. 28 B; Liley and North, 1952). As yet no explanation is available for the double phase of potentiation observed after brief tetani (Fig. 67 B). Possibly the early phase is suppressed after long tetani because there is exhaustion of the chemical transmitter (cf. p. 138).

If, as suggested above (pp. 166–70), transmission at both excitatory and inhibitory synapses is due to chemical mediators, it is possible that post-tetanic potentiation is caused by an increased availability of such transmitters due, for example, to increased manufacture or to passage from the bound into the free state in the presynaptic fibre. However, at present it is unnecessary to make such additional assumptions, for the swelling hypothesis would seem to offer an adequate explanation on the basis of effects demonstrated in peripheral axons.

2. *Polysynaptic reflexes*

The polysynaptic flexor reflex was found by Lloyd (1949) to show little evidence of post-tetanic potentiation. However, fairly large potentiations have been observed (cf. Fig. 73 B; Downman, Eccles, and McIntyre, 1952), so it may be assumed that there is no fundamental difference from the monosynaptic reflex, but merely less opportunity for revealing potentiation. For example, the primary synaptic relay in the dorsal horn may be so effective that almost all of the bombarded neurones normally discharge impulses and few are left in the subliminal fringe to signal potentiation (cf. Lloyd, 1949). Post-tetanic potentiation has even been observed to reveal polysynaptic reflexes that were not seen in control responses of extensor muscles (cf. Eccles and McIntyre, 1952).

3. *Peripheral junctions*

The principal interest for our purpose is that post-tetanic potentiation closely resembling that in the central nervous system is given by the cholinergic junctions in the mammalian sympathetic ganglion and skeletal muscle. Thus post-tetanic potentiation is certainly a property of junctions which are exclusively chemical in transmission.

Larrabee and Bronk (1947) investigated in detail post-tetanic potentiation in the mammalian sympathetic ganglion. As with central synapses, this effect is restricted to the synaptic excitatory action of the tetanized presynaptic fibres (Fig. 69 A) and there is no accompanying increase in the excitability of the ganglion-cells either to other presynaptic impulses or to acetyl-choline. Furthermore the time-course of the potentiation is measured in minutes (Fig. 69 B) and hence is comparable with that at central synapses. There is even potentiation after a single pre-

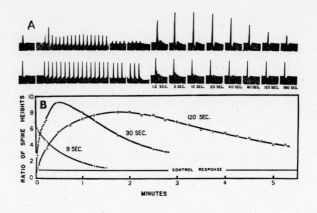

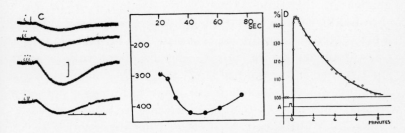

FIG. 69 A. Action potentials recorded from postganglionic nerve of stellate ganglion and set up by stimulation of preganglionic nerve in upper record, and of postganglionic nerve in lower record. Note control response to single testing volley at start, then onset and later stages of a 10-second conditioning tetanus at about 15 a second. Note subsequent development and subsidence of post-tetanic potentiation of responses to preganglionic volleys. The absence of any appreciable change in the lower record shows that the potentiation in the upper record is attributable to response of a larger number of ganglion cells and not to changes in spike size of individual postganglionic fibres (Larrabee and Bronk, 1947).

FIG. 69 B. Plotting as in Fig. 67 A of post-tetanic potentiations of stellate ganglion determined as in Fig. 69 A. Conditioning tetanus 24 a second for indicated durations (Larrabee and Bronk, 1947).

FIG. 69 C. Positive 'synaptic potentials' recorded from isolated superior cervical ganglion as in Fig. 32 after soaking in strong tubocurarine (1.6×10^{-4} M). Note initial small response, i, and in ii to iv development and subsidence of potentiation subsequent to preganglionic tetanus (60 a second for 15 seconds). Inset shows plotting of time-course of this potentiation, ordinates being percentages of control response plotted downwards (R. Eccles, 1952a).

FIG. 69 D. Time-course of post-tetanic potentiation of single test e.p.p.'s set up in curarized rat diaphragm (cf. Figs. 28 B, 29 B). Conditioning tetanus at 300 a second for 15 seconds. Ordinates, size of e.p.p. relative to control (Liley and North, 1952).

ganglionic volley (Larrabee and Bronk, 1947; Job and Lundberg, 1952). Similar post-tetanic potentiation is observed in ganglia where synaptic transmission has been blocked by tubocurarine, there being potentiation of both the negative and positive synaptic potentials (Fig. 69 c; R. Eccles, 1952a). All results are explicable by an increase in the output of chemical transmitter.

A recent systematic study of post-tetanic potentiation at the curarized mammalian neuro-muscular junction has given comparable results (Liley and North, 1952). Potentiation of the end-plate potential runs a time-course that is also measured in minutes (Fig. 69 D), but there is no change in the time-course of the potential or in the threshold level at which it sets up muscle impulses. When a brief tetanus is employed as a test, the end-plate potentials produced by the third and subsequent volleys are smaller than in the control (Fig. 28 B). This suggests that the store of acetyl-choline in the nerve terminals is not increased during post-tetanic potentiation, which merely causes more liberation and hence earlier depletion.

4. Conclusion

It may be concluded that, as with central synapses, post-tetanic potentiation at peripheral junctions is also satisfactorily explained by a swelling of the tetanized presynaptic nerve-fibres. Possibly this potentiation is a general property of all junctional regions. However, in itself, posttetanic potentiation has little physiological significance, for it is not effective in increasing the relatively prolonged discharges that are characteristic of natural movements (Ström, 1951). Also it has not been possible to evoke it by repetitive afferent discharges such as occur when muscles are stretched and contracted (Ström, 1951). But, as seen below, it may be highly significant in initiating other processes of still longer duration.

C. SYNAPTIC ACTIVITY AND PLASTICITY

1. *Effect of disuse on synaptic function*

Prolonged and total disuse of monosynaptic reflex arcs has been secured by severing the dorsal roots just distal to their ganglia, thus retaining functional continuity between parent cell bodies and the central projections within the spinal cord of their silenced fibres (Eccles and McIntyre, 1951, 1952). Several weeks after this operation the reflex responses evoked by stimulation of these disused dorsal roots are compared with the control responses on the other side. As shown in Figs. 70 A and B and 71 A, volleys in the disused dorsal roots (O responses) are always much less effective in evoking monosynaptic reflexes into either flexor or extensor muscles. Post-tetanic potentiation is, however, effective in restoring much of the lost function, but it is still far below the potentiated control response, as may be seen by comparing the O and N records in the second responses of Figs. 70 A and B and in the potentiated series of Fig. 71 A.

The question at once arises: to what extent can reflex deficiency on the operated side be attributed to changes in the presynaptic pathways other than mere absence of the normal impulse barrage? Histological examination revealed two possible causes, but there was good evidence that only part of the discrepancy could be so explained. For example there was in some, but not in all, experiments destruction of some dorsal root-fibres either at the initial operation, or subsequently by scarring. Again, there was some shrinking of the dorsal root-fibres (about 10 per cent.), which is probably attributable to diminished turgor consequent on the regenerative outgrowth from the ganglion cells into the peripheral stump (Gutmann and Sanders, 1943; Sanders and Whitteridge, 1946). It is not possible directly to refute the suggestions that the synaptic knobs shrink more than the main axonal shafts from which

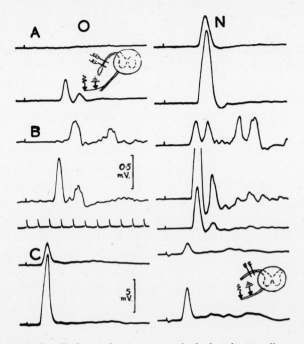

FIG. 70. Reflex discharges in response to single dorsal root volleys maximal for group I fibres. The L_7 and S_1 dorsal roots were severed just distal to ganglia 40 days previously. The O column shows reflex responses on this operated side, the N column being control responses recorded symmetrically on other side. In A upper records show reflex discharge into Gastrocnemius nerve evoked by a volley in L_7 and S_1 dorsal roots (see inset), being zero for O side. Lower records, responses after same degree of post-tetanic conditioning for O and N sides.

In B, responses evoked as in A, but recorded in the conjoint Biceps-Semitendinosus nerve. With unconditioned O there is a minute monosynaptic spike, which is post-tetanically potentiated to a large spike, about one-quarter of control side similarly potentiated (lowest record of B on N side is potentiated response at one-fourth amplification). Note in O and N the later polysynaptic discharges of flexor reflex.

In C, responses evoked by single volleys in L_6 dorsal root and recorded in L_6 ventral root (see inset diagram). Time-scale shown in msec. for all records (Eccles and McIntyre, 1951).

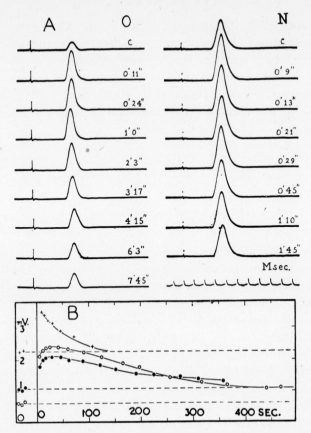

FIG. 71 A. Monosynaptic reflex discharges evoked as in Fig. 70 A and recorded in Gastrocnemius nerve 40 days after extraganglionic operative section of the dorsal roots stimulated in the *O* records. The topmost record (*C*) of *O* and *N* series is the reflex response before any tetanic conditioning. The remaining series show potentiated responses after a conditioning tetanus of 6,000 volleys at 400 a second (cf. Fig. 66). The figures above each response show the time, in minutes and seconds, at which it was elicited after cessation of the conditioning tetanus. Amplification same for *O* and *N* responses (Eccles and McIntyre, 1952).

FIG. 71 B. The crosses plot the *N* observations of Fig. 71 A and the open circles the *O* observations partly shown in Fig. 71 A. The vertical line marks the end of the conditioning tetanus, points plotted to left being preliminary controls (*c* of Fig. 71 A). Horizontal broken lines give respective mean control heights of reflex spikes. The filled circles are also *O* responses some 2 hours later than the open circles. Note that initial control level is same as level of residual potentiation surviving at end of first potentiation (open circles to right). Abscissae, time after end of conditioning tetanus (Eccles and McIntyre, 1952).

they spring, their depressed reflex excitatory power being thus explained. However, observations to be described in the next two sections would seem effectively to exclude that possibility as a complete explanation, and to show that the defectiveness of function is at least partly attributable to disuse and thus of great interest and significance. That argument will be developed later (p. 209).

2. *Effect of increased usage on synaptic function*

The effect of increased usage has been indirectly obtained from study of the reflex activity evoked by the dorsal root immediately rostral to those operatively divided (Eccles and McIntyre, 1951, 1952). As shown in Fig. 70 c the monosynaptic reflex into the corresponding ventral root was always much larger than on the control side and this asymmetry was also present when both reflexes were post-tetanically potentiated. This asymmetry may reasonably be attributed to the development of some compensatory reaction to the operative disability, particularly in muscles that have been partly deafferented. It was found, for example, that there was always a large increase in the monosynaptic reflex into the nerve to the hip extensor muscle, semimembranosus. But, on the other hand, with flexor muscles the enhancement was small or absent. Thus the compensation would seem to involve monosynaptic reflexes to extensor rather than flexor muscles.

The simplest explanation of this compensatory reaction is that the operative disability has thrown more mechanical stress on stretch-receptors of the partly deafferented group of synergic muscles, particularly the weight-supporting extensors. On account of the partial severance of afferent fibres, the monosynaptic reflexes would not be so effective in protecting the muscle-spindles from stretch (cf. p. 186). The increased stimulation of the spindles would thereby lead to an increased monosynaptic bombardment of motoneurones through the dorsal root-fibres immediately adjacent to those severed; hence the increased synaptic efficacy of these fibres.

3. *Effect of repetitive activity on the operatively inactivated reflex pathway*

It has already been seen that post-tetanic potentiation is at least as well developed with the operated roots as on the control side (Figs. 70 A, B; 71 A). However, it differs from normal in two characteristic respects, indicating that the disused knobs have acquired special properties (Eccles and McIntyre, 1951, 1952).

As shown in Figs. 71 A and B, after a standard conditioning tetanus, the post-tetanic potentiation of the reflex evoked from the disused roots ran an abnormally slow time-course, reaching a later summit and decaying much more slowly. Usually the time scale has been two to three times longer than normal.

Furthermore, after a conditioning tetanus the reflex evoked from the disused roots is abnormal in that it does not return to the initial size, but exhibits a residual potentiation which continues for hours (cf. Fig. 71 B). For example, the initial sizes of the monosynaptic reflexes after five weeks quiescence are plotted for Gastrocnemius and Biceps-Semitendinosus nerves in Fig. 72 at about 5.50 p.m. as filled and open circles respectively. Subsequently, three successive tetani (shown by the vertical lines) lifted the reflexes to the sizes shown at 6.30 p.m. Two post-tetanic potentiation curves are also drawn, the first for Gastrocnemius, the second for Biceps-Semitendinosus. After over two hours of complete rest the residual potentiation was still prominent, the return towards the initial value being just over one-quarter for Biceps-Semitendinosus and to about half for Gastrocnemius. At 8.45 p.m. an injection of Nembutal lowered both reflexes and the residual potentiation was again built up by tetanization, and finally showed a little diminution after a rest of over an hour. Residual potentiation is also shown in Fig. 71 B, where the first post-tetanic potentiation (open circles) decayed to a level at about 8 minutes, which was found to be still maintained 2 hours later (initial set of filled circles).

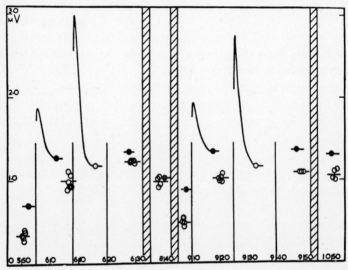

FIG. 72. Plotting of post-tetanic potentiation and residual potential as in Fig. 71 B, but on a much reduced time-scale, note time-scale in hours and minutes on abscissae. Ordinates give sizes of monosynaptic reflex spike in millivolts. L_7 and S_1 dorsal roots severed extraganglionically 38 days previously. The open circles about 5.50 p.m. give reflex spikes in Biceps-Semitendinosus nerve in response to single volleys in the combined L_7 and S_1 dorsal roots, and the filled circle the mean control spike in Gastrocnemius nerve, these same conventions being used throughout. The first tetanic conditioning (7,500 volleys at 500 per second) is shown by vertical line at 5.55 p.m., and the five other tetanic conditionings (of similar severity) are likewise indicated. The post-tetanic potentiation curves are shown for Gastrocnemius and Biceps-Semitendinosus after first and second conditioning respectively in each of the test series. As indicated by abscissae the vertical shaded columns mark lapses of 2 hours, 20 minutes, and 55 minutes respectively, and during the second an injection of Nembutal was given (Eccles and McIntyre, 1952).

The gradual changes which unavoidably occur in the reflex excitability of a preparation (attributable for example to changes in anaesthesia and in circulation) prevent any precise determination of the time constant of decay of residual potentiation but probably half decay takes at least 3 hours, which would make it about 160 times slower than the decay rate for the normal post-tetanic potentiation after a similar conditioning tetanus.

4. *Discussion on use and disuse*

Thus we are introduced to the concept that activity enhances the functional effectiveness of disused synapses over a much longer period than the several minutes of ordinary post-tetanic potentiation. We may infer that disuse is indeed a principal factor responsible for deficiency of monosynaptic reflexes after dorsal root section, and that such disused synapses are capable of 'learning' to operate more effectively as a result of intensive presynaptic stimulation. This phenomenon can be regarded as the positive counterpart of the negative effect brought about by disuse, and is thus a necessary corollary to the postulate of plastic properties, even in the simplest reflex arc. However, residual potentiation seems to decay slowly over several hours, while this does not seem to occur for the compensatory potentiation in the adjacent segment. Presumably this discrepancy is attributable to the different character of the activation. Residual potentiation has been induced in our experiments by brief bursts of high frequency tetanus, whereas the compensatory potentiation has been attributed to the prolonged low intensity activity produced by the discharge of receptor organs. For the same reason the progressive diminution of synaptic function during disuse would be expected to be a much slower process than the decay of residual potentiation.

Residual potentiation would thus be a special illustration of the enhancement of synaptic function by usage. It appears to be a residuum of the post-tetanic potentiation (cf. Figs. 71, 72) and hence is probably explicable by the same postulate of swelling with activity (cf. p. 198). Thus it can be envisaged that the normally occurring bursts of impulses in the presynaptic fibres bring about frequent

P

minor distensions of the synaptic knobs, which are hence maintained at a normal level of size and effectiveness. With disuse, as in the experiments here described, the absence of these repeated distensions results in a gradual shrinkage of synaptic knob size and hence leads to defectiveness of function. However, it would be likely that such shrunken knobs would be particularly sensitive to distension by the osmotic swelling of induced repetitive activity. Further, it may be expected that a prolonged plastic residuum of such swelling would survive for hours and thus cause the residual potentiation. Even the slower time-course of the post-tetanic potentiation of disused knobs (Fig. 71) may in this way receive an explanation.

5. *Conclusion*

In conclusion it can be stated that in the simplest mammalian reflex (the monosynaptic myotatic reflex) direct experimental evidence has been obtained in support of the hypothesis that usage leads to increased functional efficiency of synapses and disuse to defective function. The plasticity which has been postulated for higher nerve centres in explanation of conditioned reflexes and of memory would appear to be an important attribute even of the synapses of the simplest spinal reflex pathway.

Three processes have now been described in which synaptic activation increases the effectiveness of a later testing synaptic stimulus. The facilitation attributable to the post-synaptic potential decays with a time constant of 4 msec.; the post-tetanic potentiation following some thousands of conditioning volleys decays with a time constant of about 80 seconds, i.e. 20,000 times slower; finally, the residual potentiation that follows the post-tetanic potentiation of disused synapses decays with a time-constant of about 16,000 seconds, i.e. 4×10^6 times slower than the facilitation. It has been argued above that there is a still slower decay in the synaptic efficacy that is produced by the prolonged low intensity bombardment from naturally stimulated receptors. Before proceeding to show how these prolonged effects may be employed in constructing hypotheses of learning and conditioning, it will be convenient to consider another type of plastic change in motoneurones.

D. PLASTICITY AS REVEALED IN CHROMATOLYSING MOTONEURONES

It has long been known that, when motoneurones have their axons severed, they undergo a prolonged series of histological changes known collectively as chromatolysis. Recent study of the physiological reactions of chromatolysed motoneurones has revealed that functionally they undergo an even more remarkable cycle of reversible changes (Downman, Eccles, and McIntyre, 1951, 1952). Chromatolysis of motoneurones has been effected by aseptic extradural section of one or more ventral roots, and their responses to afferent volleys have been tested at intervals of 5 days to 8 weeks thereafter by recording from the appropriate ventral roots. Motoneurones with unsevered axons, either contralateral or ipselateral, have served to give control reflex responses, which of course have been recorded under identical conditions.

From 5 to 12 days there is progressive failure of monosynaptic reflexes. From 13 to 30 days group I afferent volleys from a whole series of muscle nerves give reflex responses that have such long central delays, i.e. transmission times through the spinal cord, relative to the control reflexes, that it is concluded that monosynaptic reflexes have failed and been replaced by disynaptic and still more delayed polysynaptic responses. For example, in Fig. 73 A the shortest central delay for reflexes from the chromatolysed motoneurones is 1·65 msec. as against 1·25 msec. on the control side, while after post-tetanic potentiation the respective delays have shortened to 1·4 and 0·9 msec. respectively. But it is to be noticed that in contrast to the control response the chromatolysed response is

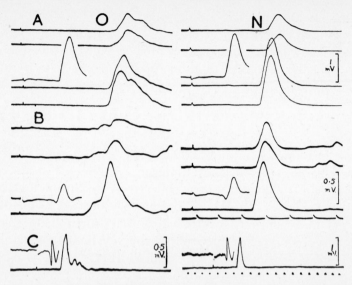

FIG. 73. Reflex spike discharges set up by afferent volleys in Gastrocnemius nerve (maximum for group I fibres) and recorded in the S_1
ventral root which had been previously severed by aseptic operation on
one side (*O* responses), the *N* responses being controls symmetrically
recorded on other side. In *A* root severance 13 days previously and on
each side two reflex spikes before and two during height of post-tetanic
conditioning. The earlier monophasic spikes show Gastrocnemius volleys
recorded subsequently in respective dorsal roots. *B* as in *A* but after 36
days chromatolysis, the first *O* volley being submaximal and only one post-
tetanic response on each side. The dorsal root volley was recorded in
volume by a contact electrode. *C* recorded after 57 days chromatolysis and
on slower time base, note millisecond scales. No post-tetanic responses.
Dorsal root spikes recorded as in *B* (Downman *et al.*, 1952).

grossly asynchronous with some central delays almost 3
msec. in duration, and this feature occurs even with the
weakest afferent stimulation (cf. Fig. 73 B). Note in Fig.
73 the records of dorsal root spikes, which allow central
delays to be calculated.

By 36 days some motoneurones have recovered to give
monosynaptic responses, as may be seen particularly in
the potentiated reflex in Fig. 73 B, where the shortest
central delay is 0·95 as against 0·8 msec. from the control
motoneurones. However, the reflex response is still domi-
nated by polysynaptic discharges which are generated by

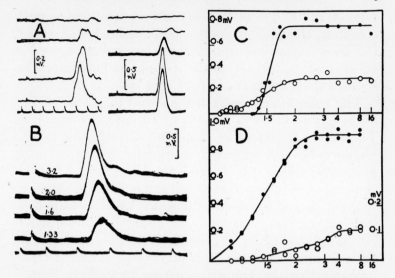

FIG. 74 A. Reflex spikes set up by various sizes of afferent volleys from nerve to Flexor Longus Digitorum and recorded to left in the L$_7$ ventral root, severed 19 days previously, and to right in the L$_6$ ventral root, unsevered until time of experiment. In left series stimulus strengths are 1·14, 1·33, 1·78, and 2·28 times group I threshold, and in right series the respective strengths are 1·33, 1·4, 1·46, 1·78, and 2·28. Time-scale, msec.
FIG. 74 B. Monophasic responses (twenty superimposed records) of dorsal root volleys when stimuli at indicated strength (relative to group I threshold) applied to Flexor Longus Digitorum nerve. Note after large group I spike the small group II spikes in all but weakest response.
FIG. 74 C. Plotting of records illustrated partly in A, the open circles for chromatolysed and the filled circles for normal motoneurones. Stimulus strengths relative to group I threshold as abscissae, reflex spike heights as ordinates.
FIG. 74 D. Plotting of spike heights in dorsal root as ordinates, against stimulus strengths as abscissae for series partly shown in B. Same abscissal scale as C. Filled circles group I spike, open circles group II spike (Downman et al., 1952).

impulses in the lowest threshold afferent fibres—presumably by group Ia afferent impulses. In the two unpotentiated responses there is a tendency for the discharges to be grouped at intervals of about 0·7 msec. This effect is frequently observed and may indicate interpolation of an additional synapse for each successive discharge.

In the further stages of recovery the monosynaptic reflexes progressively increase, while the polysynaptic regress. In Fig. 73 C at 57 days recovery to normal is nearly complete, though some polysynaptic reflexes still remain. However, the polysynaptic reflexes are still generated by an afferent volley too small to evoke monosynaptic responses (Downman et al., 1952, Fig. 4).

The reflex effectiveness of the lowest threshold afferent fibres is illustrated in Fig. 74 at 19 days chromatolysis. The same afferent volley in the nerve to Flexor Longus Digitorum evokes reflexes from chromatolysed and normal motoneurones in the L_7 and L_6 segments respectively (Fig. 74 A). It is seen in Fig. 74 C and D that a polysynaptic reflex is evoked by an afferent volley which is little more than 10 per cent. maximum for group I, while it has to be almost 40 per cent. in order to evoke the smallest reflex from L_6 motoneurones. Such observations make it highly probable that the group Ia afferent fibres have become very effective polysynaptic excitors of chromatolysed motoneurones, in contrast to their normal almost exclusive monosynaptic excitatory action (cf. p. 111). Group Ib fibres are known to be excitatory to antagonist motoneurones (Laporte and Lloyd, 1951), but their action can be excluded in those experiments where an afferent volley from the knee flexors gives the usual polysynaptic reflexes in S_1 and L_7 ventral roots which do not innervate the antagonistic knee extensors.

Thus during chromatolysis we have two events which appear to be complementary, but which actually may not be interrelated: the diminution, loss, and eventual return of monosynaptic reflexes; the development and regression of polysynaptic reflexes.

By recording the post-synaptic potentials it has been shown that the monosynaptic excitatory action of group Ia fibres is not completely lost. It is merely weakened to a sub-threshold intensity. It is possible that the initial stage of diminishing effectiveness of monosynaptic excitatory action is attributable to the swelling of the neurone which has been observed histologically (Bodian and

Mellors, 1945). The swelling could cause strain and even separation of the synaptic junctions. The return after 5 weeks suggests that a process of growth of new synapses is occurring from the reflexo-motor collaterals in order to replace the defective synapses.

The enormous development of polysynaptic reflexes is the most remarkable occurrence during chromatolysis. It would appear that one has to postulate not merely an increased effectiveness of existing polysynaptic paths, but actually a development of new paths. Possibly some chemical evocator is generated by chromatolysing neurones which causes the sprouting and growth of neighbouring nerve-fibres, much as has been observed in partially denervated muscles (Weiss and Edds, 1946; Hoffman, 1950) and when cell mitosis occurs in close proximity to a nerve-fibre (Speidel, 1940). The development of polysynaptic connexions is not restricted to reflex paths activated by group Ia impulses, for there is also an increased effectiveness of polysynaptic paths from skin afferents and high-threshold muscle afferents (Downman et al., 1952). The simplest initial postulate would be that a chromatolysed neurone was non-specific in its evocatory action on adjacent nerve-fibres. A related phenomenon has been described in the developing spinal cord, where the growth of the dendrites of the primary neurones appears to evoke the outgrowth of axons from potential neuroblasts (Barron, 1952). An alternative postulate would be that dendritic outgrowth from the chromatolysed motoneurones gave opportunity for the development of new polysynaptic connexions.

Recently, closely related observations have been made on sympathetic ganglia (Brown, McLennan, and Pascoe, 1952). After section of postganglionic fibres, failure of all synaptic transmission into them develops over much the same time-course as with chromatolysed motoneurones. Since there are no interneurones in the ganglia, there is no opportunity for development of polysynaptic paths;

hence these observations reveal that chromatolysing gang-lion-cells parallel as far as possible chromatolysing moto-neurones. This ganglionic investigation is particularly important because it should discover whether the failure is attributable to diminishing sensitivity of the chromato-lysing ganglion-cells to the chemical transmitter, or whether more gross structural changes have to be envisaged as above. If a diminishing sensitivity of the ganglion-cells to ACh explains the synaptic block in the ganglion, it becomes highly probable that there is diminished sensitivity of chromatolysed motoneurones to the monosynaptic trans-mitter (cf. p. 166), and in addition the development of polysynaptic excitation is possibly attributable to an in-creased sensitivity to other chemical transmitters.

In the absence of histological correlates of these physio-logical observations further speculation is unwarranted, but it is evident that, whatever the eventual detailed ex-planation of the changes in reflexes during chromatolysis, the simplest reflex levels in the spinal cord exhibit a re-markable lability either structural or chemical in respect both of degenerative and regenerative processes. This lability, moreover, would seem to have functional meaning because the loss of group Ia monosynaptic reflexes was fully compensated by developing polysynaptic connexions. However, if this lability is structural, it would be at a cruder level than the changing efficacy of synapses de-scribed in the preceding section.

E. EXPLANATION OF LEARNING AND CONDITIONED REFLEXES BY PLASTIC CHANGES IN SYNAPSES

1. *Introduction*

It is usual to give a very broad meaning to the term learning so that it covers the conditioned reflexes of Pavlov on the one hand, and on the other such multifarious mani-festations as occur in 'adaptive change in individual behaviour as a result of experience' (Thorpe, 1950). A more precise definition is given by Konorski (1950):

By learning we shall denote a process leading to the lasting changes in the manner in which an organism reacts to a stimulus which are due to the application of this stimulus... and which are not caused by any destructive effects which the applied stimulus might produce.

The stimulus must act on the receptive side of the nervous system, not on the effector side. In general, learning is regarded as being dependent on plastic changes in the nervous system.

For our present purpose of attempting to show in principle how learning can be explained by the actually observed reactions of the central nervous system, it will be sufficient to consider the simplest example of learning— the conditioned reflex of Pavlov. Following Konorski (1950) we may give the following general description of this reflex.

If two stimuli s_1 and s_2 are applied in overlapping sequence, the stimulus s_1 being antecedent, then, with repetition of such combination, a plastic change in the nervous system is formed, consisting in the stimulus s_1 acquiring the ability to elicit the response of the same kind as the stimulus s_2.

Pavlov (1927) attempted to develop physiological explanations, or rather physiological concepts, in order to reduce the immense variety of his experimental observations to some coherent pattern. However, as Konorski (1948) has shown, these physiological concepts of Pavlov have never had any neurophysiological or neuroanatomical meaning, e.g. such concepts as internal and external inhibition, extinction, irradiation, induction, and differentiation.

2. *Hypothesis of self-maintaining patterns of impulses*

There have been several quite independent attempts to develop physiological models that would in principle explain learning, but none has had a secure physiological foundation. For example, Rashevsky (1938), Young (1938), Hilgard and Marquis (1940), and Householder and Landahl (1945) have attributed learning to specific dynamic patterns created by impulses circulating continuously in closed self-re-exciting chains of neurones.

Lorente de Nó (1933, 1934, 1943) in particular has demonstrated that the anatomical arrangement of neurones in the cerebral cortex makes it possible that impulses could continuously circulate around in complex neuronal pathways, which he called closed self-re-exciting chains. Recently Burns (1951) has found that such circulating activity may continue for seconds in an isolated slab of cerebral cortex (cf. p. 240). Of course it is not envisaged—as is sometimes shown diagrammatically—that there is a simple propagation of a single impulse which is synaptically transmitted through a series of neurones and so back to its starting-point. Presumably each synaptic transmission depends on the convergence of many impulses. Thus a closed self-re-exciting chain would have many neurones in parallel as well as in series, as is shown diagrammatically for a segment of a pathway in Fig. 76 (cf. p. 242). Furthermore it may be assumed that the neuronal composition of such a closed chain would show some variability at least on its 'fringe', the impulses in part traversing now some neurones now others in successive circuits through the chain, much as is believed to occur in auricular fibrillation of cardiac muscle. In continuously circulating around any particular chain of neurones, the impulses would give a specific pattern of activity in space and time, which of course could form the basis of specific sequelae, e.g. conditioned reflexes or memories (cf. p. 266).

Repetitive activity in such closed chains doubtless accounts for functional changes of brief duration (cf. Hebb, 1949; Gerard, 1949), but grave difficulties arise when this explanation is applied to enduring memories or to conditioned reflexes (Konorski, 1948), for on that hypothesis a memory or a conditioned reflex must be irretrievably lost if the circulating activity ceases. The above demonstration of prolonged plastic changes at synapses (Eccles and McIntyre, 1951, 1952) removes the necessity for making the improbable postulate of dynamic patterns of circulating impulses that continue during sleep, deep anaesthesia, concussion, and convulsive seizures.

3. *Hypotheses based on postulated plastic changes*

Konorski (1948, 1950) has developed an explanation of conditioning that is based on plastic changes in the nervous system, but unfortunately plastic changes of the type that he envisages have not been demonstrated and *a priori* seem improbable. He postulates (cf. Fig. 75 A): (i) a centre of the stimulus to be conditioned (the emitting centre, EC); (ii) a centre of the unconditioned stimulus (the receiving centre, RC); (iii) potential connexions between these two centres (dotted lines in Fig. 75 A) which are transformed into 'actual excitatory connections' when excitation in the first centre coincides in time with a rise of excitation in the second centre, this process consisting in a growth and multiplication of synapses. Though this last postulate may be considered to be an example of increased synaptic effectiveness with usage, as described on p. 209, it actually differs radically therefrom, for it is assumed to occur not simply on account of activation of the emitting centre and discharge of impulses therefrom, but only when this coincides with a rise in activation of the receiving centre. Thus a special process is postulated for which we have no experimental evidence.

Shimbel (1950) has proposed a very simple model from which he develops a theory of learning. His approach has the attractive feature that he applies it to randomly interconnected neural networks, and shows how the development of specific responses may occur. However, the basic postulate has no experimental foundation, and now seems unnecessary, for it attributes learning to a *non-specific* lowering of the threshold of neurones that have been excited, i.e.

he postulates a general change in the neurone and not an increased efficacy that is restricted to the activated synaptic knobs. Thus in Fig. 75 B an impulse in the afferent

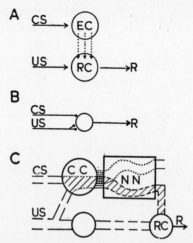

FIG. 75. Diagrams illustrating attempts to explain conditioned reflexes by plastic changes in synaptic connexions. Full description in text. CS and US show input into central nervous system of conditioned and unconditioned stimuli respectively. In A the arrows indicate nervous pathways, while B is a redrawing of a highly simplified model in which Shimbel (1951) shows converging synaptic connexions of the CS and US lines. In C nervous pathways are drawn as broad bands along which conduction occurs as indicated in Fig. 76, particularly in the neuronal network, NN. The interruptions in the bands indicate synaptic relays. Nerve centres containing large populations of neurones are indicated by circles, while the neuronal network, NN, would be an extremely complex neuronal system, for example, an area or areas of the cerebral cortex. Further description in text.

fibre excited by the unconditioned stimulus (US) is assumed to be adequate to excite a discharge from the neurone and so evoke the response, R, whereas an impulse in the afferent fibre excited by the conditioned stimulus (CS) is normally inadequate, as shown conventionally by one synaptic knob instead of the two for the US line. However, it is postulated that the threshold of the neurone is lowered more or less permanently if the super-threshold and sub-threshold impulses impinge upon it in a sufficiently close temporal contiguity, and hence the CS line becomes an adequate stimulus. This prolonged lowering of the threshold to heterosynaptic excitation has not been observed experimentally. Moreover it gives rise to a serious problem in attempting to extract from such a system an adequate degree of specificity when the lowering of threshold is non-specific for all synapses on a neurone. This is the problem of redundant conditioning, as it is appropriately called by Shimbel.

There have been many attempts to explain learning and conditioning by the growth and development of synapses (Tanzi, 1893; Cajal, 1911; Hebb, 1949), but no model has been presented that conforms with known neurophysiological properties of neurones, and at the same time accounts for the simplest phenomena of learning, i.e. conditioned reflexes of the Pavlov type.

4. *A neurophysiological hypothesis of conditioned reflexes*

As a preliminary it will be necessary to study the propagation of impulses in a neuronal network. A small segment of a network is represented in very simplified form in Fig. 76. The convention is adopted that synaptic excitation by two knobs is necessary to generate an impulse, and furthermore the cells discharging impulses have axons drawn as continuous lines. The same network is shown with two different inputs. In the upper diagram neurones A2, 3, and 4 discharge impulses and eventually neurones D2, 3, and 4 also discharge. In the lower diagram the input is altered merely by the substitution of A_1 for A_4 as an initially discharging neurone; yet the eventual output is now completely different, being D_1 only. This is an example of the effect of 'partially shifted overlap' in giving a quite different output after only three synaptic relays. It will be seen, moreover, that the same neurones can contribute to two different patterns of activity in the network. When allowance is made for the extreme simplifications adopted in Fig. 76, it will be realized that a neuronal network constructed from millions of neurones can give an immense variety of patterned activities (cf. Chapter 8).

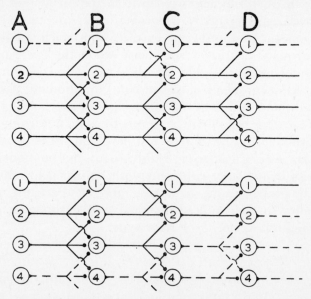

FIG. 76. Two drawings of the same neuronal network to show different response to a changed input. Full description in text.

The neurophysiological hypothesis of conditioned reflexes will be illustrated by the model shown in Fig. 75 C. It will be noted that the connexions are shown by columns or bands rather than single neurones. Propagation along each such column, particularly in the neuronal network, would occur in the manner illustrated in Fig. 76.

There is firstly the simple unconditioned reflex arc US to R via the receiving centre, RC. The conditioned stimulus causes the discharge of afferent impulses along the CS pathway to a centre where they converge on neurones also excited by impulses in collaterals from the US afferent path (the convergence centre, CC). Two changes are thereby brought about: synaptic facilitation due to the postsynaptic potential causes the discharge of impulses from some otherwise quiescent neurones in the convergence centre, the hatched area representing the active zone of neurones; there is increased efficacy of synaptic knobs on account of usage, those of the CS pathway being particularly important in conditioning. The discharge of impulses from the convergence centre will develop a special spatio-temporal pattern of impulses in the neuronal network, as shown by hatched path in NN. Since, on account of convergence and summation in CC, this spatio-temporal pattern is developed in part by impulses from the US afferents, it would be expected, as shown in Fig. 75 C, to cause eventually a discharge of impulses onto the same receiving centre, RC, that US operates more directly in evoking the unconditioned response. It is evident that, if discharges of impulses into NN are set up by CS and US in close temporal sequence and with an adequate number of repetitions, the increase in synaptic efficacy in the hatched zone both in the convergence centre (CC) and in the neuronal network (NN) will cause impulses from CS alone to be effective in evoking a pattern of impulses in NN that leads to the response R, i.e. a conditioned reflex has been set up. Before further discussion it is important to answer two criticisms that immediately suggest themselves.

(i) On this explanation would not repetition of CS by itself a sufficient number of times also be expected to give the conditioned response, R? Under such conditions there would be the same growth and development of synaptic knobs of CS in the convergence centre, and hence impulses from CS alone would be just as effective as if they had been combined with US impulses throughout the conditioning. However, the significant difference would arise at the next stage in the neuronal network. With CS impulses alone, the spatio-temporal pattern of impulses fed in from CC to NN would differ both in intensity and form. The intensity would always be lower than with CS plus US because in the convergence centre synaptic efficacy is supplemented by spatial summation. The form of the spatio-temporal pattern would be different because it is the convergence of impulses from US that causes the neurones of CC to discharge with sufficient intensity and into that particular spatio-temporal pattern (hatched path) in the neuronal network, NN, which eventually activates the neuronal pathway leading to RC. Thus, if combined with another type of US, CS would be expected to become effective in causing a type of response appropriate to that particular US, as shown for example by the path bounded by dots in NN, and so on, as may be appreciated from the two diagrams of Fig. 76. Therefore for two reasons repetition of the CS alone would not be effective eventually in giving the response R.

(ii) Would not a conditioned reflex once developed be expected to survive indefinitely provided that CS alone be repeated with adequate frequency, which is contrary to all experimental evidence (cf. Pavlov, 1927; Konorski, 1948)? This criticism may also be answered by reference to the conduction of impulses in neuronal networks as illustrated in Fig. 76. Even when fully developed, the conditioned reflex elicited by CS alone will be evoked by a smaller discharge from CC, and hence a lower degree of intensity in the spatio-temporal pattern of impulses in NN, which could for example be represented by a narrower hatched path. As a consequence many of the synaptic knobs normally activated by discharges evoked from CC by CS and US together will be activated to a lower degree or not at all (cf. Fig. 76 with input only in A2 and 3). Hence there will not be the same maintenance of synaptic efficacy in the neuronal network, and this would be serially progressive through the network as the various converging lines on each neurone become less effective, causing it to discharge less frequently so that in turn its own synaptic knobs become less effective. Thus with CS alone there will be progressively less activation of synaptic knobs in the neuronal network, which will consequently regress; and so an explanation is provided for the gradual extinction of a conditioned reflex when it is not continuously being reinforced by the unconditioned stimulus.

It may also be noted in passing that an explanation has been provided for the fact that the conditioned stimulus alone does not evoke the unconditioned response, as Pavlov implied, but actually a new response which has elements of the unconditioned response, e.g. salivation but not eating movements (Hilgard and Marquis, 1940; Hebb, 1949). Since in Fig. 75 c the input into the neuronal network from CS alone differs from that to CS plus US, CS alone would be expected to evoke a different patterned activity in NN and hence the different output that is observed.

Admittedly the neuronal model in Fig. 75 c is much more complex than other models, but that need not be regarded as a defect because conditioned reflexes can be set up only in those regions of the nervous system where very complex neuronal networks are available. Additional complications would be necessary in order to account for other features of conditioned reflexes. For example, it is not clear from Fig. 75 c why CS has slightly to precede US in order that conditioning may occur. Possibly the powerful excitatory effects of US on the neuronal network would prevent the development of spatio-temporal patterns stemming in part from CS. Hence CS would not develop its own specific spatio-temporal path through NN to RC. At least it can be claimed that most of the features of the simple conditioned reflex are satisfactorily explained by postulating that the neuronal model of Fig. 75 c exhibits only the experimentally demonstrable properties of neurones. It may seem anomalous that the two outputs shown from CC to NN have a considerable number of fibres in common and yet within NN there is rapid separation to two completely different paths. Fig. 76 illustrates in detail how this comes about. It would seem that further development of models on the principles illustrated in Fig. 75 c would provide an explanation of more complex

Q

types of conditioned reflexes and also for other kinds of learning.

Perhaps the most unsatisfactory feature of the hypothesis is that the experimental demonstrations of changing synaptic efficacy required thousands of impulses or relatively prolonged periods of disuse (Eccles and McIntyre, 1951, 1952). In contrast, conditioned reflexes are established by relatively few presentations of CS together with US, and unique events can be remembered for a whole lifetime. A probable explanation is that prolonged reverberatory activity occurs in the neuronal network, so that a single event may activate each link in a spatio-temporal pattern thousands of times within a few seconds. Hebb (1949) makes a related postulate when he supposes that 'a reverberatory trace might co-operate with the structural change, and carry the memory until the growth change is made'. A similar suggestion has been made by Gerard (1949). Furthermore we may suppose that the plastic changes are susceptible to reinforcement by the replaying of the specific spatio-temporal patterns each time that the memory is recalled. It is also possible that synaptic plasticity may be much more highly developed in the cerebral cortex.

F. THE STORAGE OF INFORMATION

At the end of the last chapter there was a general summary of the functioning of the nervous system in the section on transmission of information. Consideration was restricted to the short-term events that persisted for no longer than the propagation of impulses and their synaptic excitatory and inhibitory actions. Attempts have been made to account in this same way for all storage of information, it being postulated that even enduring memories are due to self-maintaining patterns of circulating impulses. As pointed out above, there is no need for this improbable postulate, because there is now direct evidence for plastic changes at synapses whereby their excitatory effect is increased by usage and depressed by disuse.

If, as seems likely, this is a general property of synapses, it could plausibly account for the storage of information at all parts of the central nervous system. This has been illustrated above for the conditioned reflex, but in general it can be postulated that a particular pattern of afferent input would tend to cause the development of specific spatio-temporal patterns of activity in the neuronal networks of the central nervous system. This activation would result in increased synaptic efficacy throughout this patterned structure, which would consequently tend to become a more probable pattern of activity for subsequent afferent inputs resembling the initial one. A structural basis is thus provided for the storage of information, and will be referred to later (p. 266) in discussing memory.

VII

THE CEREBRAL CORTEX

A. INTRODUCTION

IT is beyond the scope of these lectures to examine the behaviour of nerve-cells in the diverse subcortical centres of the brain, where at best we have but fragmentary knowledge. The recent intensive investigation in these regions has been of necessity largely topographical (cf. Fulton, 1949), for precise physiological investigation has to await the construction of reliable maps of the nerve connexions. However, it seems probable that the behaviour of these nerve-cells will be adequately described by the principles that have been developed in connexion with the reflex responses of the spinal cord in Chapters 4, 5, and 6. No such assumption can be made gratuitously for the nerve-cells of the cerebral cortex, where in some mysterious way patterns of neuronal activity are in liaison with mind. This problem will be considered in the final chapter. Here the attempt will be made to see how far the nerve-cells of the cerebral cortex conform in their behaviour with those that we have studied in detail in the spinal cord. Sherrington (1951) summarized this problem well.

Every nerve-cell of the millions in it (the cerebral cortex) is clearly at a glance a nerve-cell. But nerve-cells as a class are elsewhere not specially concerned with mind. It is partly conjecture whether the properties of all these nerve-cells, their fibres, their cell-contacts (synapses), their cell-bodies, have rigidly those characters observed in the more accessible cells of the spinal cord and elsewhere. That the properties will not differ fundamentally from those elsewhere seems safe to suppose.

As elsewhere, the most valuable data on the behaviour of nerve-cells in the cerebral cortex is derived from a study of their electrical responses. But the attempt at interpretation of these electrical responses is confronted by two major difficulties: the cerebral cortex is an extremely complex structure with large numbers of cells arranged in unimaginably complicated patterns; under ordinary experimental conditions the cerebral cortex is in a state of continuous activity. Before attempting any explanation of the spontaneous activity, we will consider firstly the essentials of the histological structure of the cerebral cortex and then the more easily analysed responses evoked by some specific types of stimulation: by direct electrical stimulation; by afferent volleys; and by antidromic volleys.

No attempt will be made to give an account of the specific functions of the various areas of the cerebral cortex, which is beyond the scope of the general treatment adopted in this book, and which is very thoroughly given by Fulton (1949). For example, the specific properties of the sensory receiving areas and of the motor projection areas derive from the fact that these areas are the channels by which 'information' enters or leaves the cerebral cortex. However, so far as is known, the structural and functional properties of such areas are otherwise very similar to the remainder of the cerebral cortex, at least the isocortex, hence the justification for the general treatment here adopted.

B. THE HISTOLOGICAL STRUCTURE

Fig. 77 A gives some idea of the density of the nerve-cell population in the grey matter. Counts in the human cerebral cortex average about 50,000 per sq. mm. for the surfaces of the convolutions, and rather less in the sulci (Thompson, 1899). When a very small fraction of the cells is stained by the Golgi method (Cajal, 1911; Lorente de Nó, 1933, 1934, 1943; Chang, 1951), the complex branching structure of each cell can be seen as in Fig. 77 B. Notable are the large pyramidal cells (11, 12, 13), which have apical dendrites running up to and ramifying in the superficial molecular layer, and axons which project into the subjacent white matter and so to other parts of the cortex of the same or opposite side, or even to more remote parts of the central nervous system, e.g. to form the pyramidal tract. Before leaving the grey matter these axons give off collaterals which appear to establish synaptic contacts with a large variety of cells (Lorente de Nó, 1934).

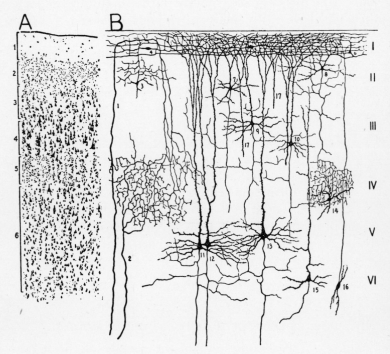

FIG. 77 A. Cytoarchitectonic picture of a representative area of the human cerebral cortex, only the cell bodies of the neurones being stained. The various layers of the cortex are indicated to the left (Campbell, 1905).

FIG. 77 B. Composite picture showing drawings of Golgi preparations of cerebral cortex of rat and mouse, and giving general plan of arrangement of the various kinds of neurones. Further description in text (Chang, 1951).

By far the most numerous cells in the human cerebral cortex are small nerve-cells (3, 14) whose axons branch profusely in the immediate neighbourhood of the cell body. Such cells are assumed to be of great importance in

providing the enormous wealth of detailed patterned linkage in the cortex. Other varieties are small and medium
pyramidal cells (7, 8, 9, 10) whose axons terminate in
the deeper layers of the grey matter, and the horizontal
cells (4, 5, 6) that have axons travelling for considerable
distances in the superficial molecular layer and making
numerous synaptic contacts on the apical dendrites of the
pyramidal cells. The other structures of great importance
in Fig. 77 B are the afferent fibres that usually run the
course of fibre 2, branching profusely in the fourth layer,
and making numerous synaptic contacts therein. An alternative course is shown by fibre 1 which runs up to the
molecular layer and then descends to the fourth layer, but
it may also contribute many branches in the molecular
layer (Lorente de Nó, 1934).

Every part of the cerebral cortex is provided in this way
with afferent and efferent fibres between which lie a vast
assemblage of interneurones. Thus, as a first approxima-
tion, any small area may be regarded as a very complex
reflex centre, incoming impulses exciting the discharge of
impulses from the large pyramidal cells by means of complex polysynaptic reflex pathways. Lorente de Nó in particular has studied the linkage of cortical neurones into
functional chains such as those illustrated in diagrammatic form in Fig. 78. Afferent impulses enter by the
fibres a and a^1, and successive synaptic transmissions are
indicated by s_1, s_2, s_3, &c. It can be seen that there are
complex pathways even for this highly simplified diagram,
for very few cells are drawn and very few synaptic contacts are shown for any one. Yet Fig. 78 is very valuable,
for it gives some concept of the complexity of synaptic
pathways in the cortex. Of course a small cortical area is
never isolated in this way, for in the grey matter there are
always profuse lateral interconnexions. It should be noted
that synaptic knobs are not a prominent feature in the
cerebral cortex. Possibly many functional contacts are
made without histologically identifiable knobs.

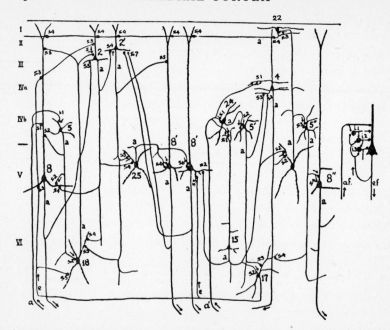

FIG. 78. Diagram of some of intracortical chains of neurones. The axons of cortical cells are marked a, and afferent fibres as *a* and a^1. The synaptic junctions are indicated by *s* and a knob-like expansion of the axon. It is assumed that synapses marked with an arrow transmit the impulses, and the synapses are numbered s_1, s_2, &c., in serial order of activation. The small diagram on the right shows a simple version of a series of inter-locking closed self-re-exciting chains (Lorente de Nó, 1943).

C. DIRECT ELECTRICAL STIMULATION OF THE CEREBRAL CORTEX

There is general agreement that a weak electrical stimulus applied to the surface of the cerebral cortex produces a brief negativity of the adjacent cortex relative to an indifferent electrode (Adrian's superficial response). A stronger stimulus generates in addition a later response which is characterized by a negativity of the deeper parts of the cortex with positivity of the surface (Adrian's deep response). The investigation of these responses has been greatly aided by Burns's (1950, 1951) technique of the isolated cortical slab, following earlier work of Bremer (1938, 1949), and of Kristiansen and Courtois (1949), which has the great advantage of providing an area of cortex with normal blood-supply, and yet free from all extraneous nervous influences and hence normally quiescent even in the unanaesthetized preparation.

1. *Superficial response*

Fig. 79 A shows in the inset a drawing of the brief negative wave that characterizes the superficial response as recorded about 2 mm. from a stimulated focus. It has a brief rising phase and a slower decay with a total duration of about 20 msec. The plotted points of Fig. 79 A reveal that the superficial response increases to a maximum as the stimulus is increased about five-fold from threshold. When the recording electrode is moved away from the stimulated focus, the superficial response progressively decrements to disappear at about 10 mm. and it also has a more delayed onset as is illustrated by the drawings at the top of Fig. 79 B.

It has been concluded (Eccles, 1951*b*) that, as illustrated in Fig. 79 B, the superficial response of the cerebral cortex corresponds with the focal record of the post-synaptic potentials that would be set up in the apical dendrites of the pyramidal cells by impulses in the nerve-fibres of the molecular layer (axons of horizontal cells and the afferent fibres to the cortex, Figs. 77 B and 78). The experimental evidence may be listed as follows.

(i) The time-course has a general resemblance to that of post-synaptic potentials of motoneurones (cf. Fig. 42), the only significant difference being the slower rising phase, which is several milliseconds in duration. This difference may plausibly be attributed to such factors as the growth of local responses in the apical dendrites (cf. p. 142), and the effect of a multitude of presynaptic paths having widely different conduction times.

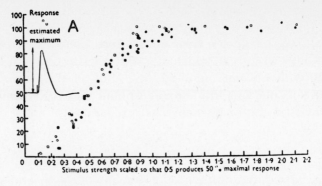

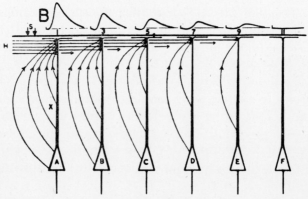

FIG. 79 A. Inset shows drawing of superficial response recorded monopolarly, and points show its size measure at about 2 mm. from the
stimulated focus and plotted against stimulus strength, which is scaled
in a series of experiments on the isolated cortical slab so that an abscissal
value of 0·5 gives 50 per cent. of the maximal response (Burns, 1950).
FIG. 79 B. Diagram illustrating the postulated mechanism generating the
superficial response. The vertical scale is more highly magnified than
the horizontal. S shows stimulating electrodes applied to the cerebral
cortex and the records at 1, 3, 5, 7, 9, and 11 show the superficial responses
recorded monopolarly at the corresponding number of millimetres from
the stimulating electrode (derived from the records of Burns and Chang).
Six deep pyramidal cells (A to F) are shown at corresponding intervals
with only the apical dendrites drawn, the remaining dendrites being
omitted for diagrammatic simplicity. Five axons (H) of horizontal cells or
afferent fibres are shown that would all be stimulated by a sufficiently
strong stimulus at S. They terminate at various distances therefrom and
each is shown contributing a synaptic knob to each apical dendrite that it
passes or ends on. Horizontal arrows indicate direction of impulse propagation in the horizontal fibres, while the lines of extrinsic current flow are
drawn from sources on deep parts of pyramidal cells to sinks on the apical
dendrites, the approximate intensity of current flow being indicated by
density of lines (Eccles, 1951b).

(ii) As shown in Fig. 79 B the synaptically depolarized foci on an apical dendrite would cause currents to flow from sources on the deeper part of the apical dendrite and on the body of that pyramidal cell. Thus an electrode at point X, being close to sources, should pick up a positive potential of comparable time-course, as has actually been observed (Chang, 1951; Burns, 1952).

(iii) The decremental spread would be attributable to the random distribution of the meshwork of longitudinally arranged fibres in the molecular layer (cf. Figs. 77 B and 79 B). Burns (1950) has shown that the decrement from the stimulated focus corresponds quantitatively to mathematical prediction from this arrangement if the fibres are about 10 mm. in length, which is a probable value for the axons of the horizontal cells.

(iv) The effect of increasing strength of stimulus would depend on the number of fibres stimulated, a stimulus about 5 times threshold exciting all those that are in the neighbourhood of the stimulating electrodes; hence the attainment of a maximum response with this strength of stimulus.

(v) The progressively delayed onset of the spreading superficial response gives it a conduction velocity of about 2 metres a second, which reasonably may be attributable to the conduction velocity of the fibres in the molecular layer.

(vi) Besides this conduction time there is some evidence of an additional delay of rather less than 1 msec., which would be attributable to the synaptic delay in setting up the post-synaptic potential (cf. p. 130).

It has further been shown (Eccles, 1951b) that other explanations of the superficial response encounter grave difficulties. It may therefore be concluded that the superficial response is attributable to a primary stimulation of nerve-fibres in the molecular layer, which in turn evoke a post-synaptic potential in the apical dendrites of the pyramidal cells as shown in Fig. 79 B.

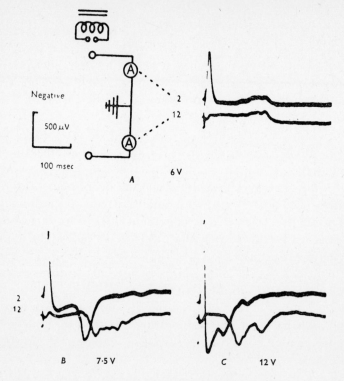

FIG. 80. Responses to surface stimulation of the isolated cortex at 2 and 12 mm. from a stimulated point (monopolar recording), see inset diagram. With a 6 V stimulus (*A*) there is a large superficial response which is recorded at 2 mm. not at 12 mm. With a 12 V stimulus (*C*) the superficial response at the 2 mm. position is larger and quickly reverses to a positivity which signals the negativity of activated foci deep in the cortex (the deep response). This surface positivity appears at about 60 msec. later in the record at 12 mm. distant. The 7·5 V stimulus (*B*) is just threshold for eliciting a deep response, which is very delayed at the 2 mm. record and almost as large as the *C* response in the 12 mm. record (Burns, 1950).

2. *Deep response*

There is general agreement that, when the strength of the stimulus is increased to several times above the threshold for the superficial response, this surface negative wave terminates in a surface positivity, i.e. the response becomes diphasic, source following sink, as shown in Fig. 80 (Burns, 1950, 1951; Chang, 1951). This positive wave arises close to the stimulating electrode and propagates slowly outwards in approximately an all-or-nothing manner and at a velocity of about 20 cm. a second. As already mentioned the sinks for this superficial source are found by a penetrating micro-electrode to be deeper in the cortex, hence the name 'deep response'. The general explanation of this deep response is illustrated in Fig. 81.

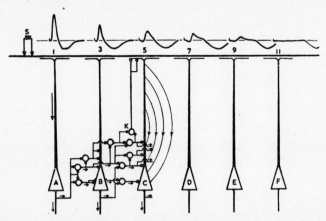

FIG. 81. Diagram as in Fig. 79 B but illustrating the postulated mechanism by which a strong stimulus generates a deep response. Again the potentials (the initial superficial and later deep response) are shown at 1, 3, 5, 7, 9, and 11 mm. from the stimulating electrodes at S. Note that time-scale is more contracted and that superficial responses are assumed to be the same as in Fig. 79 B. The arrows on pyramidal cell A indicate propagation of impulse from its apical dendrite to soma and along its axon and axon collateral. Synaptic excitation of numerous short-axon neurones is shown and also of the deep pyramidal cells B and C. It can be seen that the process of progressive synaptic excitation would likewise spread to pyramidal cells D, E, F, &c. The lines of extrinsic current flow are shown for the pyramidal cell (C) going from sources on the apical dendrite to the sinks on those deeper parts of the dendrites and the soma that are synaptically excited by the spreading deep response. K is a cell with ascending axon that could cause the deep response to spread to the surface and give the second component of Chang (Eccles, 1951b).

It is firstly assumed that, when the post-synaptic potential on the apical dendrites of a pyramidal cell reaches a critical value, it generates an impulse which propagates over the surface of the pyramidal cell (A in Fig. 81), then down its axon and along the axon collaterals (cf. Fig. 78).

As expected according to this explanation, Adrian (1936) found that there was a discharge of impulses in the pyramidal tract when a stimulus set up a deep response of the motor cortex. If impulses are in this way set up in many pyramidal cells, some neurones deep in the cortex will have sufficient synaptic excitation from the axon collaterals to cause the generation of impulses, and these in turn will excite other neurones and so on. In particular the short-axon cortical neurones would be very effectively involved in this serial synaptic excitation, for they are particularly designed to give heavy synaptic bombardment on adjacent neurones.

The first stages of this spreading synaptic excitation are illustrated in Fig. 81, where the small circles represent the short-axon neurones. It will be seen that, if there is an adequate convergence on each successive shell of neurones, this wave of excitatory involvement will propagate indefinitely outwards in an approximately all-or-nothing manner, which is actually observed (Fig. 80 c) and is shown in the drawings of Fig. 81. The extreme richness of the inter-connexions between the cortical nerve-cells (cf. Lorente de Nó, 1933, 1934, 1943) would account for the approximate all-or-nothing nature of the spreading deep response. If one millisecond be assumed as the time for each serial neuronal invasion, i.e. synaptic delay plus conduction time, then the velocity of 20 cm. a second indicates a mean distance of 200 μ for each serial neuronal invasion. This seems a reasonable value, for the neuronal density in the cortex is such that a single nerve-cell occupies on the average a cube with sides of about 80 μ. Direct evidence supporting the interpretation given in Fig. 81 has been reported by Adrian (1936) who found that a pure surface positive wave was set up by stimulation at 1·5 to 2 mm. deep to the cortical surface.

Burns (1950, 1951) has shown that the superficial response initiates the deep response when it is above a critical intensity. In the unanaesthetized cortex an indefinitely spreading deep response is set up by a superficial response about 30 per cent. maximum. With light anaesthesia the critical value is twice as high (cf. Fig. 80 B), while with deep anaesthesia even a maximum superficial response is ineffective. The postulate that the superficial response is a post-synaptic potential offers a satisfactory explanation of these observations, since anaesthesia raises the threshold level at which a post-synaptic potential generates an impulse (cf. Brooks and Eccles, 1947c).

As would be expected from Fig. 81, the deep response has virtually an all-or-nothing character when observed many millimetres from the stimulation point (cf. Figs. 80 B, C at 12 mm.). Stimuli which are too weak to generate a deep response at such a distant observation point nevertheless set up a small decrementally spreading response giving the typical surface positivity (Burns, 1950). It dies out within a few millimetres, but by facilitation due to two or more stimuli in succession (Adrian, 1936; Burns, 1950) it can be made to grow up to the indefinitely spreading deep response. Presumably in the single submaximal deep response the number of excited neurones is inadequate to give the convergence of synaptic bombardment that is necessary for continuous propagation outwards (cf. p. 238). Thus there may be sufficient convergence to generate the discharge of impulses in some neurones, and these in turn may cause others to discharge, and so on, but this convergence would become progressively more inadequate so that eventually no neurones would be caused to discharge and the deep response would be extinguished. However, application of a second stimulus before the onset of extinction would excite more neurones and so effectively add to the convergence, hence the facilitation.

The duration of the surface positivity that is observed during the deep response (30 to 100 msec.) is much too long for it to be produced mainly by impulses in neurones or their axons. Presumably it is largely attributable to the developing post-synaptic potentials that precede the generation of impulses in the neurones of the deeper cortical layers. It would be expected that with any neurone there would be a synaptic bombardment of many milliseconds before the post-synaptic potential had been built up to the intensity requisite for generating an impulse. However, the deep response probably is in part attributable to asynchronously discharged impulses. A further inference is that during the spreading deep response impulses generated in the deeper levels of the pyramidal cells do not completely invade the apical dendrites, otherwise it would seem difficult to account for the effectiveness of the surface sources as indicated by the recorded surface positivity. On the other hand, when large, the deep response is often followed by a later surface negative wave (cf. the second component of Chang, 1951), which may be attributable to activation of the horizontal cells and apical dendrites in the molecular layer by cells with ascending axons (e.g. cell 16 in Fig. 77 B and cell K in Fig. 81). However, Burns (1952) finds that in part at least this late surface negativity is attributable to the spread of the deep response to adjacent gyri.

3. *Rhythmic activity of the cerebral cortex*

When it is set up in an unanaesthetized cortical slab, the deep response is always much more complicated than in Fig. 80 (Burns, 1951). A single stimulus then gives rise to a surface positivity which persists for several seconds and on which is superimposed a fairly regular wave-form at a frequency of about 65 a second (Fig. 82). There is good evidence that this complex response is caused by continuously circulating activity in neuronal chains, the so-called closed self-re-exciting chains for which Lorente de Nó (1933, 1934, 1943) has produced histological evidence. It may be regarded as a local convulsion in the cortical slab.

The most convincing evidence given by Burns (1951) in support of the explanation by circulating impulses is

derived from experiments where stimuli of varying strengths
are applied to the cortical slab during its rhythmic response. A very strong stimulus causes an immediate cessation of the repetitive activity, presumably because it would

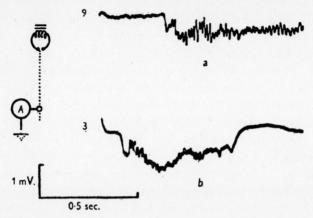

FIG. 82. Single stimuli, just above threshold for deep response, are
applied to unanaesthetized cortical slab and recorded at over 10 mm. away
(see inset diagram) so that no superficial response is seen. *A* shows prominent rhythmic wave during prolonged surface positivity—it persisted for
about 3 seconds. *B* shows unusually brief response in another cat, the
rhythmic wave being also less prominent (Burns, 1951).

excite virtually all neurones in the cortical slab and make
them refractory, hence blocking all chain activity. After
a weaker stimulus there is merely a temporary local quiescence. Presumably only a localized area of neurones would
then be excited and made refractory, and reinvasion of
this area later takes place from the more distant areas
where the repetitive activity has been unaffected by the
stimulus. Other important evidence for circulating impulses is the finding that the phase of the electrical wave
changes with movements of the recording electrode of
only 1 mm. In the intact cortex it is likely that thalamo-
cortical circuits would also contribute to the rhythmic
responses.

The conditions responsible for the onset of the repetitive wave are not shown in Fig. 81, but, in order that it

could occur, the advancing invasion of the deep response must fail to generate impulses in a considerable proportion of the neurones, which are thus available for synaptic excitation by impulses that circulate back from the advancing wave front. The next wave of the rhythmic series would be generated in this way, and so a circus activity would be set up, somewhat analogous to the circus activity in auricular fibrillation. In each rhythmic cycle the circulating impulses would not follow stereotyped neuronal chains. One may assume that the course of the advancing wave front would be determined by the degree of convergence of excitatory impulses on each individual neurone. Then the advancing wave front would be in a whole assemblage of neurones more or less in parallel as illustrated in the simple diagram of Fig. 76, which shows a fragment of a circulating neuronal path.

Here simplification is achieved by the standard convention of showing only a small fraction of the interneuronal connexions, and by assuming that synaptic excitation by only two impulses in close temporal sequence is necessary for generating an impulse. If there are impulses in A2, 3, and 4 neurones, then B2, 3, and 4, C2, 3, and 4 and D2, 3, and 4 will discharge in serial sequence as shown in the upper diagram. On the other hand, if there had been an impulse in A1 and none in A4, then B1, 2, and 3, C1 and 2, and D1 would be the discharging neurones, i.e. a very different neuronal pattern would develop. The circulating pattern of impulses would thus be extremely labile, even for the over-simplified situation of Fig. 76. It is difficult to imagine the complexity actually obtaining in neuronal chains where each neurone could be linked to perhaps 100 other neurones and the convergence of many impulses would be necessary in order to make any one neurone generate an impulse (cf. p. 132).

Since the probable assumption may be made that the transynaptic propagation of impulses in the cerebral cortex resembles that in the spinal cord, the following general propositions would be expected to hold for impulses propagating through neuronal networks (cf. p. 251 and Fig. 76).

(i) In order to generate the discharge of an impulse from any neurone, there must be within a few milliseconds convergence on to it of impulses from many neurones; hence there must be an advancing wave front in many neurones in parallel. If the activated number falls below a critical level, propagation through the network would rapidly decrement to zero.

(ii) At each stage of synaptic transmission there will be all levels of excitation in different neurones, some being just supraliminal for discharge, others just subliminal; hence there will be a considerable degree of lability in the neurones occupied by the advancing wave front. At any stage impulses converging from other paths can greatly modify the neurones that are activated and hence the subsequent development of the advancing wave front (cf. Fig. 76).

(iii) Any one neurone can be activated in several different wave fronts, for the impulse it discharges will aid in the activation of different neurones according to the synaptic distribution of the other neurones that are activated in parallel with it. For example, in the upper diagram of Fig. 76, neurone B2 is essentially concerned in the activation of neurones C2 and D2, whereas in the lower diagram it is essentially concerned only in the activation of two different neurones, C1 and D1.

(iv) Since the cortex frequently exhibits fairly regular rhythmic activity (Figs. 82, 86, 87), it may be assumed that any one neurone discharges impulses at fairly regular intervals. But it must not therefore be supposed that it is part of some closed self-re-exciting chain of stable character. The lability noted above would ensure that there was a considerable variability in the neurones involved in successive circuits of the wave front, if it is allowable to give an identity to something so variable as the wave front.

The sudden end of a rhythmic response (cf. Fig. 82) is probably attributable to the build-up of positive after-potential and the resultant depression of excitability in the repetitively discharging neurones, much as has been described for motoneurones (cf. p. 128). Reference to Fig. 76 will show how the cessation of a small proportion of the neuronal discharges would effectively damp out a whole pattern of circulating impulses; for example A2 and 3 alone would cause no D neurones to discharge impulses.

Repetitive cortical stimulation is particularly effective in causing prolonged rhythmic discharges which continue after the end of the stimulation (Adrian, 1936; Rosenblueth and Cannon, 1942). Recently Jung and Tönnies (1950) have systematically investigated these convulsive seizures, both the conditions causing their development and those terminating and following the seizure. These observations are too complex for interpretation at present, particularly as they were not done on isolated cortical slabs. However, in general it seems that closed self-re-exciting chains of neurones would provide a satisfactory explanation of the convulsions.

In conclusion it will be agreed with Burns (1951) that the experimental evidence virtually excludes, for the post-stimulation repetitive responses, the alternative hypothesis that would attribute rhythmic cortical activity to a basic rhythmic response of the individual neurones (cf. Bremer, 1949). It appears probable that the spontaneous electrical activity of the cortex is likewise generated by impulses circulating in a labile fashion in chains of neurones. However, more direct experimental investigation is desirable, particularly with intracellular recording from pyramidal cells, which should be technically possible. Meanwhile, it is already evident that the simple principles of operation of neuronal chains such as in Fig. 76 are of the greatest importance in attempting to give an account of the activity of the cerebral cortex.

4. Conclusions

For our purpose the important conclusion to be drawn from these investigations of the superficial, the deep and the rhythmic responses of the cerebral cortex is that they can be satisfactorily explained on the basis of the known neuronal structure of the cerebral cortex and the electrical responses that characterize other neurones where investigation has been more rigorous, particularly the motoneurones of the spinal cord. Thus the present experimental analysis of superficial, deep, and rhythmic responses supports the general assumption that cortical neurones do not differ fundamentally from other neurones. In particular the time-course of decay of the superficial response indicates that the electric time-constant of the surface membrane of the apical dendrites is approximately the same as for motoneurones (cf. p. 142). It is also of importance that there is good evidence from the deep response that impulses are generated at a critical degree of depolarization of pyramidal cells. However, the interpretation here offered must be regarded as provisional, for an accurate electrical study can be made only by the technique of intracellular recording, that so far has been restricted to neurones of the spinal cord.

D. CORTICAL RESPONSES EVOKED BY AFFERENT IMPULSES

There is general agreement that all afferent volleys to the cerebral cortex generate therein an initial surface-positive wave that is sharply restricted to the cortical region in which the volley terminates (cf. Eccles, 1951*b*). Subsequently the wave form is often complex, the positive wave being usually followed by a more prolonged negative wave (upper record, Fig. 83 A). A wide variety of afferent volleys has been investigated; for example, stimulation of cutaneous receptors or the cutaneous afferent pathway (Adrian, 1941; Marshall, Woolsey, and Bard, 1941; Marshall, 1941); stimulation of visual receptors or the optic pathway (Chang and Kaada, 1950);

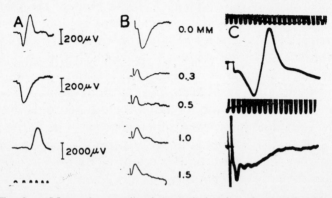

FIG. 83 A. Monopolar recording from cortical surface of potentials evoked by application of a single stimulus to symmetrical point in other hemisphere. Upper record is a typical normal diphasic response with initial positivity. The centre record was similarly evoked except that the cortex at the recording area had been anaesthetized by nembutal. In the lowest record the nembutal had been removed and 1 per cent. strychnine sulphate added. Note lower amplification. Time-scale marks 60 cyc. a second (Curtis, 1940).
FIG. 83 B. Records taken from nembutalized cortex as in Fig. 83 A, centre record, but recording electrode was inserted at the indicated depths in millimetres below the surface. Note reversal at about 0·3 mm. (Curtis, 1940).
FIG. 83 C. Electrical responses recorded monopolarly in the pyramidal cortex of the monkey in response to a single volley in the pyramidal tract. The fast record shows initial diphasic response, initially positive, due to antidromic invasion of large pyramidal cells by impulses in their large fast-conducting axons. Time, 0·1 msec. The lower record shows much slower potential wave set up by the high threshold low velocity pyramidal fibres (Woolsey and Chang, 1948).

stimulation of acoustic receptors or the auditory pathway (Bremer, 1943); stimulation of opposite side of cortex with mediation by the corpus callosum (Curtis, 1940); stimulation of afferent fibres to the hippocampus (Renshaw, Forbes, and Morison, 1940); stimulation of various thalamic nuclei (Morison and Dempsey, 1942; Dempsey and Morison, 1942). For a systematic treatment reference may be made to two reviews (Whitteridge, 1950; Eccles, 1951*b*).

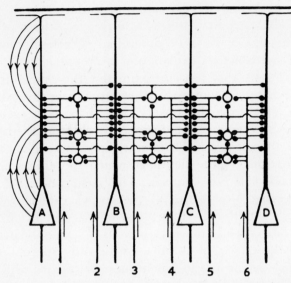

FIG. 84. Diagram as in Figs. 79 B and 81, but illustrating the postulated mechanism by which an afferent volley generates an initial positive wave on the cortical surface. The afferent impulses reach the cortex along fibres 1 to 6 as shown by arrows. When they reach layer IV, these afferent fibres branch profusing and end in numerous synaptic knobs either on the dendrites of pyramidal cells *A*, *B*, *C*, and *D* or on interneurones (cf. Figs. 77 B, 78), which in turn may give synaptic knobs to the pyramidal cells. The lines of extrinsic current flow are drawn for *A* from sources both on the superficial parts of the apical dendrites and on the soma to sinks on the relatively deep dendritic regions of the pyramidal cell (Eccles, 1951*b*).

When it is set up by a single afferent volley, the initial surface-positive wave has a duration of 10 to 20 msec. if it is relatively uncomplicated by later waves. It has been argued (Eccles, 1951*b*) in agreement with some investigators (Renshaw *et al.*, 1940; Bremer, 1943; Chang and Kaada, 1950), but not all (cf. Adrian, 1941), that the initial positive wave is attributable to the synaptic excitatory action of afferent impulses generating post-synaptic potentials on the deeper parts of the apical dendrites and the bodies of the pyramidal cells as in Fig. 84 (cf. also terminations of a and a^1 in Fig. 78). Most afferent fibres branch profusely and terminate in the fourth cortical layer (cf. Fig. 77 B). When depolarization is produced on the pyramidal cells, current will flow as in Fig. 84, the superficial and still deeper parts of pyramidal cells being sources. Hence a satisfactory explanation is provided for the surface positivity that has approximately the time-course of a post-synaptic potential. Further support for this explanation is given by the observation that, as a recording micro-electrode is inserted progressively from the cortical surface, there is reversal from initial positivity to negativity at approximately the depth at which the afferent fibres make their synaptic contacts. This is shown in Fig. 83 B (Curtis, 1940), for fibres of the corpus callosum which end more superficially than those of thalamic origin.

The later surface negative wave is presumably attributable to the effects of impulses which the afferent volley generates in the cortical neurones. In accord with this explanation it is greatly increased by strychnine and other convulsant drugs and depressed or abolished by the local application of narcotics, while in both cases the initial surface positive wave is but little affected (Fig. 83 A), as would be expected if it were a post-synaptic potential (cf. Eccles, 1951b). However, much more experimental data is needed before it will be possible to give a detailed account of the manner in which this secondary wave is generated (cf. Eccles, 1951b). There is good evidence that reverberatory circuits from the thalamus contribute to the more delayed electrical responses that are set up by an afferent volley in the cerebral cortex (Dempsey and Morison, 1942; Chang, 1950).

In respect of the electrical responses generated in the cortex by afferent volleys, it may likewise be concluded that, so far as present evidence goes, a satisfactory explanation is possible by assuming that cortical neurones give electrical responses that closely resemble those of motoneurones.

E. CORTICAL RESPONSES EVOKED BY ANTIDROMIC IMPULSES

As shown in Fig. 83 c an antidromic volley in the fibres of the pyramidal tract evokes a diphasic response in the motor cortex, a brief initial surface positivity reversing to negativity, the total duration of the diphasic complex being about 1·5 msec. (Woolsey and Chang, 1948). With stronger stimuli this spike is complicated by later waves which are attributable to slower conducting fibres.

The brief diphasic spike corresponds very closely to the focal potential generated by antidromic invasion of moto-neurones, where it has been established that the initial positivity is due to the soma and dendrites acting as a source to the sink formed by the antidromic impulse propagating up the motor axon, while the subsequent negativity signals the invasion of the soma and dendrites (Lorente de Nó, 1947b; Barakan et al., 1949; Lloyd, 1951a; Brock et al., 1952 c). Thus the cortical potentials gene-rated by an antidromic volley (Fig. 83 c) are explicable as an initial 'source' phase when the antidromic volley is traversing the axons and even the deeper parts of the soma and dendrites of the pyramidal cells, and a subsequent 'sink' phase when the antidromic invasion spreads up the pyramidal cells and involves the apical dendrites. Presum-ably the sources would then be the axons, now recovered from the antidromic invasion.

This interpretation is supported by the observation that, in contrast to the initial surface-positive wave, the surface-negative wave is depressed when the testing antidromic volley is preceded by a conditioning antidromic volley at intervals of many milliseconds. This effect is presumably attributable to axon-soma blockage, which is similar to that observed with motoneurones for a second antidromic impulse (Figs. 39, 41 A).

F. GENERAL CONCLUSIONS ON EVOKED
POTENTIALS

The attempt has been made to interpret the potentials evoked in the cerebral cortex on the basis of two sets of data: (i) the neurohistology of the cortex; (ii) the electrical responses that neurones have been observed to give in those regions of the central nervous system which have been most precisely analysed, in particular the spinal motoneurones. It may be claimed that satisfactory explanations have been offered for the cortical action potentials evoked by three different procedures: by direct electrical stimulation; by volleys in afferent fibres to the cortex; by antidromic volleys passing up efferent fibres from the cortex. However, with the first two methods of stimulation, complex and variable potential waves may follow the initial waves and further investigation is necessary before a comprehensive interpretation of these later waves is possible.

It would appear that the post-synaptic potential generated in neurones by synaptic bombardment provides the basis of most of the cortical potentials. When recorded by an intracellular micro-electrode the post-synaptic potential of a motoneurone has a duration of about 20 msec., which corresponds well with the durations of the initial potentials evoked in the cortex by direct stimulation or by afferent volleys. It is postulated that the subsequent potentials are also in large part attributable to such potentials evoked by impulses set up after one or more synaptic relays in the cortex, but of course these impulses themselves also presumably contribute to the recorded potentials, though usually they are so asynchronous that no corresponding spike potentials are detectable. Motoneurones also generate prolonged positive after-potentials, particularly after the passage of impulses over their surfaces (Fig. 37), but further analysis is desirable before any specific contributions of such potentials are recognizable in cortical responses.

G. SPONTANEOUS POTENTIALS OF THE CEREBRAL CORTEX

1. *Introduction*

The explanations that have accounted satisfactorily for the evoked potentials in the cortex should form the basis of an interpretation of the spontaneously occurring potentials. Thus the 'random spike' discharge described by Jasper (1949) would seem to be identical with the superficial response not only in time-course, but also in its localized character and in the ensuing surface positive wave that often follows random spikes above a critical size. This positive wave, like the deep response, propagates over the surface of the cortex and may be associated with discharge along efferent paths from the cortex. Again, since there is now good evidence that the rhythmic after-discharges following cortical stimulation are due to impulses circulating in closed self-re-exciting chains of cortical neurones, it is probable that the spontaneous cortical rhythms are likewise due to closed chain activity and not to an inherent rhythmicity of individual neurones (cf. Burns, 1950, 1951).

2. *The simplest model of a cortical network*

In the formulation of problems concerning activity in neuronal networks it is of value to have a model of the simplest possible network (Fig. 85 A; cf. Burns, 1951, Fig. 10). Each neurone is assumed to have only two excitatory synaptic knobs on its surface and its axon has only two excitatory knobs on two other neurones. Further it is assumed that the synaptic connexions so formed are of a pattern that allows the neurones to be arranged schematically in the rectangular net-like form of Fig. 85 A, where it will be noticed that there is virtual radial symmetry from any point and the possibility of indefinite extension in every direction. If each neurone receives and gives three synaptic contacts, a similar construction with radial symmetry is possible in a three-dimensional network (Fig. 85 B). As shown in Fig. 85 this construction would give alternating direction of transmission in the successive lines in any plane. Similarly, if each neurone gave and received n synapses, the pattern could be accommodated to an n-dimensional network.

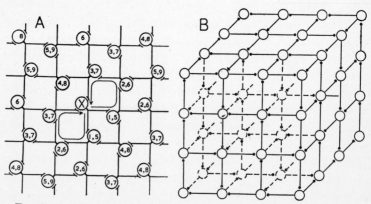

FIG. 85 A. Schematic representation of simplest type of neuronal network that would give indefinite outward spread from an excited focus and also provide closed self-re-exciting chains of all degrees of complexity. Each neurone is assumed to have only two synaptic knobs on its surface and in turn to have an axon which has only two knobs on other neurones. This net could be extended in any direction and there would be virtual radial symmetry from any point. For example, the numerals on each neurone give the number of synapses traversed in leading to its first (and second) activation in spread from neurone X, and the two simplest closed chains (4-neurone arcs) are shown by arrows. Next simplest are six 8-neurone arcs, then 12-neurone arcs, and so on (Eccles, 1951a).

FIG. 85 B. Diagram with similar conventions to those of Fig. 85 A but with each neurone receiving and giving three synaptic contacts. Unfortunately, owing to the complexity of the diagram, it has been impossible to draw the full connexions for more than a very few neurones. Moreover, only the surface neurones of the deeper layers (3 and 4) are shown. Connexions and cells in the depth of the cube are shown by broken lines. Note same convention as in Fig. 85 A, namely that in any plane the adjacent transmission lines alternate in direction.

It will be seen that even the extremely formal and simple neural network of Fig. 85 A potentially contains an enormous variety of neural circuits. For example, if neurone X discharges an impulse, the simplest circuits back to X are shown by the arrows, that is, there are two 4-neurone arcs, and next simplest are six 8-neurone arcs. In addition, it is potentially possible for a progressive invasion to spread over the net. The numerals on each neurone give the number of synapses traversed in leading to its first (and second) activation, there being with each a continued arithmetical progression of four due to the return circuits. In the operation of such a network it may be provisionally assumed that a single impulse impinging at a synapse on a neurone is adequate to generate the discharge of an impulse, and the probable value of 1·0 msec. may be assumed for synaptic delay plus conduction time to its own axonal terminals (the axonal length in the human cerebral cortex is very short for the majority of neurones). Thus, there are chains with possible circuit times of 4 msec., 8 msec., 12 msec., &c., which would form the so-called closed self-re-exciting chains. Actually, such short circuits would be most improbable on account of the prolonged (at least 0·1 sec.) and deep (for 20 msec. or so) depression that a neurone suffers after discharge of an impulse (cf. Fig. 41). In the next chapter these formal networks will be employed in calculations of the numbers of neurones which could be affected in a short interval of time by an impulse discharged by a single neurone.

3. *An explanation of the alpha rhythm*

The common alpha rhythm (Fig. 86) at about 10 a second is readily explained if it is due to circulation of impulses in closed self-re-exciting chains. After the discharge of an impulse a neurone develops a positive afterpotential (Fig. 37) and an associated phase of depressed excitability (Figs. 41, 46). Admittedly these effects have only been fully investigated in motoneurones, but they also have been shown to occur in the thalamic neurones on the somaesthetic sensory path (Marshall, 1941), and in sympathetic ganglia (Eccles, 1936). Recovery from deep depression begins at about 15 msec., and is almost complete by 100 msec. (Fig. 41).

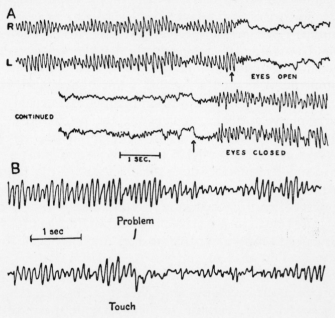

FIG. 86 A. Effect of opening eyes in suppressing the alpha rhythm recorded simultaneously from the right (R) and left (L) occipital poles of the human cerebrum , and return of rhythm on closing eyes. Note similarities of electro-encephalogram on the two sides (Jasper, 1941).
FIG. 86 B. Effect of brain activity in mental arithmetic and afferent stimulation in causing temporary cessation of alpha rhythm (Adrian and Matthews, 1934).

It may be assumed that, in neuronal networks such as in Fig. 85, paths of all durations are possible for circulating wave fronts of activity. The alpha rhythm is only observed in conditions of low cortical activity, inattention in man and light anaesthesia in animals (Adrian, 1947). Under such conditions it may be assumed that any neurone is subjected to a continuous bombardment of low intensity. Hence it is improbable that the synaptic excitation will be intense enough to generate the discharge of an impulse from a neurone that is deeply depressed after a preceding discharge. The probability of a discharge will rise as recovery progresses and will reach a maximum at about 100 msec. Later discharges are improbable because, if the synaptic bombardment is likely to excite the neurone, it will probably already have done so as recovery nears completion at about 100 msec. after the preceding discharge (cf. the argument on rhythmic responses of motoneurones on p. 177). Thus, at low background levels of activity, the most probable rhythm of neuronal discharge is at about 10 a second.

It is to be noted that fixed neuronal circuits are not invoked in this explanation. Successive discharges from the same neurone would be evoked by whatever impulses happen to bombard it at about 100 msec. after a preceding discharge. In this context it is interesting to recall that cortical bombardment from the medial thalamus at frequencies from 8 to 12 a second rapidly builds up a rhythmic response of the cortex which appears to be identical with the spontaneous alpha rhythm (Morison and Dempsey, 1942; Dempsey and Morison, 1942).

Two opposed explanations have been offered for the alpha rhythmic activity of neurones: that it is due to an inherent rhythm of the neurone (Bremer, 1938, 1949), or that it is due to circulation of impulses in closed neural chains. The present concept may be regarded as a compromise, for the frequency of the rhythm would be set by two factors, on the one hand the time curve of recovery of the neurones, which is a factor inherent in the neurone, and on the other hand the intensity of synaptic bombardment, which is a function of the activity of closed neural chains that have no fixed circuits. On a rather imperfect analogy it may be stated that there would be wide variations in the closed-chain pathways traversed by the successive impulses that were being discharged by any one neurone into the neuronal network of the cortex (cf. Fig. 85), much as is presumed to occur for the circulating impulses in auricular fibrillation (cf. Burns, 1951).

4. *Explanations of cortical potentials under various conditions*

Since Burns (1951) finds that, even in the unanaesthetized animal, the isolated cortical slab remains quiescent unless stimulated, it must be assumed that the normal cortical activity is dependent on the continued influx of impulses, which would largely come from the thalamus and other diencephalic centres. Hence, apart altogether from the problematical role of specific thalamo-cortical circuits in controlling the frequency of cortical rhythm, a continuous barrage of thalamo-cortical impulses is of the greatest importance in maintaining the intensity of cortical excitation at an adequate level for its continuous activity, i.e. the continuous input of impulses is necessary for sustaining the rhythmic cortical responses (cf. Morison and Dempsey, 1942; Dempsey and Morison, 1942). In the absence of such impulses the cortex is quiescent, but easily aroused to relatively prolonged activity (Burns, 1951, 1952); hence it is just below the excitatory level for continuous self-excitation.

It will be seen in Fig. 86 A that opening the eyes causes an immediate cessation of the alpha rhythm and that on closing the eyes the alpha rhythm rapidly returns (cf. Adrian and Matthews, 1934; Adrian, 1947). Similarly, any active cerebral process such as mental arithmetic (the eyes being kept closed) diminishes or abolishes the alpha rhythm while the calculation is in progress (Fig. 86 B). A similar result is produced by various sensory inputs (Fig. 86 B). In all such conditions the alpha rhythm is replaced by fast, small, irregular waves. Evidently the increased activation of the cortical neurones by the immense afferent barrage from the retina, or by intense mental activity prevents their phasic activation at about 10 a second. The intensity of synaptic bombardment must then be adequate to evoke neuronal discharges at intervals much shorter than the 100 msec. needed for a virtually full recovery of excitability (p. 255). Moreover it may be assumed that there are specific spatio-temporal patterns of neuronal activation, i.e. the random bombardment at low intensity is replaced by specific patterns of activation at high intensity (Adrian, 1947). Since the cerebral activity is recorded from the immensely complicated neuronal network immersed in a volume conductor (the tissue of the brain, skull, &c.), relatively high voltage waves would be expected only when large numbers of neurones are activated in phase, as is assumed for the alpha rhythm, while intense and finely patterned activity would give action potentials of negligibly small amplitude. It is relevant to note that a flickering light on the retina drives the cortical potentials in phase at frequencies up to 20 a second (Adrian and Matthews, 1934; Adrian, 1947). Here there is intense activation by the powerful visual pathway, but it is an input by synchronous bursts of discharges and not by a fine pattern of activation.

The cortical potentials recorded in sleep (cf. Jasper, 1941) may be explained in much the same way. In Fig. 87 the fine irregular waves of intense cortical activity give place firstly to an alpha rhythm, and this later fails in the drowsy state presumably because the intensity of impulses in the cortex is not even adequate to maintain the alpha rhythm. Finally large slow irregular waves appear with sometimes, as in the fourth record, brief bursts of rapid impulses (the so-called spindles). It is doubtful how far these delta waves are due to discharges of impulses by cortical neurones. It is possible that they are largely attributable to potentials generated in the cortex by barrages of impulses from sub-cortical centres (cf. pp. 245-9).

The application of severe mechanical trauma to the head results in a loss, often temporary, of all cerebral function, the state of concussion. There is an immediate complete cessation of all electrical activity, and recovery is signalled firstly by the appearance of waves characteristic of deep sleep or anaesthesia (Williams and Denny-Brown,

1941; Denny-Brown, 1945). Possibly the trauma causes mechanical damage to the synaptic mechanism, but damage to sub-cortical centres also presumably plays a part, cutting off the continuous input of impulses that is necessary

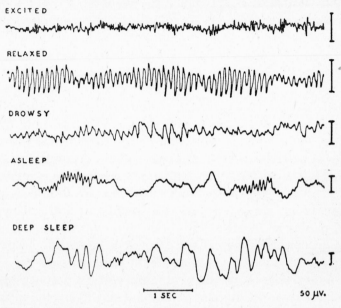

FIG. 87. Human electroencephalograms during excitement, relaxation (the alpha rhythm) and varying depths of sleep, with 'sleep spindles' in the fourth record and large delta waves in the lowest record (Jasper, 1941).

for cortical activity. The usual residuum of retrograde amnesia is good evidence of damage to the synaptic function of the cerebral cortex. It has already been suggested that mechanical trauma caused by swelling of chromatolysed motoneurones may be responsible for the temporary loss of monosynaptic activation (p. 214).

The present account has necessarily been restricted to the simplest type of cortical potentials and a few modifications thereof. It has been impossible adequately to cover the enormous amount of observational data collected during the last two decades (Jasper, 1941; Walter, 1950), and as yet no effective effort has been made to relate this data to activity of cortical neurones (cf. Whitteridge, 1950). From the above attempt it is evident that at present only general explanations can be offered for even the simplest conditions.

5. *The nature of the cortical potentials*

It is not possible as yet to assess accurately the contributions made by the various types of neuronal potentials to the spontaneous electrical responses of the cerebral cortex. Since post-synaptic potentials seem to contribute so largely to induced potentials, it may be assumed that they contribute largely to the spontaneous potentials also. But asynchronous spike potentials presumably also contribute substantially (cf. Adrian and Matthews, 1934), for they are observed to do so in monopolar records of potentials in the spinal cord. Finally the positive after-potentials of neurones cannot be neglected, for intracellular recording has established that they are much larger than with axons in peripheral nerve (cf. p. 118), and their duration of about 100 msec. is of the order of many spontaneous action potentials. Recording from pyramidal cells by intracellular micro-electrodes should enable a reliable assessment to be made of the composition of spontaneous cortical potentials, for it may be assumed that potentials led from the surface of the cortex are almost exclusively generated in pyramidal cells. Such cells, with their long vertical apical dendrites, are singularly well orientated for producing the 'open fields' of electrical currents (cf. Lorente de Nó, 1947*b*) that would give the surface potentials.

There is as yet no certain evidence on the nature of synaptic transmission in the cerebral cortex, but presumably it occurs by various transmitter substances, as seems to be the case in the spinal cord (p. 166). Feldberg (1950 *a*, *b*) has recently summarized the evidence which suggests that acetyl-choline is a transmitter substance. But it may be assumed, on analogy with the spinal cord, that other substances also act as transmitters. Clearly there is an immense and still almost unexplored field for investigation, but it may be doubted if much effective progress will be made until more is known about synaptic transmitter mechanisms in the much simpler regions of the central nervous system.

VIII

THE MIND–BRAIN PROBLEM

A. INTRODUCTION

WE now come to the problem posed at the beginning of these lectures which may be covered by the general question: Who are we? The answer of this question is according to Schrödinger (1951) 'not only one of the tasks, but *the* task, of science, the only one that really counts'. Much of the content of this chapter has appeared as a lecture published recently in *Nature* (Eccles, 1951*a*).

In attempting to see how far that question can be answered by use of the scientific method, we have firstly considered the body as a machine operating according to the laws of physics and chemistry, and on that basis explanations have been developed in the preceding seven chapters for the essential features of the known behaviour of the nervous system from the single peripheral nerve or muscle-fibre to the cerebral cortex. The physiology of the other systems of the body is of less immediate interest, because the special purpose of this inquiry is the nature of man, and it is the way in which the brain achieves liaison with mind that is the essence of the problem. It can be stated that all other systems, e.g. the circulatory system or the endocrine system, produce their effects on the 'mind' or 'self' secondarily to their direct or indirect action on the brain.

Since there is so much confusion in the usage of words in discussions of this kind, some preliminary statements are desirable. The term 'mind' will be restricted to 'conscious mind' in all its general operational field of perceiving, feeling, thinking, remembering, and willing. As such, mental phenomena are facts of experience, though each of us experiences the operations only of his own mind; for example, one can have awareness of being angry or happy by direct apprehension, apart from sensory perception. This definition is allied to one given by Russell (1948) who says, 'I hold that whatever we know without inference is mental'. A related statement is made by Russell Brain (1951): 'Mental experiences are the events in the universe of which we have the most direct knowledge.' Likewise Sherrington (1951) refers to mind as the 'non-sensual concept' saying,

Our mental experience is not open to observation through any sense organ.... (It) has no such channel of entrance to the mind.... The mental act of 'knowing'...is experienced not observed.

Again Sherrington says,

The one concept is just as much based on factual observation as is the other. Strictly, the observation and fact underlying the non-sensual concept and its 'I' are, we may think, more at first hand and more unimpugnable than are those underlying the spatial concept and its 'things'. The latter are after all an inference. If either as fact is more unquestionable than the other it should be the unextended 'I', being the more immediately established.

An instructive illustration of the problem of perception is given by the following series in a scale of perception from direct apprehension on the one hand, to the perception of a 'thing' in the external world on the other: self-consciousness or mere awareness of being; awareness of self in an emotional state, e.g. anger, happiness, or anguish; awareness of self having a vague pain, e.g. a headache or a deep visceral pain; perception of a sharp localized pain, e.g. a prick of the skin; perception of contact with an external object as signalled by, for example, touch, temperature, and pain receptors in the skin as well as by proprioceptive impulses from muscles, joints, ligaments, &c., the combined sensation giving us perception of a 'thing'; finally, perception of distant objects by means of such distance receptors as visual, auditory, and olfactory, though additional experience by direct contact is necessary in unfamiliar situations. It can be claimed that all transitions exist between any two successive members of this series, which is not surprising if every perception is dependent on a particular state of activity in the brain, as will be argued later (p. 280).

It has been maintained that the private and restricted nature of the observations relating to mind excludes mind from that class of observable phenomena which are publically observable and hence by general agreement regarded as facts of experience. But all observation is of course in the first instance just as private and restricted, the public character being given by symbolic communications between observers, in particular through the medium of language. The problems thus created in regard to perception will be postponed to page 280. Our present point is that, by means of this same method of communication, the private observation of one's 'self-consciousness' achieves public status, and may therefore be ranked as a fact of experience, as would likewise occur for awareness of self in an emotional state for example. Thus we report our mental experiences to others and discover that they have like experiences to report to us. Such procedures serve to assure us that our private experiences are not hallucinations, or more strictly we may say that hallucinatory experiences are discovered by this procedure. We may conclude that our mental experiences cannot be rejected as hallucinations, nor is solipsism a tenable explanation. Mental experiences are reported by all human beings with whom we take the trouble to communicate at the appropriate level.

It is the task of scientists to attempt to explain in principle all natural phenomena, or, alternatively, we may say that scientists attempt to discover the principles on which are based the explanations of all natural phenomena. The above argument establishes that mental experiences have the same validity that attaches to our perceptual experiences of 'things'. Hence the observations relating to mind, i.e. mental phenomena, are part of the experiences that a scientist should recognize as providing problems which are suitable for scientific investigation. It is a purely arbitrary and biased procedure to exclude such experiences from the fields of investigation where science may properly operate.

Another word that needs comment is 'self'. It will be used to connote a unity that derives from a linking by memory of conscious states that are experienced at widely different times—spread over a life-time. Thus, in order that a 'self' may exist, there must be some continuity of mental experiences and, particularly, continuity bridging gaps of unconsciousness. For example, the continuity of our 'self' is resumed after sleep, anaesthesia, and the temporary amnesias of concussion and convulsions. On the other hand mental experiences restricted to the so-called 'specious present' exist without such continuity of memory linkage. For example, in a brief interval of time we have a multitude of transient mental experiences that are not linked together and vanish past all recall in a few seconds. Perhaps such mental experiences are all that animals and very young children have, all their learning processes being subconscious and strictly speaking unremembered; hence they would lack a 'self' as defined above.

B. EXISTING HYPOTHESES RELATING TO THE MIND–BRAIN PROBLEM

The Cartesian dualism of mind and matter necessarily involved the problem of how mind and brain could interact in perception and in willed acts. It is easy of course to discredit Descartes's explanation of this interaction because at that time scientific knowledge of the brain was virtually non-existent and he developed a crude mechanical explanation. Many philosophers (for example, Burtt, 1932; Stout, 1931; Ryle, 1949) but by no means all (for example,

Broad, 1929; Popper, 1952) now argue that the hopeless difficulties of this problem have rendered untenable both dualism and the interactionist view of brain–mind liaison. On the other hand, many scientists (for example, Eddington, 1939; Sherrington, 1951; Adrian, 1947; Le Gros Clark, 1950) find in dualism and interaction the most acceptable initial postulates in a scientific approach to the problem of mind and brain. In such an approach the question arises: What scientific hypotheses may be formulated that bear in any way on the hitherto refractory problem of brain–mind liaison? It should be noted that such hypotheses would represent an extension of natural science to a field of non-sensual concepts, and even to a field outside the matter–energy system of the natural world, as has been convincingly argued by Sherrington (1951).

There are firstly various subsidiary hypotheses that have already been formulated, most notably by Sherrington (1951) and Adrian (1947), and which relate merely to the events in the brain when it is in liaison with mind. They may be formulated under four headings.

1. Mind liaison with brain occurs primarily in the cerebral cortex, though diencephalic centres may be also concerned, particularly as continued bombardment by impulses therefrom is necessary for sustaining activity in the cerebral cortex (cf. p. 256; Bremer, 1949; Burns, 1950, 1951). Presumably this explanation accounts for the finding that experimental interference with the diencephalon causes loss of consciousness (Penfield, 1937, 1947; Hess, 1948).

2. Only when there is a high level of activity in the cortex (as revealed by the electro-encephalogram) is liaison with mind possible. By activity is meant the active neuronal responses, i.e. generation of impulses in the neurones of the cerebral cortex (cf. p. 256). It would appear that unconsciousness supervenes instantly the activity is lowered below a critical level, as, for example, in anoxia, anaesthesia, concussion, sleep (cf. Fig. 87; Williams and

Denny-Brown, 1941; Blake, Gerard, and Kleitman, 1939; Denny-Brown, 1945; Brazier, 1948). Dreams are associated with bursts of electrical activity in the electro-encephalogram (Blake *et al.*, 1939).

3. The uniqueness of each percept is attributable to a specific spatio-temporal pattern of neuronal activity in the cortex (Adrian, 1947). In general, it may be postulated that any thought pattern in the mind has a counterpart in a specific spatio-temporal pattern of neuronal activity, which we may call the evocative neuronal pattern.

4. Memory of any particular event is dependent on a specific reorganization of neuronal associations (the engram) in a vast system of neurones widely spread over the cerebral cortex (Lashley, 1950). Lashley has convincingly argued that 'the activity of literally millions of neurons' is involved in the recall of any memory. His experimental study of the effects of cortical lesions on memory indicates that any particular memory trace or engram has multiple representation in the cortex. Furthermore, Lashley concludes that any cortical neurone does not exclusively belong to one engram, but on the contrary each neurone and even each synaptic junction are built into many engrams. The functional and structural bases of this conclusion have already been illustrated in a simple form in Fig. 76, which shows how the same neurone can be built into different patterns. A further observation is that activation of synaptic knobs leads to their increased functional efficacy (cf. p. 209), hence we may regard the engram as a patterned association of neurones which is called into existence, and maintained, by the increased synaptic function caused by usage (Eccles and McIntyre, 1952). There will thus be a tendency for this particular pattern of neuronal activity to be evoked by a particular predisposing or triggering neuronal activity and/or excitatory afferent input (Adrian, 1947). We may say that the remembered thought appears in the mind as its specific spatio-temporal pattern is being replayed in the cortex. It may therefore be

postulated that the initial development of effectiveness in certain synaptic junctions is a sequel to the primal event that is remembered, and this effectiveness is sustained and even enhanced by each subsequent replaying in the brain (and remembering in the mind). The role of reverberatory circuits has already been mentioned as a probable means of ensuring sufficient usage to give an effective residuum of synaptic efficacy (p. 226).

In summary we may state that these four hypotheses relate merely to the two sides of the apparently unbridgeable gulf, between the matter–energy system of the brain and the non-sensual concept of the mind, which has remained unassimilable into the matter–energy system (Sherrington, 1951). They give an account of the specific events in the brain which are linked with specific states in the mind, but say nothing concerning the 'how' of that linkage.

C. DYNAMIC PROPERTIES OF ACTIVE CEREBRAL CORTEX

There is one partial approach to the key problem of the 'how' of mind–brain liaison that hitherto has not been essayed. It arises from the questions: How does it come about that liaison with mind occurs only in special states of the matter–energy system of the cerebral cortex? Is there any special property of this system that places it in a separate category from all the remainder of the matter–energy, or natural world, and even from its own matter–energy system when it is not in this special state of activity? It is here contended that such a special property in outstanding measure is exhibited by the dynamic patterns of neuronal activity that occur in the cerebral cortex during conscious states, and the hypothesis is developed that the brain by means of this special property enters into liaison with mind, having the function of a 'detector' that has a sensitivity of a different kind and order from that of any physical instrument.

In the preceding chapter it has been shown that the spontaneous electrical activity in the cerebral cortex is explicable by impulses circulating in spatio-temporal patterns in the unimaginably complex neuronal network of the cerebral cortex, simplified fragments being shown in Figs. 77 and 78. There are some ten thousand million neurones in the human cerebral cortex (Thompson, 1899), and each is a node in the network whose strands are woven from the numerous processes (dendrites and axons) that provide the multiple synaptic contacts. Each node would be the convergent point of scores of paths and each in turn would project to scores of other nodes.

During inattentive, but awake, states the predominating rhythmic wave of the electro-encephalogram at about 10 a second (the alpha wave) indicates that the most probable circuit time of all the available neuronal circuits approximates to $0 \cdot 1$ sec., that is, to the period needed for almost complete recovery of each neuronal element (cf. p. 255), and, allowing 1 msec. for each link, it would be expected that roughly there would be about a hundred neurones in one such circuit. But to conceive of such an isolated circuit is an abstraction, for, as illustrated schematically in Figs. 76 and 85 each link of any one circuit is held in common with a great variety of other circuits. At each neuronal node in the network impulses either may be ineffective synaptic excitors and hence be extinguished (for example A_2 to B_1 and B_2 to C_1 in the upper diagram of Fig. 76), or may fuse in their influence by synaptic summation (for example A_2 plus A_3 on to B_2, B_2 plus B_3 on to C_2, &c., in the upper diagram of Fig. 76), so generating a new impulse that in turn disperses to other nodes, there likewise to be extinguished or fused. A third possibility is that summation may give synaptic excitation in excess of that necessary for generating an impulse (for example A_2, A_3, and A_4 on B_3 in the upper diagram, or

B1, B2, and B3 on C2 in the lower diagram of Fig. 76). Such excess excitation is valuable in withstanding inhibition (cf. p. 158) or the defection of an excitatory line (for example the B1 line on C2 and the A4 line on B3 in the respective upper and lower diagrams of Fig. 76). During inattention much of the rhythmic neuronal activity appears to be due to relatively synchronized responses of great numbers of neurones, adopting on the whole the dominant alpha rhythm. The responses of large numbers of neurones appear to be loosely coupled together without any specific patterning (Adrian, 1947).

When the brain is active, for example, during perception, mathematical calculation, or skilled action (Fig. 86), this formless or amorphous activity with its approximate synchronization of large groups of neurones is broken up (Adrian, 1947). We may interpret this as due to the formation of specific spatio-temporal patterns of activity in the neuronal net. Sherrington (1951) vividly and aptly pictures this net as an 'enchanted loom where millions of flashing shuttles (the nerve impulses) weave a dissolving pattern, always a meaningful pattern, though never an abiding one; a shifting harmony of sub-patterns'.

We have in imagination to develop the two-dimensional and formal net of Fig. 85 A to one of many dimensions, each node or neurone being at the confluence of many paths and itself projecting to many other nodes; and at each node the time of discharge is determined by the microscopic spatio-temporal pattern of the synaptic bombardments on its surface from millisecond to millisecond. The excitatory efficacy of the synaptic knobs of any one neurone will be related to its usage (cf. p. 209). Hence, in response to certain spatio-temporal patterns of afferent input into the cortex, the developing cortical patterns will to some extent be determined by this developed structural specificity, as has already been discussed in relation to memory (pp. 227, 266). That is, we are envisaging the pattern of activity in the cortex at any instant as being determined by two factors: (i) the immediate (and very recent) afferent input; (ii) the developed structural specificity (inherited and acquired).

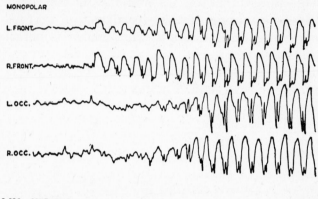

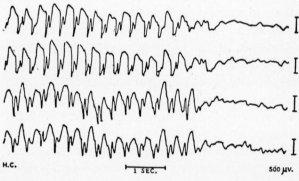

FIG. 88. Recording of electro-encephalograms before, during, and after a brief convulsive seizure. The sites of the four recording electrodes are indicated. Note that the large convulsive waves started in the frontal area some time before the occipital area was invaded. Note also the simultaneous involvement of corresponding areas on the two sides (Jasper, 1941).

It is to be noted that unconsciousness is an invariable accompaniment of a neuronal net that, as shown by the electro-encephalogram, is at rest or only active in low degree (Fig. 87) or active in a driven stereotyped way as in a convulsion of epilepsy (cf. Adrian, 1947; Fig. 88) or shock therapy, that is, the net as such is not in liaison with mind. Adrian (1947) even brings forward evidence that the part of the neuronal net giving the alpha rhythm is not in liaison with mind. It is important, therefore, to fix attention on the special properties of the neuronal net during the specific patterned activity (as indicated by a rapid, irregular, and low voltage electro-encephalogram) that occurs when there is liaison to mind. The special detector properties of such a neuronal net will be discussed in giving an explanation of the way in which the spatio-temporal patterns of activity could be modified by a 'mind influence' or 'will'.

D. HYPOTHESIS OF THE MODE OF OPERATION OF 'WILL' ON THE CEREBRAL CORTEX

1. *Introduction*

It is beyond the scope of these lectures to discuss philosophically the problem of the freedom of the will, but reference may be made to the excellent discussion by Campbell (1937). It is a psychological fact that we believe we have ability to control or modify our actions by the exercise of 'will', and in practical life all sane men assume that they have this ability. By stimulation of the motor cortex it is possible to evoke complex motor acts in a conscious human subject. The subject reports that the experience is quite different from that occurring when he 'willed' a movement. The distinction arises not in the differences between the movements, but in their different antecedents. In the one case there was the experience of having 'willed' an action which was missing in the other.

It is not here contended that all action is willed. There can be no doubt that a great part of the skilled activity devolving from the cerebral cortex is stereotyped and automatic, and may be likened to the control of breathing by the respiratory centres. But it is contended that it is possible voluntarily to assume control of such actions, even of the most trivial kind, just as we may within limits exercise a voluntary control over our breathing.

The principal grounds for the theoretical belief that this control is an illusion are derived from the assumptions that science gives a deterministic explanation of all natural phenomena and that we are entirely within this deterministic scheme. In this context reference may be made to the recent discussion by Popper (1950) in which he concludes that not only quantum physics but even 'classical mechanics is not deterministic, but must admit the existence of unpredictable events'. There are thus no sound scientific grounds for denying the freedom of the will, which virtually must be assumed if we are to act as scientific investigators.

2. *The neurophysiological problem of will*

An important neurophysiological problem arises as soon as we attempt to consider in detail the events that would occur in the cerebral cortex when, by exercise of 'will', there is some change in response to a given situation. We can say firstly that, assuming will to be operative, there will be a changed pattern of discharge down the pyramidal tract and this change must be brought about because there is a change in the spatio-temporal pattern of influences playing upon the pyramidal cells in the motor cortex. If the 'will' really can modify our reactions in a given situation, we have somewhere in the complex patterned behaviour of the cortex to find that the spatio-temporal pattern which is evolving in that given situation is modified or deflected into some different pattern.

For example a fragment of a spatio-temporal pattern in the neuronal network of the cortex is drawn in Fig. 89, the same conventions being adopted as in the neuronal path of Fig. 75 c. The arrows show the direction of propagation along the paths. The input, A, branches in an abortive path at B, while at C and D there are two other branches that coalesce at F giving mutual reinforcement by synaptic summation. After another branch at E, the path returns to confluence with A, thus forming a closed self-re-exciting chain. A possible modification of the spatio-temporal pattern by 'will' is shown by the broken lines. The branch at *B* is increased and is no longer abortive, while the branch at *C* is decreased so that it is abortive

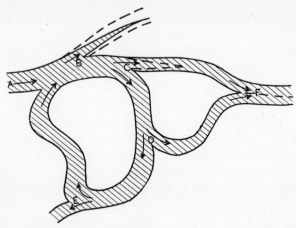

FIG. 89. Schematic diagram illustrating a fragment of a spatio-temporal pattern of neuronal activity in the cerebral cortex, and drawn according to the same conventions as those adopted in Fig. 75 c. It is assumed that by will the pattern can be altered as shown by the broken lines. Full description in text.

and the *D* branch is thus no longer reinforced by confluence at *F*. This is the sort of modification of the spatio-temporal patterns which the 'will' must bring about if it really is effective in exercising some control over action under given conditions.

3. *Quantitative aspect of spread of activity in neuronal networks*

The problem of the mode of action of the will can be simplified and sharpened by considering firstly the behaviour of a single neurone in the active neuronal network of the cortex. Suppose some small 'influence' were exerted at a node that would make a neurone discharge an impulse at a level of synaptic excitation which would otherwise have been just ineffective, that is, in general to raise the probability of its discharge. Such a discharged impulse would in turn have an excitatory effect on all the other nodes on which it impinges, raising the probability of their discharge, and so on. If we assume, as above, that the transmission time from node to node occupies 1 msec., then, even on the two-dimensional net of Fig. 85 A, a spread to a large number of neurones is possible in, say, 20 msec., a time that is chosen because it is at the lower limit of duration of discrete mental events.

In order to frame a precise problem we can firstly consider the schematic neuronal networks of Fig. 85 and make the postulates that at zero time a neurone (for example X in Fig. 85 A) is caused to discharge an impulse into the quiescent network and that activation of one synapse is adequate to cause a neurone to discharge an impulse. For the network of Fig. 85 A, the total number of neurones, N, caused to discharge impulses is given by the formula (Sawyer, 1951):

$$N = 2m^2 - 2m + 2 \qquad (12)$$

where m is the number of nodes traversed. In 20 msec. $m = 20$, the internodal time being assumed as 1 msec.; hence the number of neurones activated is 762.

On the same assumptions, but with a multi-dimensional network constructed according to the conventions of Fig. 85 (cf. p. 251), the number of activated neurones, N, is given, where m is large relative to n, by the general formula (Sawyer, 1951):

$$N \sim \frac{2^n}{n!} m^n. \qquad (13)$$

When $m = 20$ (i.e. within 20 msec.) and with $n = 3$ (Fig. 85 B), N is of the order 10^4. With $n = 4$ and 5 respectively, N is of the order 10^5 and 8×10^5.

These calculations are intended merely to give some indication of the large number of cortical neurones that could be affected by a discharge originating in any one. In order to apply them to our problem of how 'will' *could* act on the cerebral cortex, it is necessary to take into account the evidence that 'will' can act on the cortical neuronal network only when a considerable part of it is at a relatively high level of excitation (p. 265), i.e. we have to assume that, for 'will' to be operative, large populations of cortical neurones are subjected to an intensive synaptic bombardment and are stimulated thereby to discharge impulses which bombard other neurones. Under such conditions it may be conservatively estimated that, out of the hundred or more synaptic contacts made by any one neurone, at least four or five are *critically effective* (when summed with synaptic bombardments by other neurones) in evoking the discharge of neurones next in series. The remainder would be ineffective because the recipient neurones would not be poised at this critical level of excitability. This ineffectiveness of the recipient neurones would be attributable either to a too low level of excitation, or to a too high level, so that the neuronal discharge occurs in any case without this additional synaptic bombardment (cf. p. 268). Thus, as postulated below, at any instant the 'critically poised neurones' would be the effective detectors and amplifiers of the postulated action of the 'will'.

So long as the assumed number of *critically effective* synaptic excitatory actions by each neurone is kept at a value of about 4 or 5, it is probable that the conventions of the network structures of Fig. 85 give an approximate method of allowing for all the mass of feed-back connexions that occur in the closed-chain linkages of the cerebral cortex (Lorente de Nó, 1933, 1934, 1943). Further, since the cortex is approximately 3 mm. thick and the mean density of neurones 40,000 per sq. mm. of surface (Thompson, 1899), the spread to some hundreds of thousands of neurones can be treated as spreading indefinitely in all directions without serious restriction by the sheet-like structure of the cortex. Hence from Eq. 13 we may conclude that, when a region of the cortical neuronal network is at a high level of activity, the discharge of an impulse by any one neurone will have contributed directly and indirectly to the excitation of hundreds of thousands of other neurones within the very brief time of 20 msec.

An alternative method of calculation may be based on the experimentally observed rate at which a wave of excitation spreads radially through the cortical network from an artificially stimulated focus (cf. p. 237). The approximate all-or-nothing character of the spread (Burns, 1951) indicates that, during the invasion, a large proportion of the neurones are being excited to discharge impulses. Basing the calculation on the value of 50,000 neurones per sq. mm., which is the average for gyri (Thompson, 1899), an initially excited focus of 1 mm. radius would include about 150,000 neurones, and at the observed radial rate of spread of 20 cm. per sec. there would be a total invasion of about 4×10^6 neurones in 20 msec. The invasion of each neurone is attributable to the converging excitatory impulses that impinge on it and cause it to discharge. By means of the many synaptic terminals of its axon, each of the initially excited neurones thus contributes to the invasion of many neurones, and each of these in turn to many more, and so on for the twenty or so successive neurone discharges that occur along an outward spreading chain in 20 msec. Again we have the indication that an impulse discharged by any one neurone has in 20 msec. contributed directly and indirectly to the excitation of hundreds of thousands of neurones.

4. *A neurophysiological hypothesis of will*

As a restatement of the conclusion of the preceding section we may say that in the active cerebral cortex within 20 msec. the pattern of discharge of even hundreds of thousands of neurones would be modified as a result of an 'influence' that initially caused the discharge of merely one neurone. But further, if we assume that this 'influence' is exerted not only at one node of the active network, but also over the whole field of nodes in some sort of spatio-temporal patterning, then it will be evident that potentially the network is capable of integrating the whole aggregate of 'influence' to cause modification of its patterned activity, that otherwise (cf. p. 270) would be determined by the pattern of afferent input and its own inherent structural and functional properties. Such integration would occur over hundreds of thousands of nodes in a few milliseconds, the effects exerted on any and every node being correlated in the resultant patterned activity of the surrounding hundreds of thousands of neurones. Thus in general, the spatio-temporal pattern of activity would be determined not by two factors (cf. p. 270), but by three factors: (i) the micro-structure of the neural net and its functional properties; (ii) the afferent input; (iii) the postulated 'field of extraneous influence'. For example, in Fig. 89 the spatio-temporal pattern determined by factors i and ii is shown diagrammatically by the shaded structure bounded by the continuous line, while a possible modification by factor iii is indicated by the paths outlined by broken lines at B and C (cf. p. 273).

It can be claimed that no physical instrument would bear comparison with the postulated performance of the active cerebral cortex as a detector of minute 'fields of influence' spread over a microscopic pattern and with temporal sequences of milliseconds. The integration, within a few milliseconds, of 'influences' picked up at hundreds of thousands of nodes would be unique, particularly when it is remembered that the integration is no mere addition, but is exerted to modify in some specific way 'a shifting harmony of sub-patterns' of neuronal activity, achieving expression through the modifications so produced.

Thus, the neurophysiological hypothesis is that the 'will' modifies the spatio-temporal activity of the neuronal network by exerting spatio-temporal 'fields of influence' that become effective through this unique detector function of the active cerebral cortex. It will be noted that this hypothesis assumes that the 'will' or 'mind influence' has itself a spatio-temporal patterned character in order to allow it this operative effectiveness.

5. *The physical implications of the hypothesis*

When considering the manner in which mind could operate on matter, Eddington (1939) discussed two hypotheses.

(i) It was postulated that mind could control the behaviour of matter within the limits imposed by Heisenberg's Principle of Uncertainty (cf. Eddington, 1935). Eddington rejected this partly because the permitted range would be exceedingly small. Presumably he was thinking of an object as large as a neurone. However, a neurophysiologist would consider the much smaller synaptic knob as the key structure on which a 'mind influence' might work. The synaptic knob is approximately a sphere $1 \cdot 0 \, \mu$ in diameter (Haggar and Barr, 1950) and so would have a mass of about 5×10^{-13} gm. If, as Eddington implies, the uncertainty principle is applicable to an object of this size, then it may be calculated that there is an uncertainty in the position of such an object of about 20 A in 1 second and almost 3 A in 20 msec. Such distances are very small; but it is conceivable that the excitatory efficacy of a synaptic knob would be appreciably affected by an uncertainty of this order, for the distance between the knob and the subjacent membrane is probably less than 1,000 A, and the excitatory efficacy would be expected to be very sensitive to changes in this value on either a chemical or an electrical mechanism of transmission (cf. pp. 143, 166–7).

Furthermore, as shown above, minute 'influences' thus exerted on a large population of neurones would be rapidly integrated in the form of a changed spatio-temporal pattern of activity in the neuronal net. There is thus in the active cortex a mechanism that could effectively amplify by thousands of times minute effects exerted on the individual synaptic knobs, provided of course, as postulated above, these influences have some 'meaningful' pattern and are not random. It is therefore possible that the permitted range of behaviour of a synaptic knob may be adequate to allow for the effective operation of the postulated 'mind influences' on the active cerebral cortex. However, Eddington rejected this hypothesis for the further reason that it involved a fundamental inconsistency. First, behaviour according to chance was postulated in making a calculation of the permitted limits according to the uncertainty principle, then it was restricted by a non-chance or volitional action (the mind influence), which necessarily must be introduced if mind is to be able to take advantage of the latitude allowed by the uncertainty.

(ii) Hence, Eddington was led to an alternative hypothesis of a correlated behaviour of the individual particles of matter, which he assumed to occur for matter in liaison with mind. The behaviour of such matter would stand in sharp contrast to the uncorrelated or random behaviour of particles that is postulated in physics, and, as he stated, may be 'regarded by us as something "outside physics"' (Eddington, 1939).

Either of Eddington's hypotheses could form the physical basis of the neurophysiological hypothesis that has here been developed for mind–brain liaison. This latter hypothesis has the merits of relating the occasions when the mind can operate on the brain to the observed high level of neuronal activity during consciousness, and of showing how an effective action could be secured by a spatio-temporal pattern of minute 'influences'.

E. NEUROPHYSIOLOGICAL PROBLEMS IN PERCEPTION

The usual sequence of events is that some stimulus to a receptor organ causes the discharge of impulses along afferent nerve-fibres, which, after various synaptic relays, eventually evoke specific spatio-temporal patterns of impulses in the neuronal network of the cerebral cortex (cf. Adrian, 1935, 1947). The transmission from receptor organ to cerebral cortex is by a coded pattern that is quite unlike the original stimulus (cf. p. 189) and the spatio-temporal pattern evoked in the cerebral cortex would be again different. Yet, as a consequence of this cerebral pattern of activity, we experience a sensation (more properly the complex constructs called percepts) which are 'projected' to somewhere outside the cortex; it may be to the surface of the body or even within it, or, as with visual, acoustic, and olfactory receptors, to the outside world. However, the only necessary condition for an observer to see colours, hear sounds, or experience the existence of his own body is that appropriate patterns of neuronal activity shall occur in appropriate regions of his brain, as was first clearly seen by Descartes. It is immaterial whether these events are caused by local stimulation of the cerebral cortex or some part of the afferent nervous pathway, or whether they are, as is usual, generated by afferent impulses discharged by receptor organs (cf. Brain, 1951).

In the first instance, therefore, the observer will experience a private perceptual world which is an interpretation of specific events in his brain. This interpretation occurs according to conventions both inherited and acquired, that, as it were, are built into the micro-structure of the cerebral cortex, so that all kinds of diverse patterned sensory inputs are co-ordinated and linked together to give some coherent synthesis. We can regard the perceptual world of each observer as a kind of map built upon the spatial relations between objects of the external world, but also giving us symbolic information in terms of the secondary qualities, as is customary in ordinary maps with their conventions for rivers, towns, railways, &c. For example, colours, sounds, smells, heat, and cold as such belong only to the perceptual world of an observer and are merely symbolic of events in the physical world which they are quite unlike (cf. Brain, 1951; Smythies, 1951).

However, in various ways all the observers each with his private and unique perceptual world come to agree on the existence of a single physical world, which provides an explanation more or less complete and satisfactory of these manifold perceptual worlds. Personal experiment from earliest childhood onwards, and communication with other observers, are the standard procedures by which we learn to interpret a part of our private perceptual experiences as events in a single physical world common to other observers. Furthermore, the task of scientists has been to attempt to build up a progressively more valid or real physical world, i.e. a world more and more purified from the symbolic bias that is necessarily introduced into the perceptual world by the manner in which it is derived from the physical world. This is done by the discovery of rules by which the real physical world may be inferred from the symbolic data of the perceptual world, as for example the correlation of wave frequency in the physical world with colour of light in the perceptual world.

But the key problem in perception has remained so far beyond this discussion. We may ask: how can some specific spatio-temporal pattern of neuronal activity in the cerebral cortex evoke a percept in the mind?

In brain–mind liaison the traffic is both ways, from brain to mind in perception no less than from mind to brain in willed action. Existing knowledge of the brain provides the basis for the hypothesis relating to the operation of the mind on the brain. The reverse traffic—specific patterns of activity in the brain to percepts in the mind—is still more perplexing; but, presumably, if the mind can operate on dynamic spatio-temporal patterns of activity in the cortex, and itself have some spatio-temporal patterning (p. 278), it would be expected to be susceptible to operation in the reverse sense. That would be the operational path in all perception and in the memory of events. Perhaps electromagnetic interaction may provide a model that is valuable in this respect (Wisdom, 1952). For the interaction is symmetrical, from electrical to magnetic phenomena and vice versa, and yet each has a certain autonomy, just as is assumed for mind and brain. Yet this analogy can be helpful merely in giving a general picture of a reciprocal interaction. It throws no light on the 'how' of the interaction of brain and mind, for it would be gratuitous to assume any similarity in this respect.

F. AN HYPOTHESIS RELATING TO CONSCIOUSNESS

There is much experimental evidence indicating that unconsciousness occurs when the patterned activity of the neuronal net is depressed (p. 265). Unconsciousness is usually thought of as a failure of transmission from brain to mind, i.e. a perceptual failure, but the reverse trans- mission of mind to brain fails at the same time. In fact, in the experimental testing for consciousness of a subject, usually no attempt is made to distinguish between these two transmissions. The subject has to react in a discrimi- native way to various types of signals repeated in a random order. As consciousness is being lost, errors of reaction precede failure of reaction. Such errors could arise either on the afferent or efferent side, from brain to mind or from mind to brain, i.e. on either the transmitter or detec- tor functions of the brain.

When the cortex is at a low level of activity, it would function inefficiently as a detector, and presumably also as a transmitter, on account of the small proportion of neurones poised at the critical level of excitation and the consequent improbability of an effectively spreading in- fluence (cf. p. 275); hence an explanation is provided for the invariably observed failure of mind–brain liaison when the electro-encephalogram reveals depressed cortical acti- vity (p. 265). But it is of great interest that an explanation is also provided for the loss of consciousness in the stereo- typed and driven cortical rhythms that occur in convulsions, as may be seen in Fig. 88 (cf. Adrian, 1947), for the nodes of the cortical network would also then lack the critical poise as well as the specific patterning. In convulsions it may be assumed that the neurones are excited at a high level by the intense convergence of impulses travelling over stereotyped pathways.

It is further to be noted that according to the hypothesis only a part of the cortex is needed for liaison with mind. It may be that any area that is in the critically excited state will do. This corresponds to the clinical evidence that mind–brain liaison is not interrupted by excision of a large part of the cerebral cortex, or when a large part is occupied by activity that excludes liaison; for example, by a convulsion or even by alpha wave activity (Adrian, 1947). Maybe less than a tenth of the cortex in the right state of activity would be enough to give an effective mind–brain liaison.

G. GENERAL DISCUSSION OF HYPOTHESES

It will be sufficiently evident that the hypotheses here developed are of a fragmentary and tentative character, but it is hoped that they may be of value in further theoretical developments on mind–brain liaison. An outstanding problem for consideration would concern the postulated action of the mind in a spatio-temporal pattern, for presumably it must so act if it is to cause significant modification in patterned activity of the cortex. However, that problem would appear less formidable if there were a sufficiently rapid and detailed feed-back from brain action to mind, which in any case must be assumed for perception.

It will be objected that the essence of the hypotheses is that mind produces changes in the matter–energy system of the brain and hence must be itself in that system (cf. Schrödinger, 1951). But this deduction is merely based on the present hypotheses of physics. Since these postulated 'mind influences' have not been detected by any existing physical instrument, they have necessarily been neglected in constructing the hypotheses of physics, as was recognized by Eddington (1939). It is at least claimed that the active cerebral cortex could be a detector of such 'influences' even if they existed at an intensity below that detectable by physical instruments.

In this context it may be recalled that there are now extensive reports of well-controlled experiments that give evidence of a quite different kind that there is a two-way traffic between mind and the matter–energy system. Of particular significance for the above hypothesis of mind influence on brain are the psycho-kinetic experiments (Rhine, 1948; Thouless, 1951). These experiments as described indicate that very slight changes can be produced by mental concentration on moving physical objects such as dice, effects which are revealed only when statistical analysis is applied to relatively long series of trials. In particular, the striking decline in effectiveness with time (chronological decline) would seem to exclude all physical factors. There are, too, the very carefully controlled experiments on extra-sensory perception, where enormous odds have been established against an explanation attributable to chance—even 10^{35} to 1 (Rhine, Pratt, Smith, Stuart, and Greenwood, 1940; Rhine, 1948; Soal and Goldney, 1943; Soal, 1947). Though telepathic communication may be explicable as a direct influence of mind on mind, these results in part appear to be attributable to an interaction of physical events with mind, as indeed is also indicated by Eddington's second hypothesis (p. 279). It will be agreed with Rhine (1948) that, if the so-called psi-capacities (psycho-kinesis and extrasensory perception) exist, they provide evidence of slight and irregular effects which may be similar to the effects which have here been postulated for brain–mind liaison, where they would occur in highly developed form (cf. Smythies, 1951).

H. CONCLUSIONS

The present hypotheses would offer an explanation of the high development of matter–mind traffic in the active human cerebral cortex, the development including not only continuous operation but also exquisite subtlety in transmission. Both these features would receive explanation on the basis of the interlocking, integrating, and ever-changing pattern of activity formed by the multiple (ten thousand million-fold) detectors that exist in the cortex during consciousness.

It should be pointed out that, in this discussion of the functioning of the brain, it has initially been regarded as a 'machine' operating according to the laws of physics and chemistry. In conscious states it has been shown to be in a state of extreme sensitivity as a detector of minute spatio-temporal fields of influence. The hypothesis is developed that these spatio-temporal fields of influence are exerted by the mind on the brain in willed action. If one uses the expressive terminology of Ryle (1949), the 'ghost' operates a 'machine', not of ropes and pulleys, valves and pipes, but of microscopic spatio-temporal patterns of activity in the neuronal net woven by the synaptic connexions of ten thousand million neurones, and even then only by operating on neurones that are momentarily poised close to a just-threshold level of excitability. It would appear that it is the sort of machine a 'ghost' could operate, if by ghost we mean in the first place an 'agent' whose action has escaped detection even by the most delicate physical instruments.

But even if the hypotheses of brain–mind liaison here developed are on the right track, they are still extremely inadequate. For example, we have no concept of the nature of the mind that could exert these ghost-like influences. Again, the slight and irregular telepathic communications being excepted, it is not possible to answer the question: how is it that a given self is in liaison exclusively with a given brain? A further problem concerns the presumed spatio-temporal patterning of the mind (p. 278). Is this altered, as may be operatively desirable, as the microstructure of the brain alters with developing experience and the consequent storage of memories?

Recently Smythies (1951) has likewise been concerned to reconcile the neurophysiological knowledge of the brain with the direct experiences of 'self' and 'mind', and has developed a much more radical hypothesis than the one proposed here, for he postulates that there is a psychical world of mental experience in a higher dimensional space than the physical world. It would seem that this hypothesis is in many respects complementary to the hypotheses developed in this chapter, and that a synthesis is possible. But that development is beyond the present theme, which has been to show how recent neurophysiological developments make it possible to give in many respects a fairly adequate functional description of the nervous system that is based on physics and chemistry and that gives some clue as to the manner in which the gulf between mind and matter may ultimately be bridged. For the scientist there should be no doubt that the problem of interaction of mind and matter is a real problem and not a pseudo-problem arising from confusions in the usage of words. We may agree with Sherrington (1951) and Schrödinger (1951) that the 'nature of man' is the ultimate quest of science.

REFERENCES AND AUTHOR INDEX

Numbers in square brackets at end of each entry indicate the pages on which it is cited.

ACHESON, G. H., 1948, Physiology of Neuro-Muscular Junctions: Chemical Aspects. *Fed. Proc.* **7**, 447–57. [69, 78]

ADRIAN, E. D., 1935, *The Mechanism of Nervous Action.* University of Pennsylvania Press, Philadelphia, 103 pp. [179, 191, 279–80]

—— 1936, The Spread of Activity in the Cerebral Cortex. *J. Physiol.* **88**, 127–61. [232, 238, 244]

—— 1941, Afferent Discharges to the Cerebral Cortex from Peripheral Sense Organs. Ibid. **100**, 159–91. [246–7]

—— 1947, *The Physical Background of Perception.* The Clarendon Press, Oxford, 95 pp. [191, 254, 256–7, 265–6, 269–71, 279–80, 282–3]

—— and BRONK, D. W., 1929, The Discharge of Impulses in Motor Nerve Fibres, Part II. The Frequency of Discharge in Reflex and Voluntary Contractions. *J. Physiol.* **67**, 119–51. [174–5]

—— and MATTHEWS, B. H. C., 1934, Berger Rhythm: Potential Changes from the Occipital Lobes in Man. *Brain*, **57**, 355–85. [254, 256–7, 259]

ALANIS, J., and MATTHEWS, B. H. C., 1952, The Mechano-Receptor Properties of Central Neurones. *J. Physiol.* (in press). [114]

AMBACHE, N., 1951, A Further Survey of the Action of *Clostridium Botulinum* Toxin upon Different Types of Autonomic Nerve Fibre. Ibid. **113**, 1–17. [98]

ARVANITAKI, A., 1943, Réactions au stimulus anodique. Étude de la réponse électrique locale de signe positif. Observations sur l'axone isolé de Sepia. *J. Physiol. Path. Gen.* **38**, 147–70. [163]

—— and CHALAZONITIS, N., 1949, Catalyse respiratoire et potentiels bioélectriques. *Arch. Sci. Physiol.* **3**, 303–37. [2, 19]

BACQ, Z. M., and BROWN, G. L., 1937, Pharmacological Experiments on Mammalian Voluntary Muscle, in Relation to the Theory of Chemical Transmission. *J. Physiol.* **89**, 45–60. [70]

BARAKAN, T. H., DOWNMAN, C. B. B., and ECCLES, J. C., 1949, Electric Potentials Generated by Antidromic Volleys in Quadriceps and Hamstring Motoneurones. *J. Neurophysiol.* **12**, 393–424. [119, 121, 123–4, 249]

BARKER, D., 1948, The Innervation of the Muscle-Spindle. *Quart. J. Micr. Sci.* **89**, 143–86. [97]

BARRON, D. H., 1952, Some Factors regulating the Form and Organization of the Motor Neurones of the Spinal Cord. *Ciba Symposium* (in course of publication). [215]

BARRON D. H., and MATTHEWS, B. H. C., 1938, The Interpretation of Potential Changes in the Spinal Cord. *J. Physiol.* **92**, 276–321. [130–1]

BERNHARD, C. G., 1942, Isolation of Retinal and Optic Ganglion Response in the Eye of Dytiscus. *J. Neurophysiol.* **5**, 32–48. [179]
—— 1947, Slow Cord Potentials of Opposite Sign correlated to Reciprocal Functions. *Acta. Physiol. Scand.* **14**, Suppl. 47, 6. [136]

BERNSTEIN, J., 1902, Untersuchungen zur Thermodynamik der bio-elektrischen Ströme. Erster Theil. *Pflüg. Arch. ges. Physiol.* **92**, 521–62. [3, 84]

BISHOP, P. O., 1952. In course of publication. [148–9]

BLAIR, E. A., and ERLANGER, J., 1933, A Comparison of the Characteristics of Axons through their Individual Electrical Responses. *Amer. J. Physiol.* **106**, 524–64. [125]

BLAKE, H., GERARD, R. W., and KLEITMAN, N., 1939, Factors Influencing Brain Potentials during Sleep. *J. Neurophysiol.* **2**, 48–60. [265–6]

BODIAN, D., 1942, Cytological Aspects of Synaptic Function. *Physiol. Rev.* **22**, 146–69. [110–11]
—— and MELLORS, R. C., 1945, The Regenerative Cycle of Moto-neurones, with Special Reference to Phosphatase Activity. *J. Exp. Med.* **81**, 469–87. [214–15]

BOYLE, P. J., and CONWAY, E. J., 1941, Potassium Accumulation in Muscle and Associated Changes. *J. Physiol.* **100**, 1–63. [3, 9, 13]

BRADLEY, K., EASTON, D. M., and ECCLES, J. C., 1952. In course of publication. [152–4, 159, 168–70]

BRAIN, W. Russell, 1951, *Mind, Perception and Science*. Blackwell Scientific Publications, Oxford, 90 pp. [262, 280]

BRAZIER, M. A. B., 1948, Physiological Mechanisms underlying the Electrical Activity of the Brain. *J. Neurol. Neurosurg. Psych.* **11**, 118–33. [265–6]

BREMER, F., 1938, *L'Activité électrique de l'écorce cérébrale*. Paris, Hermann & Cie, 46 pp. [233, 255]
—— 1943, Étude oscillographique des réponses sensorielles de l'aire acoustique corticale chez le chat. *Arch. Int. Physiol.* **53**, 53–103. [246–7]
—— 1949, Considérations sur l'origine et la nature des 'ondes' cérébrales. *E.E.G. Clin. Neurophysiol.* **1**, 177–93. [233, 244, 255, 265]

BROAD, C. D., 1929, *The Mind and its Place in Nature*. Kegan Paul, London, pp. 674. [265–6]

BROCK, L. G., COOMBS, J. S., and ECCLES, J. C., 1951, Action Potentials of Motoneurones with Intracellular Electrode. *Proc. Univ., Otago Med. Sch.* **29**, 14–15. [114]

BROCK, L. G., COOMBS, J. S., and ECCLES, J. C., 1952a, The Recording of Potentials from Motoneurones with an Intracellular Electrode. *J. Physiol.* (in press). [51, 114–19, 128–33, 155–6, 162, 166]

—— —— —— 1952b, The Nature of the Monosynaptic Excitatory and Inhibitory Processes in the Spinal Cord. *Proc. Roy. Soc.* (in press). [114, 138–42, 172–3]

—— —— —— 1952c, Antidromic Propagation of Impulses into Motoneurones. *Ciba Symposium* (in press). [114, 119–28, 249]

—— —— —— 1952d. Unpublished observations. [139–42, 144–9, 156–60, 167, 197]

BRONK, D. W., 1939, Synaptic Mechanisms in Sympathetic Ganglia. *J. Neurophysiol.* 2, 380–401. [101–2]

—— TOWER, S. S., SOLANDT, D. Y., and LARRABEE, M. G., 1938, The Transmission of Trains of Impulses through a Sympathetic Ganglion and in its Postganglionic Nerves. *Amer. J. Physiol.* 122, 1–15. [99]

BROOKS, C. McC., DOWNMAN, C. B. B., and ECCLES, J. C., 1950a, After-Potentials and Excitability of Spinal Motoneurones following Antidromic Activation. *J. Neurophysiol.* 13, 9–38. [119, 128]

—— —— —— 1950b, After-Potentials and Excitability of Spinal Motoneurones following Orthodromic Activation. *Ibid.* 157–76. [136–8]

—— and ECCLES, J. C., 1947a, An Electrical Hypothesis of Central Inhibition. *Nature*, 159, 760–4. [155, 161–2]

—— —— 1947b, Electrical Investigation of the Monosynaptic Pathway through the Spinal Cord. *J. Neurophysiol.* 10, 251–74. [130–1, 134–6]

—— —— 1947c, A Study of the Effects of Anaesthesia and Asphyxia on the Monosynaptic Pathway through the Spinal Cord. *Ibid.* 349–60. [239]

—— —— 1948a, An Analysis of Synaptic Excitatory Action. *Ibid.* 11, 365–76. [135]

—— —— 1948b, Inhibitory Action on a Motor Nucleus and the Focal Potentials generated therein. *Ibid.* 401–16. [156, 159–60, 161]

—— —— 1948c, Inhibition of Antidromic Responses of Motoneurones. *Ibid.* 431–44. [161]

—— —— and MALCOLM, J. L., 1948, Synaptic Potentials of Inhibited Motoneurones. *Ibid.* 417–30. [161–2]

BROWN, G. L., 1937a, Action Potentials of Normal Mammalian Muscle. Effects of Acetylcholine and Eserine. *J. Physiol.* 89, 220–37. [70]

—— 1937b, Transmission at Nerve Endings by Acetylcholine. *Physiol. Rev.* 17, 485–513. [69–70, 100]

—— DALE, H. H., and FELDBERG, W., 1936, Reactions of the Normal Mammalian Muscle to Acetylcholine and to Eserine. *J. Physiol.* 87, 394–424. [70, 78]

BROWN, G. L., MCLENNAN, H., and PASCOE, J. E., 1952, Failure of Ganglionic Transmission after Postganglionic Nerve Section. Ibid. (in press). [215]

BUCHTHAL, F., and LINDHARD, J., 1939, Acetylcholine Block of the Motor End-plate and Electrical Stimulation of Nerve. Ibid. **95**, 59 P–60 P. [70]

BURGEN, A. S. V., DICKENS, F., and ZATMAN, L. J., 1949, The Action of Botulinum Toxin on the Neuro-Muscular Junction. Ibid. **109**, 10–24. [98]

—— and TERROUX, K. G., 1952, On the Negative Inotropic Effect in the Cat's Auricle. Ibid. (in press). [163–4]

BURNS, B. Deslisle, 1950, Some Properties of the Cat's Isolated Cerebral Cortex. Ibid. **111**, 50–68. [232–9, 251, 265]

—— 1951, Some Properties of the Isolated Cerebral Cortex of the Unanaesthetized Cat. Ibid. **112**, 156–75. [218, 232, 236, 238, 240–1, 244, 251, 255–6, 265, 276]

—— 1952. Personal communication. [235, 240, 256]

BURTT, E. A., 1932, *The Metaphysical Foundations of Modern Physical Science*. Routledge and Kegan Paul, London, 2nd ed., 343 pp. [264]

CAJAL, S. R., 1909, *Histologie du système nerveux de l'homme et des vertébrés*, Vol. I. Paris, Maloine, 986 pp. [110–12]

—— 1911, *Histologie du système nerveux de l'homme et des vertébrés*, Vol. II. Paris, Maloine. 993 pp. [221, 229]

—— 1934, Les Preuves objectives de l'unité anatomique des cellules nerveuses. *Trab. Lab. Inv. Biol.*, Madrid, **29**, 1–137. [110–11, 162]

CAMPBELL, B., 1945, The Distribution of Potential Fields within the Spinal Cord. *Anat. Rec.* **91**, 77–88. [160]

CAMPBELL, C. A., 1937, *In Defence of Free Will*. Glasgow University Press, 34 pp. [271]

DE CASTRO, F., 1932, Sympathetic Ganglia, Normal and Pathological, pp. 317–79. In *Cytology and Cellular Pathology of the Nervous System*, edited by W. Penfield, Paul B. Hoefer, New York. [99]

—— 1942, Modelación de un arco reflejo en el simpático, uniéndolo con la raíz afferente central del vago. Nuevas ideas sobre la sinapsis. *Trab. Inst. Cajal Invest. Biol.* **34**, 215–301. [99]

—— 1951, Aspects anatomiques de la transmission synaptique ganglionaire chez les mammifères. *Arch. Int. Physiol.* **59**, 479–513. [99]

CHANG, H. T., 1950, The Repetitive Discharges of Cortico-Thalamic Reverberating Circuit. *J. Neurophysiol.* **13**, 235–57. [248]

—— 1951, Dendritic Potential of Cortical Neurons produced by Direct Electrical Stimulation of the Cerebral Cortex. Ibid. **14**, 1–21. [229–31, 235–6, 240]

CHANG, H. T., and KAADA, B., 1950, An Analysis of Primary Response of Visual Cortex to Optic Nerve Stimulation in Cats. Ibid. **13**, 305–18. [246–7]

COLE, K. S., 1949, Dynamic Electrical Characteristics of the Squid Axon Membrane. *Arch. Sci. Physiol.* **3**, 253–8. [26, 36, 53]

—— and CURTIS, H. J., 1939, Electric Impedance of the Squid Giant Axon during Activity. *J. Gen. Physiol.* **22**, 649–70. [24–26, 37, 48–49]

—— —— 1941, Membrane Potential of the Squid Giant Axon during Current Flow. Ibid. **24**, 551–63. [42, 163]

CONWAY, E. J., 1946, Ionic Permeability of Skeletal Muscle Fibres. *Nature*, London, **157**, 715–17. [3]

—— 1947, Exchanges of K, Na and H Ions between the Cell and its Environment. *Irish J. Med. Sci.* Sixth Series, 593–609; 654–80. [3, 9]

COUTEAUX, R., 1945, La neurologie terminale au niveau de la synapse myo-neurale. *Compt. rend. soc. biol.* **139**, 641–3. [66–67]

—— 1947, Contribution à l'étude de la synapse myoneurale: buisson de Kühne et plaque motrice. *Rev. Canad. Biol.* **6**, 563–711. [66–67, 99]

—— 1951, Remarques sur les méthodes actuelles de détection histo-chimique des activités cholinestérasiques. *Arch. Int. Physiol.* **59**, 526–37. [71]

CREED, R. S., DENNY-BROWN, D., ECCLES, J. C., LIDDELL, E. G. T., and SHERRINGTON, C. S., 1932, *Reflex Activity of the Spinal Cord.* Oxford University Press, London, 183 pp. [109, 151, 175, 178, 182, 188, 191]

CURTIS, H. J., 1950, An Analysis of Cortical Potentials Mediated by the Corpus Callosum. *J. Neurophysiol.* **3**, 414–22. [246–8]

—— and COLE, K. S., 1940, Membrane Action Potentials from the Squid Giant Axon. *J. Cell. Comp. Physiol.* **15**, 147–57. [3, 9]

—— —— 1942, Membrane Resting and Action Potentials from the Squid Giant Axon. Ibid. **19**, 135–44. [3, 9, 13, 14]

DALE, H. H., 1937, *Transmission of Nervous Effects by Acetylcholine*, Harvey Lectures, **32**, 229–45. [69–70, 100]

—— FELDBERG, W., and VOGT, M., 1936, Release of Acetylcholine at Voluntary Motor Nerve Endings. *J. Physiol.* **86**, 353–80. [69–70]

DAVSON, H., 1951, *A Textbook of General Physiology.* Churchill, London, 659 pp. [115]

DEMPSEY, E. W., and MORISON, R. S., 1942, The Production of Rhythmically Recurrent Cortical Potentials after Localized Thalamic Stimulation. *Amer. J. Physiol.* **135**, 293–300. [246–8, 255–6]

DENNY-BROWN, D., 1929, On the Nature of Postural Reflexes. *Proc. Roy. Soc.* B, **104**, 252–301. [174, 178]

DENNY-BROWN, D., 1945, Cerebral Concussion. *Physiol. Rev.* **25**, 296–325. [257–8, 265–6]

DOWNMAN, C. B. B., ECCLES, J. C., and McINTYRE, A. K., 1951, Responses of Motoneurones undergoing Chromatolysis. *Proc. Univ. Otago, Med. School*, **29**, 4–5. [211]

—— —— —— 1952, Functional Changes in Chromatolysed Motoneurones. *J. Comp. Neurol.* (in press). [200, 211–15]

DRAPER, M. H., and WEIDMANN, S., 1951, Cardiac Resting and Action Potentials recorded with an Intracellular Electrode. *J. Physiol.* **115**, 74–94. [51]

ECCLES, J. C., 1936, Synaptic and Neuro-Muscular Transmission. *Ergebn. Physiol.* **38**, 339–444. [69–70, 100, 108, 174, 253.]

—— 1937, Synaptic and Neuro-Muscular Transmission. *Physiol. Rev.* **17**, 538–55. [69–70]

—— 1943, Synaptic Potentials and Transmission in Sympathetic Ganglion. *J. Physiol.* **101**, 465–83. [101, 105, 107]

—— 1944, The Nature of Synaptic Transmission in a Sympathetic Ganglion. Ibid. **103**, 27–54. [102–4, 106]

—— 1946, Synaptic Potentials of Motoneurones. *J. Neurophysiol.* **9**, 87–120. [111, 113, 130–1, 134, 167, 181]

—— 1947, Acetylcholine and Synaptic Transmission in the Spinal Cord. Ibid. **10**, 197–204. [167]

—— 1948, Conduction and Synaptic Transmission in the Nervous System. *Ann. Rev. Physiol.* **10**, 93–116. [3, 91, 93, 163]

—— 1949, A Review and Restatement of the Electrical Hypotheses of Synaptic Excitatory and Inhibitory Action. *Arch. Sci. Physiol.* **3**, 567–84. [89]

—— 1950, The Responses of Motoneurones. *Brit. Med. Bull.* **6**, 304–11. [109, 119]

—— 1951*a*, Hypotheses relating to the Brain-Mind Problem. *Nature*, **168**, 53–57. [252, 261]

—— 1951*b*, Interpretation of Action Potentials evoked in the Cerebral Cortex. *E.E.G. and Clin. Neurophysiol.* **3**, 449–64. [233–7, 245–8]

—— and HOFF, H. E., 1932, The Rhythmic Discharge of Motoneurones. *Proc. Roy. Soc.* B, **110**, 483–514. [175, 178]

—— KATZ, B., and KUFFLER, S. W., 1941, Nature of the 'Endplate Potential' in Curarized Muscle. *J. Neurophysiol.* **4**, 362–87. [70, 76, 82, 92]

—— —— —— 1942, Effect of Eserine on Neuromuscular Transmission. Ibid. **5**, 211–30. [80–81]

—— and KUFFLER, S. W., 1941*a*, Initiation of Muscle Impulses at Neuro-muscular Junction. *J. Neurophysiol.* **4**, 402–17. [70]

—— —— 1941*b*, The Endplate Potential during and after the Muscle Spike Potential. Ibid. **4**, 486–506. [125]

ECCLES, J. C., and MACFARLANE, W. V., 1949, Actions of Anti-
Cholinesterases on Endplate Potential of Frog Muscle. Ibid. **12**,
59–80. [80–81, 90–93]
—— and McINTYRE, A. K., 1951, Plasticity of Mammalian Monosynaptic Reflexes. *Nature*, **167**, 466–8. [203–7, 219, 226]
—— —— 1952, The Effects of Disuse and of Activity on Mammalian Spinal Reflexes. In course of publication. [200, 203–9, 219,
226, 266]
—— and MALCOLM, J. L., 1946, Dorsal Root Potentials of the Spinal
Cord. *J. Neurophysiol.* **9**, 139–60. [124]
—— and O'CONNOR, W. J., 1941, Abortive Impulses at the Neuro-
muscular Junction. *J. Physiol.* **100**, 317–28. [76]
—— and RALL, W., 1951a, Repetitive Monosynaptic Activation of
Motoneurones. *Proc. Roy. Soc.* B, 475–98. [144–7]
—— —— 1951b, Effects Induced in a Monosynaptic Reflex Path by
its Activation. *J. Neurophysiol.* **14**, 353–76. [136–8, 194–9]
—— —— 1952, Unpublished observations. [199]
—— and SHERRINGTON, C. S., 1930, Numbers and Contraction-Values
of Individual Motor-Units examined in some Muscles of the Limb.
Proc. Roy. Soc. B, **106**, 326–57. [97]
ECCLES, R. M., 1952a, Action Potentials of Isolated Mammalian Sympathetic Ganglia. *J. Physiol.* **117**, 181–95. [105, 201]
—— 1952b, Responses of Isolated Curarized Sympathetic Ganglia.
Ibid. 196–217. [106–7]
EDDINGTON, A. S., 1935, *New Pathways in Science.* Cambridge University Press, 333 pp. [278]
—— 1939, *The Philosophy of Physical Science.* Cambridge University
Press, 230 pp. [265, 278–9, 283]
EMMELIN, N. G., and MACINTOSH, F. C., 1948, Some Conditions
affecting the Release of Acetylcholine in Sympathetic Ganglia and
Skeletal Muscles. *Acta. Physiol. Scand. Suppl.* **53**, 17–18. [100]
—— —— 1952. Personal communication. [100–1]
ERLANGER, J., 1937, *Electrical Signs of Nervous Activity* by J. Erlanger
and H. S. Gasser. Univ. Penn. Press, Philadelphia, 221 pp.
[55–56]
FATT, P., 1950, The Electromotive Action of Acetylcholine at the Motor
End-plate. *J. Physiol.* **111**, 408–22. [84]
—— and KATZ, B., 1950, Membrane Potentials at the Motor End-
plate. Ibid. 46–47 P. [65, 73]
—— —— 1951, An Analysis of the End-plate Potential recorded with
an Intra-Cellular Electrode. Ibid. **115**, 320–70. [25–27, 49, 65–70,
72–75, 77–89, 96]
—— —— 1952a, Spontaneous Subthreshold Activity at Motor Nerve
Endings. Ibid. **117**, 109–128. [81, 89]

FATT, P. and KATZ, B., 1952*b*, The Electric Activity of the Motor End-plate. *Proc. Roy. Soc.* B (in press). [65, 81, 83–89]

—— —— 1952*c*. Personal communication. [26, 98–99, 164]

FELDBERG, W., 1945, Present Views on the Mode of Action of Acetylcholine in the Central Nervous System. *Physiol. Rev.* **25**, 596–642. [67, 95, 167–8]

—— 1950*a*, The Role of Acetylcholine in the Central Nervous System. *Brit. Med. Bull.* **6**, 312–21. [67, 95, 167–8, 171, 259]

—— 1950*b*, Gegenwärtige Probleme auf dem Gebeit der chemischen Übertragung von Nervenwirkungen. *Arch. Exp. Path. u. Pharmakol.* **212**, 64–88. [67, 167–8, 259]

—— 1952, Contribution to Royal Society Discussion on Excitation and Inhibition. *Proc. Roy. Soc.* B (in press). [171]

—— GRAY, J., and PERRY, W. L. M., 1952. Personal communication. [168]

FENN, W. O., and GERSCHMAN, R., 1950, The Loss of Potassium from Frog Nerves in Anoxia and other Conditions. *J. Gen. Physiol.* **33**, 195–203. [23]

FESSARD, A., and POSTERNAK, J., 1950, Les mécanismes élémentaires de la transmission synaptique. *Journ. de Physiol.* **42**, 319–446. [65, 109]

FILLENZ, M., and HANAFIN, M., 1947, Acetylcholine and Neuro-Muscular Transmission. *J. Neurophysiol.* **10**, 189–95. [81, 93]

FRANKENHAUSER, B., 1952, Saltatory Conduction in Myelinated Nerve Fibres. *J. Physiol.* (in press). [57–59]

FULTON, J. F., 1949, *Physiology of the Nervous System*, 3rd ed. New York, Oxford University Press, 667 pp. [228–9]

GASSER, H. S., 1937, *Electrical Signs of Nervous Activity* by J. Erlanger and H. S. Gasser. Univ. Penn. Press. Philadelphia. 221 pp. [54, 123, 125]

—— and GRUNDFEST, H., 1936, Action and Excitability of Mammalian A Fibres. *Amer. J. Physiol.* **117**, 113–33. [117–18, 123]

GERARD, R. W., 1941, The Interaction of Neurones. *Ohio J. Sci.*, **41**, 160–72. [162]

—— 1949, Physiology and Psychiatry. *Amer. J. Psychiat.* **106**, 161–73. [218, 226]

GESELL, R., and HANSEN, E. I., 1945, Anticholinesterase Activity of Acid as a Biological Instrument of Nervous Integration. *Amer. J. Physiol.* **144**, 126–63. [162]

—— —— and SISKEL, J., 1947, On the Electrotonic Nature of Stimulation, Inhibition, Summation, and After-Discharge of Nerve Centers. Ibid. **148**, 515–29. [162]

GIBSON, W. C., 1940, Degeneration and Regeneration of Sympathetic Synapses. *J. Neurophysiol.* **3**, 237–47. [99]

GÖPFERT, H., and SCHAEFER, H., 1938, Über den direkt und indirekt erregten Aktionsstrom und die Funktion der motorischen Endplatte. *Pflüg. Arch. ges. Physiol.*, **239**, 597–619. [70]

GOLDMAN, D. E., 1943, Potential, Impedance and Rectification in Membranes. *J. Gen. Physiol.* **27**, 37–60. [14]

GRAHAM, J., and GERARD, R. W., 1946, Membrane Potentials and Excitation of Impaled Single Muscle Fibres. *J. Cell. Comp. Physiol.* **28**, 99–117. [9]

GRANIT, R., 1947, *Sensory Mechanisms of the Retina*. Oxford University Press, London, 412 pp. [179]

—— 1950, Reflex Self-Regulation of Muscle Contraction and Autogenetic Inhibition. *J. Neurophysiol,* **13**, 351–72. [111, 153–4, 188]

—— 1952, Aspects of Excitation and Inhibition in the Retina. *Proc. Roy. Soc.* B (in press). [154, 179]

—— and KAADA, B., 1952, Influence of Stimulation of Central Nervous Structures on Muscle-Spindles in Cat. In course of publication. [187]

—— and STRÖM, G., 1951, Autogenetic Modulation of Excitability of Single Ventral Horn Cells. *J. Neurophysiol.* **14**, 113–32. [137–8, 153–4, 188]

GRAY, J. A. B., and MALCOLM, J. L., 1950, The Initiation of Nerve Impulses by Mesenteric Pacinian Corpuscles. *Proc. Roy. Soc.* B, **137**, 96–114. [179]

GRUNDFEST, H., 1940, Bioelectric Potentials. *Ann. Rev. Physiol.* **2**, 213–42. [54, 117–18, 123, 125]

GUTMANN, E., and SANDERS, F. K., 1943, Recovery of Fibre Numbers and Diameters in the Regeneration of Peripheral Nerves. *J. Physiol.* **101**, 489–518. [204]

—— and YOUNG, J. Z., 1944, The Re-innervation of Muscle after Various Periods of Atrophy. *J. Anat.* **78**, 15–43. [66–67, 96]

HAGBARTH, K. E., 1952, Excitatory and Inhibitory Skin Areas for Flexor and Extensor Motoneurones. *Acta. Physiol. Scand.* **26**, Suppl. 94, 58 pp. [160, 183]

HAGGAR, R. A., and BARR, M. L., 1950, Quantitative Data on the Size of Synaptic End-Bulbs in the Cat's Spinal Cord. *J. Comp. Neurol.* **93**, 17–35. [110, 162, 167]

HARTLINE, H. K., 1941, *The Neural Mechanisms of Vision*. Harvey Lectures, 39–68. [179]

—— and GRAHAM, C. H., Nerve Impulses from Single Receptors in the Eye of *Limulus*. *J. Cell. Comp. Physiol.* **1**, 277–95. [179]

HEBB, D. O., 1949, *The Organization of Behaviour*. New York, John Wiley & Sons, 335 pp. [218, 221, 225–6]

HELLAUER, H. F., and UMRATH, K., 1948, Über die Aktionssubstanz der sensiblen Nerven. *Pflüg Arch. ges. Physiol.* **249**, 619–30. [167]

HESS, W. R., 1948, *Die funktionelle Organisation des vegetativen Nerven-systems*. Benno Schwabe, Basel, 226 pp. [265]

HILGARD, E. R., and MARQUIS, D. G., 1940, *Conditioning and Learning*. New York, D. Appleton, Century Company, 429 pp. [218, 225]

HILL, D. K., 1950, The Volume Change resulting from Stimulation of a Giant Nerve Fibre. *J. Physiol.* 111, 304–27. [56, 198]

HODGKIN, A. L., 1938, The Subthreshold Potentials in a Crustacean Nerve Fibre. *Proc. Roy. Soc.* B, 126, 87–121. [53–4, 163]

—— 1947, The Membrane Resistance of a Non-Medullated Nerve Fibre. *J. Physiol.* 106, 305–18. [24, 25]

—— 1948, The Local Electric Changes associated with Repetitive Action in a Non-Medullated Axon. Ibid. 107, 165–81. [181]

—— 1950, Conduction of the Nervous Impulse: Some Recent Experiments. *Brit. Med. Bull.* 6, 322–5. [3]

—— 1951, The Ionic Basis of Electrical Activity in Nerve and Muscle. *Biol. Rev.* 26, 339–409. [3–5, 8, 10–13, 17–24, 32–36, 49–53, 55, 57–59, 62–64, 123]

—— and HUXLEY, A. F., 1939, Action Potentials Recorded from inside a Nerve Fibre. *Nature*, London, 144, 710. [3, 9]

—— —— 1945, Resting and Action Potentials in Single Nerve Fibres, *J. Physiol.* 104, 176–95. [3, 9, 51]

—— —— 1947, Potassium Leakage from an Active Nerve Fibre. Ibid. 106, 341–67. [34, 36, 62]

—— —— 1952a, Currents Carried by Sodium and Potassium Ions through the Membrane of the Giant Axon of *Loligo*. Ibid. 116, 449–72. [22, 36–43]

—— —— 1952b, The Components of Membrane Conductance in the Giant Axon of *Loligo*. Ibid. 473–96. [36, 44–46]

—— —— 1952c, The Dual Effect of Membrane Potential on Sodium Conductance in the Giant Axon of *Loligo*. Ibid. 497–506. [36, 54–56]

—— —— 1952d, A Quantitative Description of Membrane Current and its Application to Conduction and Excitation in Nerve. *J. Physiol.* (in press). [22, 36, 46–52, 118–19]

—— —— 1952e, Contribution to Royal Society Discussion on 'Excitation and Inhibition'. *Proc. Roy. Soc.* B (in press). [22, 39–43, 46–52, 118–19]

—— —— and KATZ, B., 1949, Ionic Currents underlying Activity in the Giant Axon of the Squid. *Arch. Sci. Physiol.* 3, 129–50. [36, 53–54, 61–62, 163]

—— —— —— 1952, Measurement of Current-Voltage Relations in the Membrane of the Giant Axon of *Loligo*. *J. Physiol.* 116, 424–48. [36–40, 42, 53–54]

—— and KATZ, B., 1949, The Effect of Sodium Ions on the Electrical

Activity of the Giant Axon of the Squid. Ibid. **108**, 37–77. [3, 9, 13, 14, 20, 22, 32–33, 47]

HODGKIN, A. L., and KEYNES, R. D., 1950, The Mobility of Potassium in the Axis Cylinder of a Giant Axon. Abstr. *XVIIIth Int. Physiol. Congr.* 258. [4, 8]

—— and RUSHTON, W. A. H., 1946, The Electrical Constants of a Crustacean Nerve Fibre. *Proc. Roy. Soc.* B, **133**, 444–79. [24–27, 72, 163]

HOFF, E. C., HOFF, H. E., and SHEEHAN, D., 1934, Reflex Interruption of Rhythmic Discharge. *J. Physiol.* **83**, 185–91. [178]

HOFFMAN, H., 1950, Local Re-innervation in Partially Denervated Muscle: A Histo-Physiological Study. *Aust. J. Exp. Biol. Med. Sci.* **28**, 383–97. [215]

HOLTON, P., and PERRY, W. L. M., 1951, On the Transmitter responsible for Antidromic Vasodilatation in the Rabbit's Ear. *J. Physiol.* **114**, 240–51. [167]

HOUSEHOLDER, A. S., and LANDAHL, H. D., 1945, *Mathematical Biophysics of the Central Nervous System*. Bloomington (Indiana), Principia Press, 124 pp. [218]

HUNT, C. C., 1951, The Reflex Activity of Mammalian Small-Nerve Fibres. *J. Physiol.* **115**, 456–69. [111, 186–7]

—— 1952, Drug Effects on Mammalian Muscle-Spindles. *Fed. Proc.* **11**, 75. [97]

—— and KUFFLER, S. W., 1950, Pharmacology of the Neuromuscular Junction. *Pharm. Rev.* **2**, 96–120. [69, 97]

—— —— 1951a, Further Study of Efferent Small-Nerve Fibres to Mammalian Muscle Spindles. Multiple Spindle Innervation and Activity during Contraction. *J. Physiol.* **113**, 283–97. [97–98, 111, 179, 183–5]

—— —— 1951b, Stretch Receptor Discharges during Muscle Contraction. Ibid. 298–315. [111, 147, 179, 183–5, 188]

HURSH, J. B., 1939, Conduction Velocity and Diameter of Nerve Fibers. *Amer. J. Physiol.* **127**, 131–9. [60]

HUXLEY, A. F., and STAMPFLI, R., 1949, Evidence for Saltatory Conduction in Peripheral Myelinated Nerve Fibres. *J. Physiol.* **108**, 315–39. [57–59, 110]

—— —— 1951a, Direct Determination of Membrane resting Potential and Action Potential in Single Myelinated Nerve Fibres. Ibid. **112**, 476–95. [29, 57]

—— —— 1951b, Effect of Potassium and Sodium on Resting and Action Potentials of Single Myelinated Nerve Fibres. Ibid. 496–508. [13, 14, 32, 57–59]

ING, H. R., 1936, The Curariform Action of Onium Salts. *Physiol. Rev.* **16**, 527–44. [95]

JASPER, H. H., 1941, Electroencephalography. Chapter 14 in: Penfield, W., and Erickson, T. C., *Epilepsy and Cerebral Localization.* Springfield, Ill., Charles C. Thomas, 623 pp. [254, 257–8, 270]

—— 1949, Electrical Signs of Epileptic Discharge. *E.E.G. Clin. Neurophysiol.* 1, 11–18. [251]

JEFFRIES, G., 1952. In course of publication. [76, 94–95]

JOB, C., and LUNDBERG, A., 1952, Presynaptic Facilitation in the Sympathetic Ganglion of the Cat. *J. Physiol.* (in press). [107, 200]

JUNG, R., and TÖNNIES, J., 1950, Hirnelektrische Untersuchungen über Entstehung und Erhaltung von Krampfentladungen: Die Vorgänge am Reizort und die Bremsfähigkeit des Gehirns. *Arch. Psych. u. Zeits. Neurol.* 185, 701–35. [244]

KATO, G., 1936, On the Excitation, Conduction and Narcotisation of Single Nerve Fibres. *Cold Spr. Harb. Symp. Quant. Biol.* 4, 202–13. [57]

KATZ, B., 1937, Experimental Evidence for a Non-Conducted Response of Nerve to Subthreshold Stimulation. *Proc. Roy. Soc.* B, 124, 244–76. [53]

—— 1939, *Electric Excitation of Nerve.* Oxford University Press, London, 151 pp. [27, 55]

—— 1942, Impedance Changes in Frog's Muscle Associated with Electrotonic and 'Endplate' Potentials. *J. Neurophysiol.* 5, 169–84. [49, 86]

—— 1947b, The Effect of Electrolyte Deficiency on the Rate of Conduction in a Single Nerve Fibre. *J. Physiol.* 106, 411–17. [28]

—— 1948, The Electrical Properties of the Muscle Fibre Membrane. *Proc. Roy. Soc.* B, 135, 506–34. [24–26, 76, 163]

—— 1949, Neuro-Muscular Transmission in Invertebrates. *Biol. Rev.* 24, 1–20. [98–99]

—— 1950a, Action Potentials from a Sensory Nerve Ending. *J. Physiol.* 111, 248–60. [180]

—— 1950b, Depolarization of Sensory Terminals and the Initiation of Impulses in the Muscle-Spindle. Ibid. 261–82. [179–81]

—— 1952, The Properties of the Nerve Membrane and its Relation to Propagation of Impulses. *Sym. Soc. Exp. Biol.* (in press). [3]

—— and KUFFLER, S. W., 1946, Excitation of the Nerve-Muscle System in Crustacea. *Proc. Roy. Soc.* B, 133, 374–89. [98]

KEYNES, R. D., 1951a, The Leakage of Radioactive Potassium from Stimulated Nerve. *J. Physiol.* 113, 99–114. [34]

—— 1951b, The Ionic Movements during Nervous Activity, Ibid. 114, 119–50. [8, 15–17, 19, 33–36, 47]

—— 1951c, *The Role of Electrolytes in Excitable Tissues.* Publ. Inst. Biol., Univ. Brasil, Rio de Janeiro. [3, 8, 16–17, 22–23, 47]

KEYNES, R. D., and LEWIS, P. R., 1951*a*, The Resting Exchange of Radioactive Potassium in Crab Nerve. *J. Physiol.* **113**, 73–98. [8, 17, 34]

—— —— 1951*b*, The Sodium and Potassium Content of Cephalopod Nerve Fibres. Ibid. **114**, 151–82. [7, 15, 34, 47, 56]

KOELLE, G. B., 1950, The Histochemical Differentiation of Types of Cholinesterases and their Localizations in Tissues of the Cat. *J. Pharm. Exp. Therap.* **100**, 158–79. [71]

—— 1951, The Elimination of Enzymatic Diffusion Artifacts in the Histochemical Localization of Cholinesterases and a Survey of their Cellular Distributions. Ibid. **103**, 153–71. [71, 102–3]

KONORSKI, J., 1948, *Conditioned Reflexes and Neuron Organization.* Cambridge University Press, Cambridge, 267 pp. [193, 217–19, 224]

—— 1950, The Mechanisms of Learning. *Symp. Soc. Exp. Biol.* **4**, 409–31. [193, 217–19]

KRISTIANSEN, K., and COURTOIS, G., 1949, Rhythmic Electrical Activity from Isolated Cerebral Cortex. *E.E.G. Clin. Neurophysiol.* **1**, 265–72. [233]

KROGH, A., 1946, The Active and Passive Exchanges of Inorganic Ions through the Surfaces of Living Cells and through Living Membranes generally. *Proc. Roy. Soc.* B, **133**, 140–200. [115]

KUFFLER, S. W., 1942*a*, Electric Potential Changes at an Isolated Nerve-Muscle Junction. *J. Neurophysiol.* **5**, 18–26. [70, 72, 82]

—— 1942*b*, Responses during Refractory Period at Myoneural Junction in Isolated Nerve-Muscle Fibre Preparation. Ibid. 199–209. [77]

—— 1942*c*, Further Study on Transmission in an Isolated Nerve-Muscle Fibre Preparation. Ibid. 309–22. [74–76, 138]

—— 1943, Specific Excitability of the Endplate Region in Normal and Denervated Muscle. Ibid. **6**, 99–110. [70–71, 96, 173]

—— 1945, Electric Excitability of Nerve-Muscle Fibre Preparations. Ibid. **8**, 77–87. [70–71, 96]

—— 1948, Physiology of Neuro-Muscular Junctions: Electrical Aspects. *Fed. Proc.* **7**, 437–46. [69, 79]

—— 1949*a*, Transmitter Mechanism at the Nerve-Muscle Junction. *Arch. Sci. Physiol.* **3**, 585–601. [69, 79]

—— 1949*b*, Le système moteur à fibres nerveuses de petit diamètre. Ibid. 613–30. [97]

—— HUNT, C. C., and QUILLIAM, J. P., 1951, Function of Medullated Small-Nerve Fibres in Mammalian Ventral Roots: Efferent Muscle Spindle Innervation. *J. Neurophysiol.* **14**, 29–54. [97–98, 185]

—— and KATZ, B., 1946, Inhibition at the Nerve-Muscle Junction in Crustacea. Ibid. **9**, 337–46. [98]

LANDSTEINER, K., 1945, *The Specificity of Serological Reactions*. Harvard University Press, Cambridge, Mass., 310 pp. [96]

LAPORTE, Y., and LLOYD, D. P. C., 1951, Disynaptic Reflex Linkage between Muscles of a Mystatic Unit. *Fed. Proc.* 10, 78–79. [152–4, 168, 188–9, 214]

—— and LORENTE DE NÓ, R., 1950, Potential Changes Evoked in a Curarized Sympathetic Ganglion by Presynaptic Volleys of Impulses. *J. Cell. Comp. Physiol.* 35, Suppl. 2, 61–106. [105, 107]

LARRABEE, M. G., and BRONK, D. W., 1947, Prolonged Facilitation of Synaptic Excitation in Sympathetic Ganglia. *J. Neurophysiol.* 10, 139–54. [200–1]

—— and POSTERNAK, J. M., 1952, Selective Action of Anaesthetics in Synapses and Axons in Mammalian Sympathetic Ganglia. Ibid. 15, 91–114. [99]

LASHLEY, K. S., 1950, In Search of the Engram. *Symp. Soc. Exp. Biol.* 4, 454–82. [266]

LE GROS CLARK, 1950, The Structure of the Brain and the Process of Thinking, pp. 12–24 in *The Physical Basis of Mind*, edited by Peter Laslett, Basil Blackwell, Oxford. [265]

LEKSELL, L., 1945, The Action Potential and Excitatory Effects of the Small Ventral Root Fibres to Skeletal Muscle. *Acta Physiol. Scand.* 10, Suppl. 31, 84 pp. [97, 185]

LEWIS, P. R., 1952, *Biochem. J.* (in press). [7]

LIDDELL, E. G. T., and SHERRINGTON, C. S., 1924, Reflexes in Response to Stretch (Myotatic Reflexes). *Proc. Roy. Soc.* B, 96, 212–42. [178]

—— —— 1925, Recruitment and some other Features of Reflex Inhibition. Ibid. 97, 488–518. [178]

LILEY, W., and NORTH, K. A. K., 1952. In course of publication. [91–92, 94, 199, 202]

LILLIE, R. S., 1925, Factors affecting Transmission and Recovery in the Passive Iron Wire Model. *J. Gen. Physiol.* 7, 473–507. [57]

LING, G., and GERARD, R. W., 1949a, The Normal Membrane Potential of Frog Sartorius Fibres. *J. Cell. Comp. Physiol.* 34, 383–96. [9, 13]

—— —— 1949b, The Membrane Potential and Metabolism of Muscle Fibres. Ibid. 413–38. [2, 19, 23]

LLOYD, D. P. C., 1941. A Direct Central Inhibitory Action of Dromically Conducted Impulses. *J. Neurophysiol.* 4, 184–90. [151–4]

—— 1943a, Reflex Action in Relation to Pattern and Peripheral Source of Afferent Stimulation. Ibid. 6, 111–19. [148, 159]

—— 1943b, Neuron Patterns controlling Transmission of Ipsilateral Hind Limb Reflexes in Cat. Ibid. 293–315. [61, 111, 137–8, 148, 160]

LLOYD, D. P. C., 1943c, Conduction and Synaptic Transmission of the Reflex Response to Stretch in Spinal Cats. Ibid. 317–26. [61, 111]

—— 1944, Functional Organization of the Spinal Cord. *Physiol. Rev.* **24,** 1–17. [110]

—— 1946a, Facilitation and Inhibition of Spinal Motoneurons. *J. Neurophysiol.* **9,** 421–38. [111, 134–6, 151–2, 158]

—— 1946b, Integrative Pattern of Excitation and Inhibition in Two-Neuron Reflex Arcs. Ibid. 439–44. [111]

—— 1949, Post-Tetanic Potentiation of Response in Monosynaptic Reflex Pathways of the Spinal Cord. *J. Gen. Physiol.* **33,** 147–70. [194–7, 200]

—— 1951a, Electrical Signs of Impulse Conduction in Spinal Motoneurons. Ibid. **35,** 255–88. [119, 123–4, 127–8, 249]

—— 1951b, After-Currents, After-Potentials, Excitability, and Ventral Root Electrotonus in Spinal Motoneurons. Ibid. 289–321. [119, 123]

—— and McINTYRE, A. K., 1949, On the Origins of Dorsal Root Potentials. Ibid. **32,** 409–43. [131]

—— —— 1950, Dorsal Column Conduction of Group I Muscle Afferent Impulses and their Relay through Clarke's Column. *J. Neurophysiol.* **13,** 39–54. [110]

LOEWI, O., 1945, Edward Gamaliel Janeway Lecture; Aspects of Transmission of Nervous Impulse; Theoretical and Clinical Implications. *J. Mt. Sinai Hosp.* **12,** 851–65. [167]

—— and HELLAUER, H., 1938, Über das Acetylcholin in peripheren Nerven. *Pflüg. Arch. ges. Physiol.* **240,** 769–75. [167]

LORENTE DE NÓ, R., 1933, Studies on the Structure of the Cerebral Cortex. I. The Area Entorhinalis. *J. Psych. Neurol.* **45,** 381–438. [218, 229, 238, 240, 275]

—— 1934, Studies on the Structure of the Cerebral Cortex. II. Continuation of the Study of the Ammonic System. Ibid. **46,** 113–77. [218, 229–31, 238, 240, 275]

—— 1938, Synaptic Stimulation of Motoneurones as a Local Process. *J. Neurophysiol.* **1,** 195–206. [110–11, 132]

—— 1943, Cerebral Cortex: Architecture, Intracortical Connections, Motor Projections, pp. 274–301 in *Physiology of the Nervous System* by J. F. Fulton, 2nd ed., Oxford University Press, 614 pp. [218, 229, 231–2, 238, 240, 275]

—— 1947a, A Study of Nerve Physiology, vols. 1 and 2, in *Studies From the Rockefeller Institute for Medical Research*, vols. 131 and 132, New York. [19, 23, 62]

—— 1947b, Action Potential of the Motoneurons of the Hypoglossus Nucleus. *J. Cell. Comp. Physiol.* **29,** 207–88. [119, 123–4, 249, 259]

REFERENCES

LORENTE DE NÓ, R., 1949, On the Effect of Certain Quaternary Ammonium Ions upon Frog Nerve. *J. Cell. Comp. Physiol.* **33**, Suppl., 1–231. [33]

—— and LAPORTE, Y., 1950, Refractoriness, Facilitation, and Inhibition in a Sympathetic Ganglion. Ibid. **35**, Suppl. 2, 155–92. [107]

LUDBROOK, J., and WHYTE, H. J., 1952. In course of publication. [76]

MACINTOSH, F. C., 1941, The Distribution of Acetylcholine in the Peripheral and in the Central Nervous System. *J. Physiol.* **99**, 436–42. [167]

MARMONT, G., 1949, Studies on the Axon Membrane, I. A New Method. *J. Cell. Comp. Physiol.* **34**, 351–82. [36, 53–54]

MARSHALL, W. H., 1941, Observations on Subcortical Somatic Sensory Mechanisms of Cats under Nembutal Anaesthesia. *J. Neurophysiol.* **4**, 25–43. [246, 253]

—— WOOLSEY, C. N., and BARD, P., 1941, Observations on Cortical Somatic Sensory Mechanisms of Cat and Monkey. Ibid. 1–24. [246]

MATTHEWS, B. H. C., 1931, The Response of a Muscle Spindle during Active Contraction of a Muscle. *J. Physiol.* **72**, 153–74. [111, 147, 179–81, 183–4, 188]

—— 1933, Nerve Endings in Mammalian Muscle. Ibid. **78**, 1–53. [as above]

MONNIER, A. M., 1949, Les bases physico-chimiques de l'action du calcium sur l'activité nerveuse. *Arch. Sci. Physiol.* **3**, 177–87. [62]

MORISON, R. S., and DEMPSEY, E. W., 1942, A Study of Thalamocortical Relations. *Amer. J. Physiol.* **135**, 281–92. [246, 255–6]

NASTUK, W. L., 1950, The Electrical Activity of Single Muscle Fibres at the Neuro-Muscular Junction. Abstr. *XVIII, Int. Physiol. Congr.* 373–4. [65, 82]

—— and HODGKIN, A. L., 1950, The Electrical Activity of Single Muscle Fibres, *J. Cell. Comp. Physiol.* **35**, 39–74. [9, 12, 32, 50, 78, 84]

OGSTON, A. G., 1952. Personal communication. [93, 104, 167]

OVERTON, E., 1902, Beiträge zur allgemeinen Muskel- und Nervenphysiologie. II. Über die Unentbehrlichkeit von Natrium- (oder Lithium-)Ionen für den Kontraktionsakt des Muskels. *Pflüg. Arch. ges. Physiol.* **92**, 346–86. [2, 33]

PATON, W. D. M., 1951, The Pharmacology of Decamethonium. *Ann. N.Y. Acad. Sci.* **54**, 347–61. [95]

PAULING, L., CAMPBELL, D. H., and PRESSMAN, D., 1943, The Nature of the Forces between Antigen and Antibody and of the Precipitin Reaction. *Physiol. Rev.* **23**, 203–19. [96]

PAVLOV, I. P., 1927, *Conditioned Reflexes: An Investigation of Physiological Activity of the Cerebral Cortex.* Oxford University Press, London, 430 pp. [217, 224]

PENFIELD, W., 1937, *The Cerebral Cortex and Consciousness*, Harvey Lectures, 35–69. [265]

—— 1947, Some Observations on the Cerebral Cortex of Man. *Proc. Roy. Soc.* B, **134**, 329–47. [265]

PITTS, R. F., 1943, The Basis for Repetitive Activity in Phrenic Motoneurons. *J. Neurophysiol.* **6**, 439–54. [174]

POPPER, K. R., 1950, Indeterminism in Quantum Physics and in Classical Physics. *Brit. Journ. Phil. Sci.* **1**, 117–33, 173–95. [272]

—— 1952. Personal communication. [265–6]

PUMPHREY, R. J., and YOUNG, J. Z., 1938, The Rates of Conduction of Nerve Fibres of Various Diameters in Cephalopods. *J. Exp. Biol.* **15**, 453–66. [60]

RASHEVSKY, N., 1938, *Mathematical Biophysics*. Chicago: University of Chicago Press. [218]

RENSHAW, B., 1942, Effects of Presynaptic Volleys on Spread of Impulses over the Soma of the Motoneuron. *J. Neurophysiol.* **5**, 235–43. [135]

—— 1946, Observations on Interaction of Nerve Impulses in the Grey Matter and on the Nature of Central Inhibition. *Amer. J. Physiol.* **146**, 443–8. [155, 162]

—— FORBES, A., and MORISON, B. R., 1940, Activity of Isocortex and Hippocampus: Electrical Studies with Micro-Electrodes. *J. Neurophysiol.* **3**, 74–105. [246–7]

RHINE, J. B., 1948, *The Reach of the Mind*. Faber and Faber Ltd., London, 188 pp. [284]

—— PRATT, J. G., SMITH, B. M., STUART, C. E., and GREENWOOD, J. A., *Extra-Sensory Perception after Sixty Years*. Henry Holt & Co., New York, 1940. [284]

ROMANES, G. J., 1951, The Motor Cell Columns of the Lumbo-Sacral Spinal Cord of the Cat. *J. Comp. Neurol.* **94**, 313–63. [115, 159, 182]

ROSENBLUETH, A., 1950, *The Transmission of Nerve Impulses at Neuroeffector Junctions and Peripheral Synapses*. New York. [65]

—— and CANNON, W. B., 1942, Cortical Responses to Electric Stimulation. *Amer. J. Physiol.* **135**, 690–741. [244]

RUDIN, D. O., and EISENMAN, G., 1951, A Method for Dissection and Electrical Study *in vitro* of Mammalian Central Nervous Tissue. *Science*, **114**, 300–2. [110]

RUSHTON, W. A. H., 1951, A Theory of the Effects of Fibre Size in Medullated Nerve. *J. Physiol.* **115**, 101–22. [60–61]

RUSSELL, B., 1948, *Human Knowledge: Its Scope and Limits*. London, 538 pp. [262]

RYLE, G., 1949, *The Concept of Mind*. Hutchinson's University Library, London, 334 pp. [264, 285]

SANDERS, F. K., and WHITTERIDGE, D., 1946, Conduction Velocity and Myelin Thickness in Regenerating Nerve Fibres. *J. Physiol.* **105**, 152–74. [204]

SAWYER, D. B., 1951. Personal communication. [274]

SCHLAPP, W., and JEFFERSON, A. A., 1952, Some Effects of Repetitive Stimulation of Afferents on Reflex Conduction. *Ciba Symposium* (in press). [136–8, 197]

SCHRÖDINGER, E., 1951, *Science and Humanism: Physics in Our Time.* Cambridge University Press, 68 pp. [261, 283, 286]

SHANES, A. M., 1946, A Neglected Factor in Studies of Potassium Distribution in Relation to the Resting Potential of Nerve. *J. Cell. Comp. Physiol.* **27**, 115–18. [9]

—— 1950, Potassium Retention in Crab Nerve. *J. Gen. Physiol.* **33**, 643–9. [23, 36]

—— and HOPKINS, H. S., 1948, Effect of Potassium on 'Resting' Potential and Respiration of Crab Nerve. *J. Neurophysiol.* **11**, 331–42. [23]

SHERRINGTON, C. S., 1906, *Integrative Action of the Nervous System.* Yale University Press, New Haven, 411 pp. [109, 151, 182]

—— 1925, Remarks on Some Aspects of Reflex Inhibition. *Proc. Roy. Soc.* B, **97**, 519–45. [191]

—— 1951, *Man on His Nature.* Cambridge University Press, 2nd ed., 300 pp. [228, 262, 265, 267, 269, 286]

SHIMBEL, A., 1950, Contributions to the Mathematical Biophysics of the Central Nervous System with Special Reference to Learning. *Bull. Math. Biophysics.* **12**, 241–75. [219–20]

SMYTHIES, J. R., 1951, The Extension of Mind. A New Theoretical Basis for Psi Phenomena. *J. Soc. Psych. Res.* **36**, 477–502. [280, 284, 286]

SOAL, S. G., 1947, *The Experimental Situation in Psychical Research.* Society Psych. Res., London, 63 pp. [284]

—— and GOLDNEY, K. M., 1943, Experiments in Precognitive Telepathy. *Proc. Soc. Psych. Res.* **47**, 21–150. [284]

SPEIDEL, C. C., 1940, *Adjustments of Nerve Endings.* Harvey Lectures, 126–58. [215]

SPERRY, R. W., 1945, The Problem of Central Nervous Re-organization after Nerve Regeneration and Muscle Transplantation. *Quart. Rev. Biol.* **20**, 311–69. [193]

STOUT, G. F., 1931, *Mind and Matter.* Cambridge University Press. 325 pp. [264]

STRÖM, G., 1951, Physiological Significance of Post-Tetanic Potentiation of the Spinal Monosynaptic Reflex. *Acta. Physiol. Scand.* **24**, 61–83. [199, 203]

TANZI, E., 1893, *Rev. sperim. d. frenatria et d. medic. legal.* **19**. (Quoted by Cajal, 1911.) [221]

TASAKI, I., 1939, The Electro-Saltatory Transmission of the Nerve Impulse and the Effect of Narcosis upon the Nerve Fibre. *Amer. J. Physiol.* **127**, 211–27. [57]

—— and MIZUGUCHI, K., 1949, The Changes in the Electric Impedance during Activity and the Effects of Alkaloids and Polarization upon the Bioelectric Processes in the Myelinated Nerve Fibres. *Biochim. Biophys. Acta*, **3**, 484–93. [49]

TAYLOR, D. B., 1951, Some Basic Aspects of the Pharmacology of Synthetic Curariform Drugs. *Pharmacol. Rev.* **3**, 412–44. [95]

TEORELL, T., 1949, Membrane Electrophoresis in Relation to Bio-electrical Polarization Effects. *Arch. Sci. Physiol.* **3**, 205–18. [18]

THOMPSON, H. B., 1899, The Total Number of Functional Cells in the Cerebral Cortex of Man, and the Percentage of the Total Volume of the Cortex composed of Nerve Cell Bodies, calculated from Karl Hammarberg's Data, together with a Comparison of the Number of Giant Cells with the Number of Pyramidal Fibres. *J. Comp. Neurol.* **9**, 113–40. [229, 268, 275–6]

THORPE, W. H., 1950, The Concepts of Learning and Their Relation to those of Instinct. *Symp. Soc. Exp. Biol.* **4**, 387–408. [216–17]

THOULESS, R. H., 1951, A Report on an Experiment in Psycho-Kinesis with Dice, and a Discussion on Psychological Factors favouring Success. *Proc. Soc. Psych. Res.* **49**, 107–30. [284]

TINBERGEN, N., 1951, *The Study of Instinct.* Clarendon Press, Oxford, 228 pp. [194]

TOBIAS, J. 1952. Personal communication. [56]

USSING, H. H., 1949*a*, Transport of Ions across Cellular Membranes. *Physiol. Rev.* **29**, 127–55. [19]

—— 1949*b*, The Distinction by means of Tracers between Active Transport and Diffusion. *Acta. Physiol. Scand.* **19**, 43–56. [18]

WALTER, W. Grey, 1950, Normal Rhythms—their Development, Distribution and Significance, pp. 203–27, in *Electroencephalo-graphy*, edited by D. Hill and G. Parr, Macdonald, London. [258]

WEIDMANN, S., 1951*a*, Electrical Characteristics of Sepia Axons. *J. Physiol.* **114**, 372–81. [21, 24–27]

—— 1951*b*, Effect of Current Flow on the Membrane Potential of Cardiac Muscle. Ibid. **115**, 227–36. [50]

WEISS, P., and EDDS, M. V., 1946, Spontaneous Recovery of Muscle following Partial Denervation. *Amer. J. Physiol.* **145**, 587–607. [215]

WHITTERIDGE, D., 1950, Physiology, pp. 92–126, in *Electroencephalo-graphy*, edited by D. Hill and G. Parr, Macdonald, London. [247, 259]

WILLIAMS, D., and DENNY-BROWN, D., 1941, Cerebral Electrical Changes in Experimental Concussion. *Brain*, **64**, 223–38. [257–8, 265–6]

WISDOM, J. O., 1952, A New Model for the Mind-Body Relationship. *Brit. J. Phil. Sci.* **2**, 295–301. [281–2]

WOODBURY, J. W., and PATTON, H. D., 1952. Properties of Spinal Cord Elements studied with Intracellular Ultramicro-electrodes. *Fed. Proc.* **11**, 175. [114]

WOOLSEY, C. N., and CHANG, H. T., 1948, Activation of the Cerebral Cortex by Antidromic Volleys in the Pyramidal Tract. *Res. Publ. Assoc. Nerv. Ment. Dis.* **27**, 146–61. [246, 249]

YOUNG, J. Z., 1938, In Evolution, pp. 179–205. *Essays Presented to E. S. Goodrich*, ed. G. R. de Beer. Oxford. [218]

—— 1939, Fused Neurons and Synaptic Contacts in the Giant Nerve Fibres of Cephalopods. *Phil. Trans. Roy. Soc.* B, **229**, 465–503. [7]

—— 1951, Growth and Plasticity in the Nervous System. *Proc. Roy. Soc.* B, **139**, 18–37. [193]

INDEX

PRINTED IN
GREAT BRITAIN
AT THE
UNIVERSITY PRESS
OXFORD
BY
CHARLES BATEY
PRINTER
TO THE
UNIVERSITY